A
COMPENDIUM
OF
COSMETOLOGY
AND AESTHETICS

TEACHINGS OF THE HEALTHY HUMAN BODY,
ITS FUNCTIONS AND SUBSEQUENT PHYSICAL CARE
FOR PROFESSIONAL AND PERSONAL STUDY

URSULA E.E. AUSTERMANN

STANLEY THORNES (PUBLISHERS) LTD

Text © 1987 Ursula E.E. Austermann
Illustration © Stanley Thornes (Publishers) Ltd, 1987

First published in Canada in 1983
This edition published in Great Britain in 1987 by:
Stanley Thornes (Publishers) Ltd
Old Station Drive
Leckhampton
CHELTENHAM GL53 0DN
England

British Library Cataloguing in Publication Data

Austermann, U.E.E.
    A compendium of cosmetology and aesthetics.
    1. Cosmetics
    I. Title
    646.7′26   TP983

ISBN 0-85950-660-6

Typeset by Tech-Set, Gateshead, Tyne & Wear
Printed and bound in Great Britain at The Bath Press, Avon.

Contents

Preface to the second edition

The second, revised edition of *A Compendium of Cosmetology and Aesthetics* has the aim to provide the professional and student with additional, updated information. An expansion of some chapters was considered necessary for the better understanding of relevant subjects benefiting the reader.

There is no major news in the field since the first edition except for a few ideas and approaches which developed and are of value in the practice of cosmetology/aesthetics.

Ursula E.E. Austermann
1987

Preface to the first edition

Knowledge is gained through experience, understanding and constant study. The study of cosmetology/aesthetics is to be informed about the latest development and scientific recognitions in physical culture and to delve back thousands of years in history as far as the human desire for eternal youth and beauty.

The ancient Greek work *'kos-mein'* – to bring order, to adorn, – has been transformed into 'cosmetology' and is now interpreted to be the practice of physical care, including the simple rules of good health and the art of beautifying. Cosmetology teaches how to look after and improve the personal appearance, as well as convey self-confidence and reassurance.

Aesthetics is rooted in Greek and formed from Latin – *aestheticus* – relating to dealing with the beautiful.

To be well groomed and to have an appropriate intellectual standard, good general education, ability to adjust and judgement of people, are provisions for personal success, to which for professional efficiency a thorough training must be added.

This book is to serve as a guide in personal care, as a guide to student and teacher during the time of training and as a reference to the cosmetologist/aesthetician in her professional career. It covers all theoretical and practical subjects representing the scientific base for the study of cosmetology/aesthetics. To keep up in the developments and changes in this extending field is indispensable to making the most of one's apperance. It is important that during and after training further education and training is obtained to be able to render the best services.

The introduction to anatomy and physiology of the human body is to make the reader realize the close interrelation between a normal functioning body system and a healthy, lovely skin. To understand the anatomic structure of the skin and the physiologic processes taking place in the skin belongs to the basics of cosmetology – aesthetics.

The ability to describe skin diseases is intended to make a professional cosmetologist aware that her field is the care, preservation and beautification of the healthy different skin types. It is to enable her to refer a client to a doctor when perhaps the person came to see her not realizing the necessity of medical treatment. It is important to note that skin diseases in the sense of dermatology belong in the hands of a doctor.

As prerequisite for the understanding of cosmetic products, a basic study of organic chemistry, herbs, vitamins, and other additives to preparations is required. The foregoing, as well as being familiar with the skin types, makes a capable, efficient consultant in skin care.

The section introducing stage make-up and related fields is to develop touch and skill in the art and for a better comprehension of make-up in general.

Continuous studying and practising leads to perfection in physical culture; during the time of professional training they are the first steps toward a successful career.

I extend my thanks to the late Dr W. Morrish for his advice and to all institutions and companies who contributed to this book as well as to Dr J.Y. Liao and Dr D.A. Kester for their additions. The mention of only a few firms in the list of examples of cosmetic formulae does not indicate any preference by the author.

Ursula E.E. Austermann
Edmonton, Alberta, Canada
1983

Acknowledgements

With such a multi-faceted book, it is impossible to name everyone who has generously donated time and effort in helping with information, research, pictures and advice. Nonetheless, the author wishes to pay special tribute to Dr Gertrud Austermann, M.D., for assistance in an advisory capacity. The author and the publishers wish to acknowledge permission to quote excerpts from:
(published and copyright as indicated)
Dragoco Cosmetic Raw Materials, DRAGOCO, Holzminden
Facts about Foods, by H.J. Heinz Company of Canada Ltd.
First Aid Handbook, by Sun Life Assurance Company of Canada
Formulations for Cosmetic and Pharmaceutical Preparations,
BASF (Badische Anilin- & Soda-Fabrik AG), Ludwigshafen
Guide to the Use of ATLAS Surfactants and Sorbitol in Cosmetic and Pharmaceutical Products, by ATLAS Chemical Industries, Inc., Wilmington, Delaware
Suggested Formulae for the Manufacture of Pharmaceutical and Cosmetic Preparations, by Henkel International GmbH, Dusseldorf
The Practice of Compositions, by Helmut Fuehrer, DRAGOCO, Holzminden
Up-to-date Dosing of Perfume Oils in Perfumery Goods and Cosmetics, and *Up-to-date Ways of Perfuming Aerosol Products,* by Helmut Fuehrer, DRAGOCO, Holzminden
Manual of Nutrition, by Ministry of Agriculture, Fisheries and Food, HMSO, London

Permission to reproduce illustrations
by the following sources is also acknowledged:
ATLAS Chemical Industries, Inc., Wilmington, Delaware
Bavarian State Opera, Photos: Sabine Toepffer, Munich
Bayreuth Festivals, Photos: Wilhelm Rauh, Bayreuth
DRAGOCO, Holzminden
Metropolitan Opera, Photos: Louis Mélancon, New York, N.Y.
Musée du Petit Palais, Paris, Photos: Ets. J.E. Buloz, Paris
Musée Carnavalet, Paris, Photos: Ets. J.E. Buloz, Paris
Musée Condé, Chantilly, Photo: Photographie Giraudon, Paris
Staatsbibliothek, Berlin, Photo: Handke und Feldhaus, Bildarchiv, Berlin
The National Gallery of Scotland, Edinburgh, Photo: ANNAN
Photographer, Glasgow

Photographs courtesy of Cosmetology Schools of Canada Ltd

PLEASE NOTE:

The professional designation of Cosmetologist or (Esthetician/Aesthetician) is used
depending upon the country.
Basically the meaning is the same, harmony and beauty.

PART I
THEORY

The history of cosmetology

Contents

Cosmetology is not a phenomenon of our time; it dates back to the earliest recorded history. Our different products and preparations for preserving the skin's youth and beauty are, in their fundamental compounds, sometimes as old as the cultural habits of the human race. This has been proven by numerous findings in places where former civilizations were rediscovered through excavation.

EARLY CIVILIZATIONS

In the valley of the Indus, archaeologists exposed the ancient town of Mohenjo-Daro and found razors, cream containers and make-up 4500 to 5000 years old. The women of the Sumerians, who occupied the lower Mesopotamian valley 3000 years ago, coloured their hair with henna and bleached it with lime. They also darkened their eyes with kohl and rouged their cheeks with vermilion or madder. To whiten their complexions they applied chalk or lead, and they reddened their lips with henna or fucus. They depilated hair, cleaned their teeth with pulverized pumice and manicured, coloured, or polished their fingernails. Cosmetics had almost reached perfection. In ancient Babylon men and women made up their faces, using stibium as an eyeliner. Body skin was smoothed and softened by rubbing it with pumice stone.

In the Old Testament we read about make-up application. II Kings 9: 30 says: 'And when Jehu was come to Jesreel, Jezebel heard of it; and she painted her face, and tired her hair . . .'. In the Suras of the Koran it is written that the houris in the Gardens of Delight had kohl-darkened eyes.

Bust of Queen Nefertiti (1390–1354 BC), State Museum, Berlin

In pre-Incan Peru about 500 BC the women shaped their eyebrows, manicured and pedicured, tinted and polished their nails. They also applied rouge to their cheeks and lips. After death, a full assortment of cosmetics was placed in the grave with the body. Many centuries before Christ in the Far East, the Chinese had refined the art of skin care and make-up, as we can see in their paintings and drawings of gracious women. A massage method was also developed there some 5000 years ago. The customs of physical care and beautification carried out by primitive peoples throughout history include face paints of yellow or red ochre, clay ornaments and tattooing. A certain amount of grooming is considered a necessity wherever groups of human beings live together, indispensable for general hygiene and individual health. The ways and means were formerly often connected with religious customs, so that all believers could be included. Ritual washing, for example, was nothing else but an education in cleanliness. To remain young, fit and attractive is and has been at all times a natural instinct for humans.

ANCIENT EGYPT

In the royal tombs of ancient Egypt, archaeologists have found make-up containers, make-up spoons, cream pots, combs and mirrors. Inscriptions or drawings on the walls of the tomb chambers give information on product ingredients and use. In addition to these findings numerous rolls of papyrus, or from later ages handwritten scripts and prints, explain cosmetic and beauty treatments. Cosmetics of all kinds were used abundantly not only by women but also by men. Both sexes wore wigs, which were not necessarily black but could be blue, green or red. It is in Egypt that the cradle of cosmetics has most likely been found. The ancient Egyptians advanced body care to a high art.

Egyptian physicians and pharmacists took great interest in the practice of cosmetology, expanding it with their knowledge. A number of their prescriptions

seem almost up-to-date: one suggests sulphur and plant extracts to improve hair growth. Another recipe called for the lining of the uterus of a cat added to the egg of a gabgu bird, and mixed with oil to massage into the scalp. Ingredients of their medicines and cosmetics that are still in use today include beeswax, olives, almond oil, animal fats, thyme, resins and milk.

For the cultivated Egyptian, cosmetology was an everyday art. Even those of lower class anointed their body daily. This was indispensable because of the light clothes preferred at that time which did not offer sufficient protection against the drying effects of the sun. The deceased were provided in the tomb with various kinds of creams, oils and at least nine different make-ups for the life after death. In the tomb of Tutankhamon, Pharaoh of Egypt about 1361–1352 BC, creams, pomades and other fragrant cosmetics were found in alabaster jars. Essential oils of flowers and herbs had been used in their preparation, as well as fats, resins or balsams.

Queen Hetephras, mother of Cheops, Pharaoh of the Fourth Dynasty (2900–2871 BC) had manicure instruments and toilet accessories resembling those of the women of today. Cleopatra (69–30 BC) took her bath in donkey's milk. Slaves creamed, massaged, and powdered her body while she relaxed on a bed covered with rose petals.

Egyptian women shaped their eyebrows and drew a black line along the upper eyelid, extending it over the outer corner. They wore a blue or green dash along the lower lid and used a kind of mascara to make their eyes appear large and shiny. They lined and coloured their lips with brushes. Their faces were made up with lead white or yellow ochre foundations, sometimes with an orange tinge, so that the complexion either appeared white like a lily or showed the effect of a golden shimmer.

Their black and green eyeliner seems to have been composed of sulphur, carbon, copper ore, lead and fatted soot. The skin creams were kept in precious jars, or in hollow, elastic plant stalks, so that the contents could be pressed out as from a tube. Lipsticks were preserved in this way too. Lip make-up and rouge consisted of a fatty, vermilion-coloured paste.

Egyptian women shaved their body hair including their scalp; they emphasized their veins with blue, and painted their nipples gold. Their fingernails were coloured yellow-red with henna, which was applied as well to the palms and the soles of the feet.

ANCIENT GREECE AND ROME

Cosmetology as practised by the ancient Egyptians influenced a great part of the antique world. Frescoes on the island of Crete show that in about 1500 BC girls knew very well how to apply their make-up. The art eventually established itself in Greece, and the country of classic beauty enriched it in many ways. The ideal of the ancient Greek epoch was the combination of a sound spirit in a healthy, well-proportioned body. Sculptures of Greek deities reveal a never-again-attained beauty. Harmonious unity was the recognized perfection, and the whole way of life was an attempt to reach this ideal, through such means as refined baths, compresses, massages and a fully-regulated diet. Physical education was promoted, and exercising was considered a necessity for fitness and beauty. Cosmetology was also looked upon as an essential fundamental for a dignified life, and the philosopher Socrates (469–399 BC) was greatly criticized for his indifference to his outward appearance.

At the time of Hippocrates, the founder of classic medicine, Greek cosmetology was well recognized and esteemed. Over-night packs were made of bread-crumbs or flour mixed to a pasty consistency with milk. In the morning the dried pack was softened and washed off with additional milk. Make-up with lead white was in use: this corrodes the skin and may be absorbed to poison the system, leading to death. Thus we find in ancient Greece the first warnings about the disadvantages of this dangerous cosmetic ingredient.

At the beginning of the Greek period there were cold water showers in the bath halls, fed by natural wells. Later in the antique period it became customary to use hot water and to have heated bathrooms. After the bath the ancient Greeks massaged their skin with scented oil. A variety of perfumes were used by both men and women. Both sexes were fond of being blond, and liked to lighten their hair.

After Greece had become a Roman province the Greek way of life and thinking greatly influenced Roman culture. With the extension of Roman power and higher living standards, the employment of cosmetics, adopted from the Greeks and originating in Egypt, became further refined.

The aristocratic Roman woman was no longer satisfied with creams based on olive oil or animal fats. She preferred those containing lizard liver oil and wine to keep her complexion young and free of wrinkles. The lower-class woman took whey for her skin. If her husband could afford it, she bathed in milk instead of water. Poppaea the wife of Emperor Nero (AD 37–68) liked donkey's milk for her daily bath, so she kept her own herd of donkeys. She dyed her lashes and eyebrows black and concealed her freckles and blemishes with a preparation of barley flour mixed with butter. Like the Greeks, the Romans thought it a sign of beauty if the eyebrows met at the bridge of the nose.

To be fair or a redhead became desirable through contact with Germanic tribes. The Roman woman sometimes coloured or bleached her hair, or wore a blonde wig. The Romans were also familiar with the favourable effect of fresh fruit on the complexion and fruit juices enjoyed great popularity with them. A guild of cream makers was founded. The fragrances for their oils and creams came mainly from Arabia. Special cosmetics and other beauty means were imported together with female slaves so that treatments could be carried out according to original

Piero di Cosimo (approx. 1462–1521): portrait of Simonetta Vespucci, Musée Condé, Chantilly

Francois Boucher: Portrait of Madame de Pompadour (1721–64), The National Gallery of Scotland, Edinburgh

methods. The luxury-loving Roman male also used cosmetics. It is said that fashionable men, even some military leaders when parading into Rome, applied make-up to their faces.

Wherever the Roman Empire reached, we still find ruins of *thermae* containing pools, as well as seat baths, showers, and steam baths. Extensive perspiration combined with a quick change from hot to cold temperature was supposed to further health by replacing physical exercise. In order to fight corpulence, a consequence of living in leisure and comfort, it was the custom to be massaged by a slave after the bath.

THE DARK AND MIDDLE AGES

After the decline of the Roman Empire, most of their cosmetic and physical-care experiences were lost. The Arabs alone continued to further the Greek and Roman development.

They not only discovered in principle the employment of herbs for cosmetics, but were the first to use alcohol as a solvent in perfumery. Alcohol is an indispensable part of present-day preparations. The Arabian physicians had our modern point of view that appearance is relative to the state of health. Make-up continued in their countries in its traditional ways.

The invasion of Germanic tribes ended the Roman bath culture in Europe. They destroyed aqueducts and *thermae*, using the metal to make weapons. Christianity in the Middle Ages placed physical concerns in a secondary position. No essential additions were made to cosmetology during these centuries. Superstition and mysticism represented spiritual power, bringing about the invention of some amusing, peculiar and occasionally dangerous formulae for beauty treatments.

The crusaders (eleventh to thirteenth century) brought cosmetics and fragrances home to Europe from their journeys to the Orient. But the crusaders also carried along diseases, and the plague called the Black Death spread through a population crammed into small cities encircled by heavy stone walls. The few public bathhouses were increasingly criticized by the clergy, and for fear of being infected nobody attended them anymore. Through lack of hygiene and cleanliness the scourge of epidemics expanded.

THE RENAISSANCE

It seems that due to the changes in fashion over the centuries, clean and negligent civilizations take their turn. About 1400 the Renaissance, a rebirth of antique spirit, started in Italy. The rising sensual joy of life and elaborate way of dressing soon made it seem too much trouble to devote time regularly to body care. The bathtub became a minute dish to wash face and hands only. Parasites spread rapidly as fragrant waters were used lavishly instead of the necessary bath. It became stylish to bleach the hair. Eyebrows were shaped to a fine arch or removed to create the impression of a high forehead. Dresses had extremely low-cut necklines, and both face and *décolleté* were made up, while accessories like gloves were scented and fragrances profusely worn by both sexes.

At the court of Catherine de' Medici (1519–89) there were no bath facilities. It is said that she had to change her residence ninety times so that the smelly rooms could be made habitable again. Mary Stuart, Queen of Scots, was an exception to the usual customs: she bathed and washed her face in wine. But later in seventeenth-century England cosmetics were considered 'sinful and the art of the Devil'.

Even if physical care was not a general practice in the Renaissance, there were some physicians and chemists who issued prescriptions to keep the skin fresh and young with bath additives. Some still serve us today, like fir needles, petals, herbs and salts.

THE SEVENTEENTH AND EIGHTEENTH CENTURIES

In the seventeenth century soap was still less common than water, and personal hygiene was not considered important. It was not unusual just to dip the hands into water and sprinkle some perfume onto the face. The extravagance in fashions and vanity of the Baroque made powder the most important part of the daily beauty treatment.

The court of Louis XIV led in dress styles, hair styles and make-up, with high wigs, light foundation, rouge and patches. Both sexes employed an abundance of scents.

To preserve a fair, fine complexion broad-brimmed hats shaded women's faces against sunlight, and a silk mask sometimes protected the skin from the elements. To underline paleness the hair frequently was dyed dark.

In the Rococo period which followed (1730–89), nothing was feared more than ageing. Ladies, young or old, plentifully applied *céruse*, a foundation containing white lead pigment. Their lipstick was a bright red colour. Powder gave the complexion the 'peach look' as it sat in the fine facial hair. Women continued to ruin their skin by improper care and products, so that a continually thicker layer had to be applied to cover the marks. Beauty patches, already customary in the Baroque, were placed on the face or the *décolleté* close to the point to which a lady wished to draw attention. For contrast to their white powdered hair, men too used plenty of make-up. Women adorned their hair with flowers and all kinds of ornaments. The harmony of the healthy female body was disfigured by a corset to create a tiny waistline, while the hoop-skirt reached large dimensions.

THE NINETEENTH CENTURY

An important change took place in the Empire period around 1804, the year of Napoléon I's coronation. Loose-fitting clothes were preferred according to Greek or Roman patterns. The style was a high-waisted dress, a kind of shirt of delicate material to reveal the shape of the body. For a better effect, the dress was sometimes slightly dampened to cling. Some remembered the Roman baths and their healthy, beautifying effect: physical exercise also had a comeback. In the houses of that time we find small wash basins with sponges, but there was a long way to go to a complete hygiene and beauty culture.

In the nineteenth century corsets were back – those of the Baroque were nothing compared to these! It is not surprising to read that women had a tendency to faint for no apparent reason. Body care was not of importance and cosmetology of little interest. Make-up was considered to be vulgar, so the use of cosmetics declined. They were limited to the stage where they could not be omitted.

From 1870 on, together with a succession of inventions and scientific progress, the caring part of cosmetology was revived.

Francois Gérard: Portrait of Madame Recamier (1777– 1849), Musée Carnavalet, Paris

THE TWENTIETH CENTURY

The twentieth century brought a constant rise, a recognition that physical care is indispensable in general progress and increase of population. We find great pioneeers starting out in all parts of the world: in Australia, Helena Rubinstein; North America, Elizabeth Arden; France, Dr N.G. Payot – to name a few. World War One (1914–18) and female emancipation made it necessary for women to appear in public and compete professionally with men. Their clothes changed to be convenient and practical. The caring part of cosmetology became general knowledge but to accept *maquillage* and its challenges was a slow process. There were still prejudices. Only powder, lipstick and nail polish were commonly applied.

After World War Two women became more make-up conscious. *Visagistes* now create a new trend every season, developing make-up into an art. Constant progress in cosmetology is taking place through research, making it accessible to everybody. More items for men have been introduced. Caring procedures and products are becoming more and more specialized, adjusted to individuals and their specific problems. Fashion today demands the use of cosmetics and general body care since more body parts are exposed.

Anatomy and physiology as applied to cosmetology

Contents

THE CELL

The human body is a structural and functional unit of tissues, organs and systems, all of them made up of cells, the smallest living matter. Each cell consists of protoplasm chemically composed for its specific task. Thus each cell is highly specialized to enable the body to carry out its vital functions: red blood cells transport oxygen by means of the blood vessels and remove carbon dioxide; nerve cells communicate and co-ordinate body systems; muscle cells let limbs move; bone cells support the body.

Protoplasm is living matter and as such represents the basis of life. As the cell is made of protoplasm, it is able to carry out all processes required for life. Like the body itself the cell responds to stimuli, conveys impulses, stores food, has a metabolism and reproduces. These are all characteristics present in the living: human, animal and plant. However, there are exceptions: some cells do not reproduce.

The body's health depends largely upon the health of the body parts, and in turn their health is subject to their building stones, the cells. If cells are starved, or their existence endangered in any way, they are unable to carry out their functions properly, and a disorder results. If a cell is injured causing discharge of protoplasm, it dies. It follows that without the regular, healthy operation of these minute structures, life does not continue in its normal course.

The cell is nourished by osmosis, an exchange occurring between the outside and inside liquids, taking in nourishment and giving away waste products. Osmosis is a diffusion through a semi-permeable wall, e.g. the cell membrane. The movement of water, gases, food or waste, and chemicals is a continuous sequence. This means that it includes two main procedures, anabolism and catabolism. Anabolism, the constructive part, is the synthesis of the chemical process in the cell. Catabolism, the destructive part, is the break-down of the compounds into simple substances. Energy derives from the chemical reactions. To produce this energy the cell must be supplied adequately with nutrients, so it may continue to live and maintain the body's health and life. The main elements in the cell are carbon, hydrogen, oxygen and nitrogen.

The cell structure

1 The cell membrane, a fine porous skin, surrounds the cell body. The membrane protects and separates the cell from its environment so that osmosis can take place through the pores. It has two layers, the external membrane and the internal membrane, also called the plasma membrane.

2 The liquid between cell membrane and nucleus is cytoplasm. Cytoplasm and nucleus comprise all of the cell's protoplasm. Numerous small bodies with definite functions, arranged in a distinct manner, are found in the cytoplasm; there are named organelles.

The organelles are:

  a) endoplasmic reticulum – a network of membranes,

  b) ribosomes – synthesize protein and consist largely of ribonucleic acids (RNA),

  c) Golgi apparatus – synthesizes carbohydrates

  d) mitochondria – the cells' power stations,

  e) lysosomes – contain enzymes to defend the cell, for example against bacteria.

The centrosome is a spherical body, surrounded by cilia, located close to the cell centre near the nucleus. This plays an important part in cell division. Inside the centrosome are two small bodies, centrioles, to organize the spindle in mitosis.

9

3 The nucleus is a spherical body in the centre of the cell, enclosed in the nuclear membrane, which is a porous, thin layer of tissue. The nucleus is the centre of cell reproduction and metabolism. It contains round, small bodies called nucleoli, nucleoplasm, granular bodies, and chromosomes, the carriers of the genes. In animals the number of chromosomes varies according to species; in human beings there are 46. Cells reproduce by division: direct cell division or amitosis, and indirect cell division or mitosis.

In amitosis, the cell stretches lengthwise and divides in the middle without any noteworthy structural changes. After the nucleus is duplicated, the cytoplasm separates into two parts and the cell falls apart along the short axis forming two daughter cells. This uncomplicated multiplying process occurs in bacteria and plants.

In mitosis, the division in humans and animals consists of five major phases:

Interphase: the cell prepares for division, chromosomes elongate and deoxyribonucleic acid (DNA) replicates.

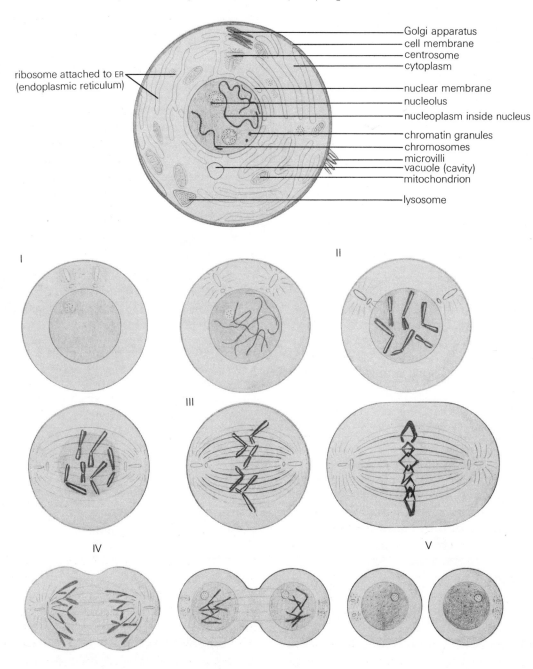

ribosome attached to ER (endoplasmic reticulum)

Golgi apparatus
cell membrane
centrosome
cytoplasm
nuclear membrane
nucleolus
nucleoplasm inside nucleus
chromatin granules
chromosomes
microvilli
vacuole (cavity)
mitochondrion
lysosome

I   II   III   IV   V

Schema of the cell structure and indirect cell division

Prophase: the centrosome divides into halves and the two newly-formed bodies, still connected by a spindle of fibres, move to the cell's poles. In the meantime, the nuclear membrane dissolves, the chromosomes thicken and turn into small rods.

Metaphase: chromosomes line up at the cell equator and attach themselves to the spindle fibres.

Anaphase: chromosomes divide into equal parts, thus doubling their number. They then separate and move towards the centrosomes at the cell poles.

Telophase: chromosomes lose their structure, become granules again, nucleoli and a new nuclear membrane are formed, while the spindle fibres disappear. The cytoplasm separates and the result is two daughter cells.

Meiosis is a special method of cell division occurring in sex cells during their process of maturing.

TISSUES

A formation of similarly-constructed cells, carrying out together the same functions, is a tissue. The cells' shape, size and arrangement determine the structure of the tissue. Body tissue is classified as epithelial tissue, connective tissue, muscle tissue and nerve tissue.

Epithelial tissue is an organization of cells closely put together with little or no intercellular liquid filling the spaces in between. It serves as a protection, for excretion, absorption, as a filter and to disseminate. The lining of the body's inner organs, cavities, mucous membranes, and the epidermis are made of ephithelial tissue. Its cells are renewed by mitosis and are nourished by the underlying tissues, as it does not itself hold any blood vessels. Epithelial tissue may consist of one or several cell layers.

Lymph and blood vessels are lined by one layer of flat cells. This simple squamous epithelium also surrounds the alveoli and covers the surface of membranes in the chest cavity. Striated squamous epithelium has several cell layers. It protects mouth and oesophagus and makes up the outer layer of the skin.

Two types of cells, goblet and columnar cells, are found in simple columnar epithelium, partly lining the respiratory tract, stomach and intestines.

Connective tissue comprises most body tissue. It supports by forming the body's framework, connects organs, bones and all other structures. The cells in the connective tissue are relatively far apart, with abundant intercellular matter. The quality of the intercellular substance, whether it is soft or firm, gelatinous or fibrous, determines the features of the connective tissue and distinguishes among the following:

Delicate, loose connective tissue which fills the spaces between organs and other tissues, (e.g. between the skin and inside body);

Dense, elastic connective tissue which builds tendons, ligaments, dermis and is the texture of scars;

Cartilage which is firm and flexible, shapes noses and ears, connects the ribs and joints and extends support to structures within the body. Bones contain an addition of calcium and phosphorus for firmness. They protect and support.

An exceptional kind of connective tissue is the fatty or adipose tissue. Fat is stored in the cell to an extent, pushing cytoplasm and nucleus towards the cell membrane. Fatty tissue, such as that found under the skin, protects, supports, and is a reserve source of energy.

Reticular tissue is an arrangement of cells and fibres resembling a network or frame such as in the spleen, lymph nodes, and bone marrow.

Haemopoietic tissue serves for the formation of blood and lymph cells. Blood is a liquid intercellular substance for the transportation of blood cells.

Muscle tissue is made of long, stretched fibrous cells which are able to contract and create body movement. The muscle tissue can be classified according to location or nerve control to which it is subject. The muscle types and their properties are discussed in a separate chapter.

Nerve tissue is spread throughout the body and is composed of greatly differentiated cells. Nerve cells are not reproduced or replaced during the entire lifetime. Nerve tissue is discussed in one of the following chapters.

The tissues develop from the three primary germ layers which form in the early stage of growth of the embryo: the outer layer or ectoderm forms skin and its appendages and the nervous system; the middle layer or mesoderm forms muscles, bones and other connective tissue; the inner layer or entoderm forms the lining of the digestive and respiratory tracts, glands and bladder.

THE SKIN AND ITS ACCESSORY ORGANS

The inside and outside of the human body is covered by membranes serving specific purposes. On the inside, the mucous membranes line all passages of the body leading to the outside, such as the mouth, nose and the excretory tracts. Serous membranes are found in the body's cavities and around the organs while synovial membranes line tendons and joint cavities.

The cutaneous membrane, or skin, covers almost the entire outside of the body. Being in direct contact with the environment like all sense organs, it has to perform continuously many-sided tasks. The skin's accessory organs enable it to fulfill these functions to perfection. The skin distinguishes itself from the body's lining tissue by its structure. In an average sized person it covers approximately 2 m², with a weight of around 4.5 kg for epidermis and dermis together. The weight of the subcutaneous tissue varies greatly in different people.

As the largest and, at the same time, one of the body's most important organs, the skin's proper, undisturbed activity is required for the process of life and preservation of health. The skin is the mirror which reflects youth and age, as well as health and sickness. Internal disorders and harmful outside influences cause rashes or skin diseases.

The skin colour is determined by a pigment, melanin, and by the thickness of the horny layer. The amount of blood in the capillaries also adds to the shade of the skin. In general, the colour is inherited and might vary from a pinkish tone to almost black, depending merely on the different quantities of melanin present in the skin's layers.

Skin functions include protection of the body against outside attacks, regulation of body fluid and temperature, excretion, and reception of nerve impulses.

The skin structure

The epidermis and dermis constitute the skin's main layers, of which the epidermis is the outer, thinner layer and the dermis the inner, thicker layer.

The epidermis or cuticle is made up of several cell layers in which the cells move upward, undergoing different changes until they reach the surface where they are shed. This is a continuous sequence. The cell

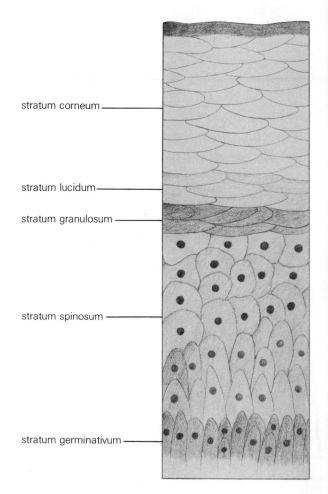

Diagram of the epidermis

is columnar at the beginning and becomes a flat horny scale at the end. The epidermis is avascular and made up of stratified squamous epithelial tissue, whereas the dermis is made of fibrous connective tissue. The parallel ridges found in the dermis form the relief of the epidermis. This differs in each person.

The thickness of the epidermis can be from less than 0.5 mm, e.g. on the eyelids, up to about 1 mm. The dermis averages around 2.4 mm.

The epidermis has four layers except on the soles of the feet and palms of the hands, where it has five. The layers are distinguished according to cell shape and functions and are as follows, from inside to the skin surface:

1 Stratum germinativum or stratum basale is a single row of columnar shaped cells. It is the only layer in the epidermis where the cells divide; this takes place at the same rate as the skin is shed. This layer deposits melanin for skin protection against ultra-violet rays (melanocytes).

In the diagram labels (top to bottom): stratum corneum, stratum lucidum, stratum granulosum, stratum spinosum, stratum germinativum

2 Stratum spinosum, the prickle cell layer, is made of several layers of irregularly-shaped cells. In a dark skin, melanin is also present here.

3 Stratum granulosum is named because of the granules to be seen in the cell cytoplasm. The cells die in this layer, turning into a horny substance.

4 Stratum lucidum is only present in the palms and foot-soles. Eleidin a translucent compound is formed in the cells from which this layer received its name.

5 Stratum corneum, the horny layer at the skin's surface, is composed of dead cells made of keratin, a water-repellant substance of protein.

It takes about three weeks for the skin cells to reach the stratum corneum from the stratum germinativum, to die and to be flaked off. Depending upon skin condition, we shed in general 10 g of skin scales daily, together with lipids, a waxy substance of fatty acids and cell-reduction products. Liquid collection between epidermis and dermis is a blister.

The dermis (derma, corium, cutis vera), also called the true skin, is made of fibrous connective tissue that gives the skin its pliability. It is a network of delicate elastic, collagenous and reticular fibres. Collagenous fibres are made of up to 75 per cent water, which is reduced if they are damaged by climatic influences and in advanced years, adding to the skin's aging process. These fibres represent the main protein contents of the skin, bones, tendons and other connective tissue. The skin's fibres are arranged in certain directions which determine the fissures of the membrane. Numerous capillaries, lymph vessels, hair follicles, arrector pili muscles, sweat glands, oil glands, and nerve endings are present in the dermis.

The two layers of the dermis are the papillary layer and the reticular layer. The upper or papillary layer contains capillaries which supply the cells of the stratum germinativum through osmosis with the necessary nourishment for reproduction. Papillae, projections reaching into the lower part of the epidermis, hold looped capillaries and nerve endings. The papillary layer contains a small amount of melanin. The reticular layer, the lower part of the dermis, is the transition zone to the adipose tissue and has already some fat cells (lipocytes).

The adipose (subcutaneous) tissue is a layer of loose connective tissue mainly consisting of fat cells which is found below the dermis. The thickness of the fatty lower layer varies according to body part, e.g. only a very fine layer surrounds the eyes, whereas hips and abdomen tend to build up adipose tissue. The fatty tissue under the skin serves the body as a protection, acts as an insulator, and also extends support and shapes the silhouette. The fat storage is an energy source for body functions and a reserve to fall back upon in case of sickness. In old age, the adipose tissue either grows to become thick and flabby or reduces, giving a person a lean look.

The appendages or accessory organs of the skin are hair, nails, and sebaceous, ceruminous and sudoriferous glands.

Hair

Hair is distributed all over the human body except for the palms and the soles. Three different kinds may be distinguished: fine or lanugo hair; short, bristly hair; and long hair.

Lanugo hair is the almost invisible fluff covering the body which is already present on the skin of the embryo and stays through all phases of life.

Bristly hair is the short hair of eyebrows (supercilia), eyelashes, (cilia), and hair in nose and ears. The latter is, in most cases, only seen in the later years of life. Bristly hair distinguishes itself from the two other kinds of hair by not being equipped with an erector pili muscle. It performs the function of protecting the sense organs from dust, sweat and insects.

Head hair, beard and long body hair comes under the heading long hair. The density of hair growth varies, as well as the strength of hair, which is an inherited characteristic. However, if the hair is fine, it grows closer than coarse hair. Approximate figures as to hair density based on hair colour, reveal that blonde heads come in first place with 140 000 hairs, next brown with 110 000, black with 100 000 and red with 90 000.

Rate of growth Human hair is not shed in a cycle like animal hair and reaches an average age of 2 to 4 years. The eyebrows renew themselves in 150 days. Scalp hair grows about 1 cm per month and faster in summer than during winter.

The number of hairs lost daily in the process of normal hair renewal is about 60. This is carried out in the same sequence in which the skin is shed. The cells in the deepest layer divide into daughter cells forcing the foregoing cells into the next upper layer. As long as the reproductive cells are not destroyed, hair is replaced. When a hair is shed, it is cut off from the supply of nourishment at the hair bulb and moves upward in the follicle to fall out.

Structure   The hair is embedded in the hair follicle, a tube-like pocket of the two skin layers, the epidermis and the dermis. The bottom of the follicle is the hair papilla, in which looped capillaries for hair nourishment are found together with the reproductive cell. The part of the hair under the skin surface which ends with the hair bulb in the papilla is the hair root; the visible part above the skin is the hair shaft.

Hair (pilus) is chiefly composed of keratin with additional quantities of carbon and other chemicals. Two layers surround the inner layer or medulla: the middle layer or cortex, and the outer scaly layer, the cuticle. Hair colour depends on the amount of melanin in the cortex and air content, which lets the hair appear lighter or darker through the reflection of light. Dry hair seems lighter than wet or oily hair, owing to the fact that fat and water particles replace air. Greying of hair is discussed in a chapter under disorders.

The hair follicle reaches into the skin at an angle, which is curved if the hair is wavy or curly. Straight hair is round, wavy hair oval and kinky hair almost flat in cross section.

Sebaceous glands (oil glands) are attached to the hair follicle in the papillary layer of the dermis. Their oil (sebum) is secreted for lubrication of skin and hair. A small involuntary muscle, the arrector pili muscle, is attached as well to the hair follicle. This muscle makes the hair stand on end by contracting and pressing it into a straight position. This way, the skin raises around the follicle, forming a goose pimple.

Nails

Nails (onyx) are a horny structure made of transparent layers of flat keratin cells which serve to protect finger and toe ends. The nail originates from the matrix underneath the skin fold or mantle at the base of the nail body.

The matrix contains the only living, reproductive cells of the nail. After the cells have been formed, they undergo a change into keratin in the transformation zone, from where they are pushed by succeeding cells into the nail root. They leave the nail root and the skin passing into the lunula, a white half-moon, which colour is due to light reflection in the

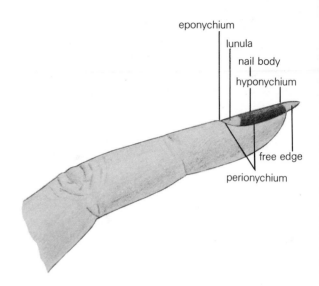

The nail

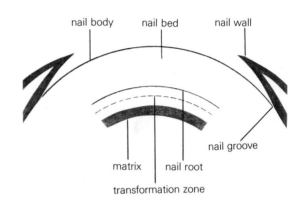

Cross-section of the nail

area where root and nail bed join. From there the nail reaches to the free edge, the part of the nail body extending over the fingertip. Like all horny substances it contains protein and sulphur.

The nail plate arches over the nail bed, which is well-supplied with nerves and blood vessels. The elevations on both sides of the nail are the nail walls, going down towards the nail body into the nail grooves. The extension of the stratum corneum overlapping the edge around the nail is the cuticle or perionychium. At the base of the lunula, it is also named eponychium. The skin under the free edge is the hyponchium.

Nails grow more slowly on toes than fingers; in an adult they grow around 3 mm a month, in a child it is more. It takes four to six months for a nail to be completely renewed from the base to the free edge.

Skin glands

The skin's glands are exocrine or duct glands which, contrary to those of the endocrine system, excrete their content by means of a duct to the body surface. The 3 minute glands of the skin are sebaceous, sweat and ceruminous.

Sebaceous glands are in the skin wherever hair grows on the body. There are only a few exceptions where they are without a hairshaft, e.g. close to the lips between the skin and mucous membrane. Even if the hair has been permanently destroyed, the oil glands continue to excrete. Footsoles and palms of the hands have no hair and consequently no sebaceous glands.

Sebaceous glands are microscopic sacks arranged in a pair or more around the hair follicle, which they use as a duct to excrete sebum. Oil glands serve to make hair and skin soft and pliable. Sebum forms a fine film on the skin, helps to keep the skin waterproof and assists in regulating the body temperature, as fat is a poor conductor.

Sudoriferous or sweat glands are embedded in the reticular layer of the dermis. From the coiled base or fundus, a tube-like duct extends perpendicular to the skin surface ending in the sweat pore. There is no connection between hair growth and sweat glands. On the contrary, sweat glands are more numerous in those areas where hair is missing, such as the palms and soles.

The two kinds of sweat gland are the apocrine and the eccrine sweat glands. Apocrine glands are found under the arm and in the groin. Eccrine glands are all over the body, and in large numbers on the forehead and in the axillae on palms and soles. Like all glands, sweat glands are well equipped with nerve fibres and blood vessels. The larger of the two, the apocrine glands, develop during adolescence.

Perspiration is controlled by the sympathetic nervous system. About half a litre of liquid is excreted by the sweat pores daily under normal conditions. Physical work, emotions, high temperatures, stimulants and drugs are among the factors increasing sweat excretion. Sweat is composed of about 99 per cent water, mineral salts and nitrogenous wastes. The chemical reaction of sweat (sudor) is acid, an important factor in the body's defence against infections (acid mantle). By excreting sweat to its surface, the skin counts as one of the excretory organs of the human body.

Ceruminous glands are situated in the external ear canal. They excrete a waxy, yellowish substance, cerumen, serving as a protection against dust and insects for the drum and inner parts of the ear.

Mammary glands, a type of a modified sweat gland, excrete only after child birth.

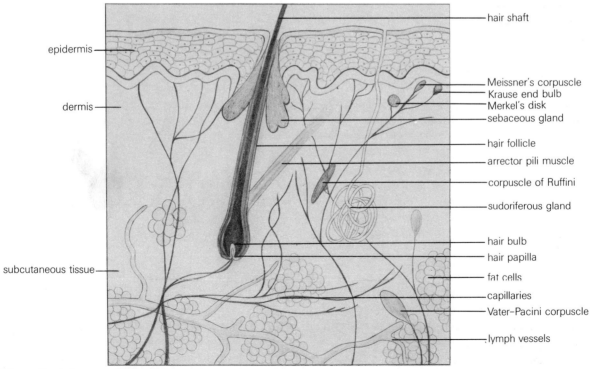

Schematized diagram of the skin

epidermis

dermis

subcutaneous tissue

hair shaft

Meissner's corpuscle
Krause end bulb
Merkel's disk
sebaceous gland

hair follicle

arrector pili muscle

corpuscle of Ruffini

sudoriferous gland

hair bulb
hair papilla
fat cells
capillaries
Vater–Pacini corpuscle
lymph vessels

Blood and lymph vessels of the skin

The skin is abundantly supplied with nourishment by blood vessels in the dermis and papillae, extending into the stratum germinativum. The layers of the epidermis above the stratum germinativum are not reached by blood vessels; however, tissue fluid is still found in the next layer, the stratum spinosum.

More than half to three-quarters of the body's total blood content is distributed to the skin. The capillaries adjust themselves to the connective tissue in the dermis and subcutis for protection, so that they are not damaged by pulling or pressure.

The capillaries of the skin serve as the main regulators of body temperature, as well as for blood storage. By blood concentration in the skin's capillaries heat from inside the body is given away to the environment. The capillaries are well equipped with nerve fibres which can cause them to expand and turn the complexion pink or red, or to contract, creating paleness. By storage of liquid the skin helps balance the body's fluid.

A network of fine canals between the cells is filled with intercellular liquid, a clear fluid supplied to the cells by osmosis. Here, dead end vessels called lymphatics originate to carry the lymph away after the exchange of nourishment and waste products. The lymph passes through lymph nodes in the subcutaneous tissue to be filtered before returning into the body.

The skin – a sense organ

The skin, the body's outer cover and largest sense organ, contains numerous microscopic nerve endings. They are present all over the body's external surface in the dermis and the subcutis. The receptors note sensations brought to the skin from outside and convey them to the central nervous system (cerebrum and thalamus). Each of these sensory nerves and their endings is irritable to a certain stimulus and has specific tasks of perceiving temperature, touch, pressure or pain. Autonomic nerve endings are attached to sweat and oil glands, skin fibres and blood vessels. The skin's nerves are a warning system, the body's protection against injuries.

Some body regions are more sensitive than others as they contain more nerve endings than the rest of the skin. An example is the fingertips. In case another sense organ is damaged, the skin takes over to assist the body to adjust itself to the situation by becoming specified and highly perceptible to minor impulses.

Heat and cold   To distinguish between sensations in temperatures the corpuscles of Ruffini function as receptors for heat and the Krause end bulbs for cold. Even minor changes in temperature in the body's environment are noticed and reported by these nerve endings. However, the sense of hot and cold is relative, and we feel neither as an absolute temperature, but as a difference when changing from one to the other. After a while, the body adjusts itself to a temperature, calling forth no more reactions. The same applies to objects with which the body comes in touch. Here another factor also plays a part: a poor conductor like cloth feels warmer than a good conductor like metal at the same temperature.

Pain is perhaps the most important of all sensations conveyed by the skin nerves, as it protects the body against harm. Without the sense of pain, the body could be seriously hurt unknowingly. All perceptions, heat, cold, pressure and touch, are painful if excessive. Through pressure, the skin becomes indented or deformed, regaining its normal shape after the cause is no longer present. This leaves the skin surface numb for a while until the compressed blood vessels and nerves take up their normal functions. Pressure is only felt at the beginning when the nerve endings (Vater–Pacini corpuscles) receive the initial impulse. The intensity of the sensations depends upon the speed and power of impact and size of skin portion affected. A complex of nerve endings is generally involved in the perception of a skin sensation.

The receptors of touch are tactile corpuscles in the papillae of the dermis (Meissner's corpuscles), Merkel's disks and the arrangements of nerve endings around the hair papillae. The slightest stroke, or only a motion close to the hairshaft, lets the hair move, and is registered by the receptors around the follicle.

Regulation of body temperature

As mentioned, the body temperature is greatly influenced by the skin capillaries, keeping it within certain degrees, around 37 °C. If the body produces increased heat, it has to get rid of it to keep the balance of its temperature. This must also be maintained under different external conditions like hot and cold climates. Approximately 80 per cent of the heat given away by the body passes through the skin; the rest is transferred through the lungs and the digestive and urinary tracts. To lose heat, energy has to be used. This is done through sweat evaporation into the surroundings. The capillaries dilate to expel heat; sweat is simultaneously excreted by the sudoriferous glands. Dry, hot climates make it easier for the body to adjust its temperature, while in a damp climate, the air is so moist that sweat cannot be evaporated as easily, and this interferes with the body's cooling system.

Body heat is transmitted through contact with objects of a lower temperature and vice versa. This process is known as heat radiation.

The skin – a body protection

The skin's anatomic structure, the elasticity and firmness of its fibres, and the under-lying adipose tissue, reduce the chance of mechanical injuries to the body. Adipose tissue, being a soft, fatty layer, is like a cushion which rebounds blows and other impacts. This is of great importance in preventing damage to the sensitive inner organs. The skin glides easily over the fatty layer without being bruised or hurt.

Keratin, a chemical and physical barrier in the epidermis, hinder penetration of water and other matter into the skin. The protection system is supported by its natural functions as an excretory organ, giving away sudor and sebum to the surface as well as shedding horny scales. These physiological processes take place from the inside to the outside and of course, represent a problem when it comes to influencing the skin in the opposite direction. However, penetration and absorption are to some extent possible by way of the skin's openings, the pores and intercellular space, when the substance is rubbed or massaged into the skin. Oil in water (O/W) emulsions, preparations on a gelatinous base and liquids are more easily accepted by the skin than fats. Gases have the greatest chance to penetrate. Melanin granules in the epidermis, keratin and sweat are our innate screen against ultra-violet rays and heat radiation in normal amounts.

(Note: Tyrosine an amino acid, is oxidated with the assistance of the enzyme tyrosinase to dopa, a dark pigment.)

The acid mantle, a fine film of sudor and sebum, covers the skin's surface and prevents it from drying out. Sweat extends to it varying acidity of 6 pH to 7 pH depending upon body portion. The acid environment counteracts the development of fungi and bacteria. After removal of the acid mantle with alkaline products it takes normal skin up to three hours to regain its pH balance. In case of reduced

gland activity normalization may take even longer. If the skin's functions are disturbed in any way, it reacts to alkali with a hypersensitivity. Therefore it is indicated that skincare preparations should have an adjusted pH.

The symbol pH stands for the measurement of the hydrogen-ion concentration of a solution. To demonstrate the alkalinity and acidity a scale is used ranging from pH 0 to 14. To explain further, a pH 7 indicates the neutrality of a solution, 0 to 7 the acidity and 7 to 14 the alkalinity.

THE SKELETAL SYSTEM

By giving the body posture and shape, the skeleton largely determines the personal appearance. The skeleton is the body's framework, made of bones and cartilage which complement each other in their task. Body cavities and organs are protected by bone structures such as the rib cage and skull. Movement is produced by the joints, a junction of two or three bones, in co-operation with the contractions of the muscles located above the articulation. In this way, bones serve as levers for all body movements. Bones store calcium, and blood cells are formed by haemopoiesis in the red bone marrow. The yellow marrow is predominantly fat.

Bones are made of living cells and a non-living intercellular mineral substance, chiefly calcium salts (calcium-phosphate).

The bone tissue is either dense or cancellous. The dense or compact tissue forms the long bone shafts and serves as cover for all other bones. The cancellous or spongy tissue is encased in short and flat bones and constitutes the epiphysis at the end of long bones. In cancellous tissue the firm matter is disintegrated by open spaces, whereas in dense tissue the units of the cells and the intercellular substance lie close together.

The periosteum is a fibrous, vascular, tough membrane surrounding the entire bone except the articular surface at the joints. Capillaries and nerve fibres reach through tiny canals (Volkmann's and Haversian canals) into the bone cavity to nourish marrow and bone tissue. The periosteum serves additionally to attach tendons and ligaments.

Instead of calcified minerals, the intercellular substance of cartilage is a gelatinous matter, giving it the flexibility of plastic material. It holds no blood vessels and its cells are nourished by osmosis. Hyaline

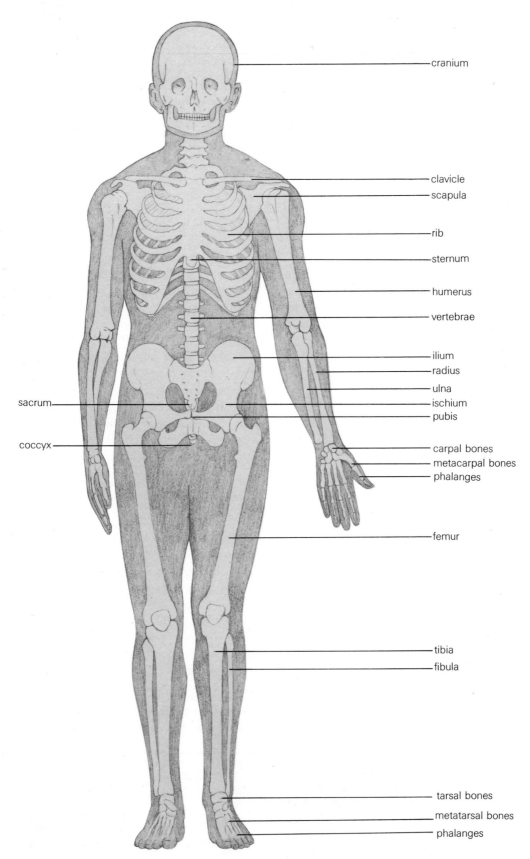

cranium

clavicle
scapula

rib

sternum

humerus

vertebrae

ilium
radius
ulna
ischium
pubis

carpal bones
metacarpal bones
phalanges

femur

tibia
fibula

tarsal bones
metatarsal bones
phalanges

sacrum

coccyx

Skeleton

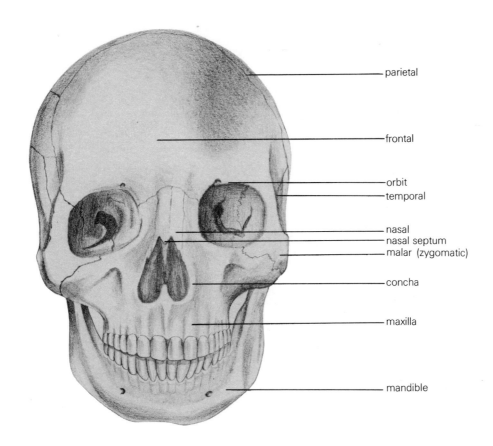

parietal

frontal

orbit
temporal

nasal
nasal septum
malar (zygomatic)

concha

maxilla

mandible

Skull front view

cartilage forms an elastic cover in joints to prevent jarring. Elastic cartilage adds to external features, and the discs between vertebrae are fibrous cartilage.

There are four bone types, divided according to their shape:

1 long bones – extremities
2 short bones – wrist and ankle
3 flat bones – skull, shoulder, ribs and pelvis
4 irregular bones – vertebrae, sphenoid, ethmoid and mandible.

The skeleton

The human skeleton may be divided into two main parts, the head and trunk, which comprises the axial skeleton with its appendages, the upper and lower limbs.

The skull is composed of two divisions contouring the head:

The cranium which protects the brain, and the facial skeleton.

The cranium consists of eight bones, two of which are paired.

1 The frontal bone forms the forehead and roof of the orbits

2 The two parietal bones, united by an immovable joint, constitute the crown of the skull.

3 The two temporal bones, located below the parietals, cover the lower sides of the cranium and contain middle and inner ear structures.

4 The occipital bone forms the base and back of the cranium. It joins with the parietals on top and the two temporals at the sides.

5 The sphenoid, an irregular bone shaped like a bat, reaches the orbits and forms part of the base of the cranium joining together the cranial bones.

6 The ethmoid, an irregular bone, lies anterior to

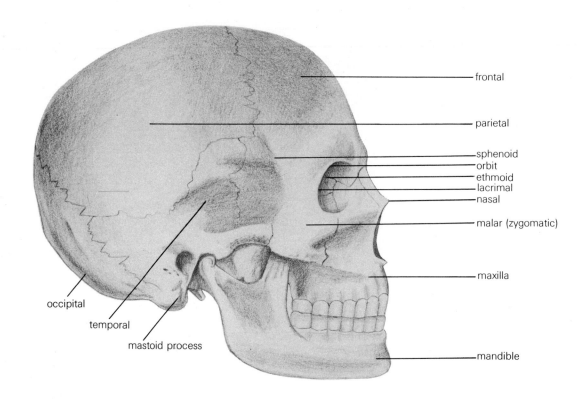

frontal

parietal

sphenoid
orbit
ethmoid
lacrimal
nasal

malar (zygomatic)

maxilla

mandible

occipital

temporal

mastoid process

Skull side view

the sphenoid and posterior to the nasal bones, shaping part of the nasal cavities.

The facial bones are fourteen bones arranged to mould the features. The framework is built of irregular bones, most of them in pairs, and is set up to form the orbits, part of the nose and to shape the mouth cavity.

1 The two maxillae are the second largest bones of the facial skeleton and are united to form part of the roof of the mouth, the floor of the orbits, floor and side of the nose and the upper jaw. The maxillae are connected with all facial bones except the mandible and, as such, act the same way in the face as the sphenoid in the cranium, to hold the entire structure together.

2 The mandible or lower jaw is a single bone and the strongest and largest of the face's architecture. It is attached to the temporal bones by movable joints, the only movable joints of the skull.

3 The two palatine bones form the back portion of the palate, the floor of the orbits and part of the nasal cavity.

4 The two zygomatics or malar bones are the cheek-bones, and as such are part of the floor and sidewalls of the orbits.

5 The two nasal bones at the bridge of the nose shape the nose in conjunction with the septum and the cartilage at their lower part.

6 The lacrimal bones are two thin bones, similar in size and form to fingernails. They are located in the inner corner of the orbits and, as indicated by their name, contain the grooves for the tear-ducts.

7 The two turbinates or turbinal bones (because of their shell-like structure also called conchae) are situated in the nasal cavity.

8 The vomer is a bone at the upper part of the septum, joining the palatines, maxillae, sphenoid and ethmoid.

The hyoid bone is a U-shaped, single bone in the neck in front of the larynx. It supports the tongue and is the only bone in the body not articulating with any other bone.

20

The vertebral column or spine The vertebral column represents the backbone and central support of the body. Situated at the body's back, it combines two important but opposing functions: namely, to be very flexible yet of great stability. A series of irregular bones compose the five regions of the spine: seven cervical vertebrae, twelve thoracic vertebrae, five lumbar vertebrae, the sacrum and the coccyx.

The vertebrae The 26 bones of the spine differ slightly in shape. The smallest vertebrae are found at the top of the column, increasing in size progressively until they reach the pelvis and from there on decreasing to end in the coccyx. The spine is curved in order to balance the body's weight.

Vertebrae articulate with each other by means of discs, enabling the body to bend to all sides. The discs are made of cartilage which acts as a cushion between the vertebrae. The entire spinal structure is held together by strong ligaments and in this way the vertebrae are impeded from slipping off each other. Each vertebra is made of a box-like body with a bony arch at its back, surrounded by three projections which serve as a muscle attachment to assist body movements. The spinal cord connects the brain by way of the spinal cavity with all other body parts.

The first two vertebrae of the neck differ in build from the rest. The first, the atlas, supports the skull and is shaped like a ring, allowing nodding of the head. The second cervical vertebra is the axis. It has a small upward process about which the atlas rotates with the movements of the head.

The thoracic vertebrae form the upper part of the back and the lumbar vertebrae the lower part. In an adult the sacrum is a fusion of five vertebrae to a single bone. The coccyx originates from four to five poorly developed vertebrae fused together.

The thorax Twelve pairs of ribs attached to the thoracic vertebrae combine with the sternum to make up the thorax. Of the twelve ribs, seven are directly and three indirectly affixed by cartilage to the sternum in front of the chest, while the last two end in muscle tissue and are therefore called floating ribs. The sternum, a flat dagger-shaped bone, articulates with the clavicles in its upper portion.

The shoulder girdle consists of the clavicles and the two scapulae or shoulder blades. The scapula is a flat, triangular bone attached to the ribs by muscles and tendons. The clavicle or collar bone lies in front of the scapula; it is joined to the scapula and to the sternum. It contains the glenoid cavity, the socket for the head of the humerus.

Arms and hands The upper extremities include the upper arm, lower arm, wrist, palm and fingers.

The humerus is a long bone shaft of which the upper end is connected with the shoulder girdle by a ball and socket joint and the lower with the bones of the forearm by a hinge joint.

Radius and ulna are the long bones of the lower arm. The radius is located on the thumb side and the ulna, a thinner bone, on the little-finger side.

Eight short, irregular bones constitute the wrist or carpus, a flexible joint held together by ligaments. The carpal bones are arranged in two rows of four each. Starting from the thumb side of the arm they are as follows: the navicular, lunate, triquetrum, pisiform, greater and lesser multangular, capitate and hamate. The skeleton of the hand is constructed of five metacarpal bones, long bones the heads of which form the knuckles of the hand.

The fourteen phalanges are the small, long bones of the fingers or digits. There are three phalanges in each finger: proximal, middle and distal phalanx; but only two in the thumb.

The pelvic girdle is made of two irregular hip bones, each combining three parts, the ilium, ischium and pubis. The pelvic bones differ in the male and female skeleton. The male pelvis is funnel-shaped while the female pelvis is broad and shallow to allow the birth of a child. The hip bones meet with the sacrum at the back and contain the socket for the head of the femur to form the hip joints. Strong ligaments affix the femur or thigh bone to the pelvic girdle.

The femur is the longest bone of the lower extremities and the largest and heaviest single bone of the human skeleton. Below the head and neck of the femur are two projections, the greater and lesser trochanter, which serve as muscle attachments. The lateral and medial condyles are the femur's processes at the lower end, where it joins the tibia or shin to form the knee.

The patella or kneecap, a sesamoid bone, protects the knee joint in front and is embedded in the tendon of the quadriceps femoris.

The tibia, the stronger and larger bone of the lower leg, carries the weight. Its thick, upper end (lateral and medial condyle) has a flat surface that articulates with the condyles of the femur. The fibula, the thinner bone in the calf, joins the lateral condyle of the tibia. The fibula and tibia form a box-like structure (the ankle socket) over the talus, one of the tarsal bones. The fibula is the long, thin outer bone of the lower leg, whereas the tibia is the inner and thicker bone.

Feet have a similar architecture to hands. However, they are adjusted to their task of carrying and balancing the entire body weight. The tarsus consists of seven short bones fashioning the ankle and heel: the talus, calcaneus, cuboid, navicular and three cuneiforms. The two largest tarsal bones are the talus and calcaneus, which forms the heel. The metatarsals are the small, long bones in the foot and the fourteen phalanges, the bones of the toes. As the thumb, the big toe has only two phalanges, whereas all other toes have three: the proximal, middle and distal.

The foot derives its strength and spring from the leg muscle tendons and from three arches which are supported and held together by strong ligaments. Tarsals and metatarsals are arranged to form two arches lengthwise: the outer, lateral longitudinal arch and the inner, medial longitudinal arch. The third arch, the transverse arch, is shaped by the metatarsals and the distal row of the tarsals.

Bones are connected in various ways to allow a great variety of movements in different body parts. Two major types of articulation are distinguished, according to their construction: freely movable joints, slightly movable and immovable joints.

Diarthroses

The majority of joints in the human skeleton are freely movable, with a joint cavity creating a space between the articulating bones. Hyaline cartilage covers the surface of the bone-ends. The joint is encased in a capsule lined with a synovial membrane, which lubricates the cavity with the sticky synovial fluid to prevent friction. Tough, flexible, fibrous tissue in the form of ligaments keeps adjoining bones firmly together.

Freely-movable joints are subdivided into:
1 ball and socket joints – shoulders, hips
2 pivot joints – neck, between radius and ulna
3 hinge joints – elbow, knee, ankle
4 gliding joints – between carpal bones
5 saddle joints – between metacarpal and carpal bones
6 ellipsoidal joints – between radius and carpals

Synarthroses

Immovable and slightly-immovable joints distinguish themselves principally from the freely-movable joints through the absence of a joint cavity. Fibrous tissue, cartilage or bone grow between them, contacting the bone surfaces. Immovable joints, connected by fibrous tissue, are the articulations (sutures) of the skull. Slightly or semi-movable joints, also called amphiarthrotic joints, articulating by means of cartilage discs are found between the vertebrae.

THE MUSCULAR SYSTEM

The muscular system includes all types of the body's muscles: those attached to bones, those enclosing organs, and the muscles forming the internal structures. The functions of the muscles are as follows:

1 To produce movement – that is, movement of the skeleton (locomotion), and inner organs to maintain the vital process;

2 To support the body's posture by making different body positions possible;

3 To produce body heat. The chemical reactions taking place in the muscle cells supply energy for movement and release heat simultaneously.

Characteristics of muscles are: Irritability: The ability to respond to natural stimuli by nerves, as well as to react to artificial stimuli such as electric current, rays, temperatures, chemicals and massage.

Elasticity: The ability to contract, shorten and thicken, and then to relax and reassume the original shape.

The normal degree of muscle tension, a continuous partial contraction, is muscle tone or tonus. It makes body posture possible. Without muscle tension the body would collapse; too much tension may result in spasms. Good posture is the natural deportment which maintains the body's best balance; poor posture counteracts gravity, and therefore strains muscles, body structures and systems.

Muscle tissue can be classified according to shape, nerve control, and location. In appearance it is distinguished between striated and non-striated tissue as to cell structure. In striated or striped muscle tissue, such as is found in skeletal and cardiac muscles, the cells show cross stripes. The non-striated or smooth muscle tissue in the walls of organs and internal structures (the visceral muscles), is made up of cells that look like slender, smooth, overlapping spindles.

Nerve control From the aspect of nerve control, the muscle tissue can be divided into two sections, voluntary and involuntary. The contractions of the voluntary skeletal muscles are controlled by the cerebrospinal nervous system and are subject to will. The movements of the involuntary muscles, like visceral and cardiac muscles, are not controlled by will; their nerve fibres belong to the autonomic nervous system.

If the nerve impulses from the cerebrospinal system are interrupted, or the nerve cells damaged, skeletal muscles are paralyzed. They, unlike visceral and cardiac muscles, cannot function without nerve stimuli. Taking all three characteristics into consideration, the muscle classification is as follows:
1 the skeletal muscle is a striated, voluntary muscle
2 the cardiac muscle is a striated, involuntary muscle
3 the visceral muscle is a non-striated, involuntary muscle.

Skeletal muscle fibres The so-called red flesh of the body is made up of skeletal muscle fibres, which are set up in different directions in relation to the muscle's activity. The muscle size and shape differs according to the grouping of the fibres. From a central tendon muscle fibres may reach out to both sides, similar to a feather. Some muscles resemble a spindle, some are broad and others narrow. They may be flat sheets or round, and can be long, stretched or a short mass as well as curved, like the ring-shaped muscles of the face. This enables the muscle to fulfill the task in its location precisely and efficiently.

A fibrous sheath of connective tissue (fascia) encloses the muscles and serves as a partition between single fibres and bundles of muscle fibres. Aponeurosis is a strong, tough, and flat fibrous tissue, connecting muscles to each other and to body structures. Tendons extend as transferers of muscle strength to parts where there is no muscle close to the location to perform movement, for example, in the fingers. They also serve as an attachment of muscle to bone.

Motor nerves transmit impulses to the skeletal muscles. The smaller the muscle supplied by a motor neuron, the more precise the movements. The facial expressions, their detailed responses and reflections, are only possible because of the presence of a number of small muscles.

A movement is a teamwork of bone, muscle and motor nerve. Skeletal muscles produce movement through contraction and relaxation, assisting the bones in their capacity as levers. Each muscle passes over one or more joints and when contracting, pulls on a bone causing it to move. Muscles bringing about movement of a limb are located close to the part affected, generally in the next upper portion of the limb. Most body actions are carried out by the coordination of several muscles. Depending upon its position, the muscle either contracts or relaxes during the procedure.

Muscle names These muscles are designated as to their main functions: *abductors* move bones away from the body; *adductors* move them toward the body; *flexors* decrease joint angle; *extensors* straighten and return a body part to normal position; *levators* raise a body part and *depressors* lower it; *tensors* tighten a part, *rotators* let a body part turn upon its axis; *sphincters* close body openings; *pronators* turn the palm of the hand downward and *supinators* turn it upward.

In addition to functions, muscle names indicate directions of fibres, number of divisions, shape, location and point of attachment. Skeletal muscles are attached to bones and receive their names from the bone or bones to which they are relatively firmly affixed, referred to as the origin of the muscle. The movable muscle attachment is the insertion of the muscle, which is usually another bone. Facial muscles are an exception: they may originate at a bone, but end freely in the skin and create facial expressions through their contractions. They are delicate, fine structures which are sometimes composed of only a few fibres and, because of this, rough pulling and expansion (i.e. improper massage) have to be avoided. A massage must be carried out longitudinally to the direction of the muscle fibres and not laterally.

Muscle stimulation Skeletal muscles are able to contract with different degrees of strength adjusted to the work demanded. A muscle continues to be firm and strong as long as it is active; therefore, it follows that exercise strengthens and enlarges muscles. A similar result is achieved by massage, as well as by muscle contraction and relaxation through artificial stimuli: however, these methods are not as effective. Strenuous physical work or exercise stimulates muscles repeatedly and may be followed by muscle fatigue, in which the muscles no longer respond to stimuli.

Bursae are small sacs of connective tissue filled with synovial fluid. They are located between bones, tendons, muscles or ligaments and act as a cushion wherever there is pressure between moving structures.

Muscles of the head

The top of the skull is covered by the epicranius or occipito frontalis, of which the occipital belly originates at the occopital bone at the base of the head. The frontal belly extends over the forehead to the tissues of the eyebrows and raises eyebrows, causing horizontal wrinkles across the forehead.

The muscles of the face are:
orbicularis oculi – encircles the eye and closes eye,
orbicularis oris – encircles the mouth and closes lips,
corrugator – originates at the frontal bone and ends in the skin of the eyebrows. It wrinkles the forehead vertically and causes frowning,
procerus – a small muscle over the bridge of the nose draws down eyebrows,
nasalis – covers the nose,
quadratus labii superioris – at the upper lip, consists of the angular head, infraorbital head and zygomatic head – draws back the upper lip and pulls up nostrils,
quadratus labii inferioris – situated at the lower lips, draws and depresses lower lip,
caninus – a small muscle under the quadratus labii superioris, raises the mouth corners,
buccinator – originates at the maxilla, ends at the side of the mouth – brings about smiles and dimples in the cheeks, permits blowing,
risorius – originates at masseter, extends to mouth corner, draws back mouth corner,
zygomaticus – originates at zygomatic bone, extends to lip corner, permits laughing by drawing corners back and upward,
triangularis – extends from the chin to the lower mouth corner, draws corners down,
mentalis – a small muscle at the chin reaching to the lips, moves bottom lip,
superior auricular – a muscle located above the ear which is practically immovable,

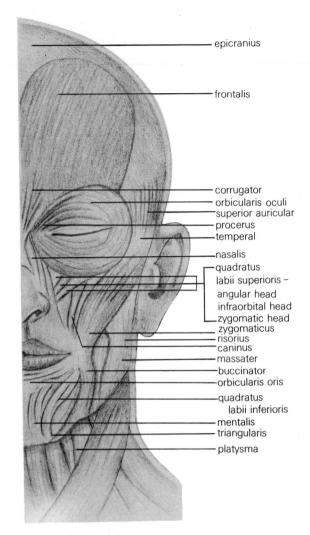

Muscles of the head

masseter – originates at zygomatic arch and extends to mandible, closes jaw, muscle of mastication,
temporal – extends from temporal bone to mandible, closes jaw and is a muscle of mastication similar to the masseter,
platysma – a sheet of muscle tissue extending from deltoid and pectoralis major to mandible, draws corners of mouth down.

Muscles of the neck and back

Sternocleidomastoid – originates at sternum and clavicle and extends to temporal bone – moves head, permits nodding,
trapezius – extends from occipital bone to scapula and clavicle – moves head, raises and lowers shoulders,
latissimus dorsi – extends from the vertebrae to humerus – moves arms down, back and inward.

24

Muscles of the chest

Pectoralis major – originates at sternum and clavicle, insertion is the humerus – moves arm forward, pectoralis minor – originates at ribs and extends to scapula – moves shoulder and scapula, serratus anterior – is attached to ribs and extends to scapula – raises arm and pulls shoulder forward.

Muscles of shoulder, arm and hand

Deltoid – reaches from clavicle and scapula to humerus – extends and moves upper arm away from body, biceps – has a long and short head; origin is the scapula and insertion the radius – flexes forearm, turns forearm and hand upward, triceps – as the name indicates, has three heads – attached to the scapula and upper humerus and reaches to the ulna – covers back of the upper arm, extends lower arm,

brachioradialis – extends from humerus along radius – flexes forearm, turns lower arm and hand inside, brachialis – reaches from humerus to ulna – flexes forearm pronators – extend from ulna and humerus to radius – stretch and pronate forearm, supinator – originates at humerus and ulna – the insertion is at radius – supinates lower arm, flexors – originate at humerus and ulna and have their insertion at metacarpals and pisiform – they bend forearm and hand and turn palm downward, extensors – reach from humerus and ulna to metacarpals – extend hand and fingers.

Muscles of the leg and foot

Muscles originating from the ilium, sacrum and coccyx and ending at the bones of the leg, like the gluteus and rectus femoris, assist in leg movements.

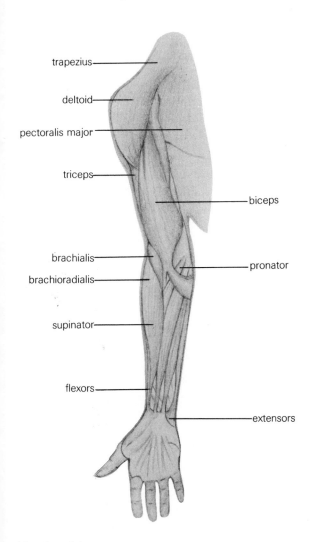

Muscles of the arm

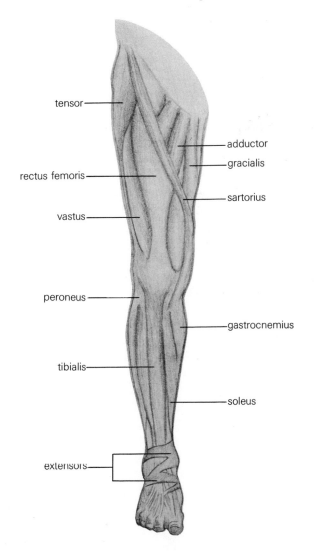

Muscles of the leg

The following are the leg muscles located in the leg itself and of interest in the study of the subject of this book:

tensor – extends from ilium to tibia – abducts thigh,

rectus femoris – originates at ilium and reaches to tibia – flexes thigh and stretches lower leg,

vastus – originates at femur, insertion tibia – extends leg,

sartorius – extends from ilium to tibia – flexes and draws leg towards body,

adductors – reach from pubis to femur and gracilis to tibia – adduct thigh and flex leg.

The following three muscles form the hamstring group:

biceps femoris – attached to the ischium and reaches the head of the fibula and from femur to tibia, flexes and extends thigh,

semitendinosus and semimembranosus – two muscles at the back of the thigh – origin ischium – insertion tibia – the same task as the biceps femoris,

peroneus – are muscles attached to tibia and fibula extending to metatarsals and first cuneiform – straighten and turn foot outside,

tibialis – originates at tibia and fibula – reaches to tarsals and metatarsals – flexes and turns foot inside,

soleus – reaches from tibia and fibula to calcaneus – straightens foot (calcaneal – achilles tendon),

gastrocnemius – is attached to femur and extends to calcaneus – flexes lower leg and straightens foot,

extensors – reach from lower leg to toes – straighten foot and toes.

THE NERVOUS SYSTEM

The body has two means of communication and co-ordination: (1) chemicals, which are the secretions of the endocrine glands, and (2) the nerve impulses. The head control station is the central nervous system, where all impulses conducted to the various body regions originate and all impressions received by the sense organs are perceived, registered and evaluated. The peripheral nervous system, whose function is to carry messages to and from body parts, is connected to the central nervous system.

The somatic nervous system comprises the brain, spinal cord and pertinent cranial and spinal nerves. It is in contrast to an entirely different independent division of the system, the autonomic (sympathetic and parasympathetic) nervous system which is in charge of the involuntary movements of the internal organs, heat regulation of the skin and all other functions beyond our conscious control.

According to location the nervous system can be divided into the central nervous system (that is, brain and spinal cord), and the peripheral nervous system consisting of cranial, spinal and autonomic nerves.

Neurons The building stones of the nervous system are neurons. Their basic function is to respond to stimuli by conveying impulses. Just as all cells are built to carry out specific tasks, the specialized structure of a neuron enables it to receive and transmit sensations. A neuron is a unit comprised

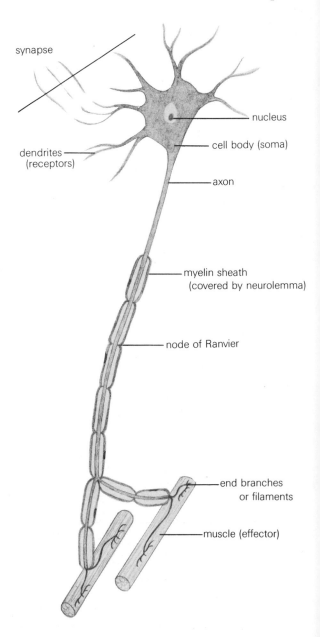

synapse

nucleus

cell body (soma)

dendrites (receptors)

axon

myelin sheath (covered by neurolemma)

node of Ranvier

end branches or filaments

muscle (effector)

Schematized diagram of a motor neuron

of a cell body with a nucleus, the dendrites, which branch out from the cell body into the surrounding tissue, and the axon. The outer ends of the dendrites act as receptors of the initial impulse. The single axon conveys the stimulus away from the nerve cell to another neuron, muscle cell or organ. An axon may vary considerably in length, from one metre to a very minor size. Axons with a small diameter conduct less rapidly than larger ones. Axons branch out when they leave their protective sheath, which is made of myelin, a somewhat fatty substance. These end branches cause voluntary muscle movements and functions of sense organs.

Nerve cells do not reproduce and when injured, only a limited repair is possible.

Neurons classified as to their activity are: sensory or afferent neurons, which carry impulses from the sensory organs to the spinal cord or brain; and motor or efferent neurons, which transmit sensations from the brain or spinal cord to a muscle or gland (muscle action is controlled in this way). The so-called intercalated neurons in the brain and spinal cord conduct impulses from the sensory to the motor neuron.

Nerve impulses A nerve impulse begins with the stimulation of the receptor and ends with the response of the effector. It is conducted via a path of neurons to and from the brain. The contact point between the axon of a nerve cell and the dendrites of another cell is called the synapse.

A change in the environment, i.e. in temperature or pressure, stimulates the sensory nerves. The stimulus travels from the receptor, the outer ends of the dendrites of the sensory nerves in the skin, to the spinal cord and to the brain. The message returns by way of the spinal cord to the motor neuron and finally reaches its effectors, the end branches of the axon in the muscles, which carry out the message.

Whether or not a nerve stimulus follows action, and the extent of the response, depends upon the intensity of the initial impulse. If there is damage to the nervous system, the message received by the receptor cannot reach the brain and therefore cannot be returned to the effector. A loss of sensation in the skin may lead, for example, to damage through temperature.

Nerve stimulation may be attained by massage, by electric current, by light and heat or by chemicals, causing muscles to contract and relax. Artificial stimuli may be followed by an involuntary response or reflex.

Proper food, relaxation and oxygenation supply nerves with the required energy. Mental strain causes nerve fatigue.

Units of the nervous system

The nervous system is constructed of only a few units: the brain, spinal cord, nerves and ganglia. A nerve is a bundle of nerve fibres (axons and dendrites) enclosed in a sheath of connective tissue. A ganglion is a cluster of neurons outside the central nervous system. The peripheral nervous system is composed of ganglia and nerves.

The brain and spinal cord The brain and spinal cord are highly sensitive organs and are protected by nature with two coverings. The outer protection is made of bone and the inner (the meninges) consists of three layers. The dura mater, a strong fibrous tissue, lines the skull and neural canal. Directly beneath it is the arachnoid, a delicate membrane resembling a spider web. The pia mater is a soft layer trapped around the organs which contains the blood vessels to provide them with nourishment. The spaces within the organs and between their coverings are filled with cerebrospinal fluid, which acts as a protecting cushion against injury.

The brain The largest part of the brain is the cerebrum, consisting of two hemispheres of grey matter, the cerebral cortex, on the outside, and white matter in the interior. The grey matter is made of cell bodies and dendrites of neurons and the white matter is axons. The surface of the cerebrum shows numerous folds containing specialized areas with important functions: the centres for control of voluntary movements of the skeletal muscles, hearing, smell, taste, sight, memory, speech, skin sensations, intelligence, emotions and personality traits. The cerebellum is the smaller part of the brain, situated at the back of the head beneath the cerebrum. It is responsible for the co-ordination of muscular movements, muscle tone and body balance.

The medulla oblongata is a bulb at the lower part of the brain stem and connects the brain with the spinal cord. At the brain stem the nerve fibres cross over so that the right hemisphere of the brain controls the left side of the body and vice-versa.

The medulla helps in supervising heartbeat, respiration and blood pressure and mediates reflexes such as

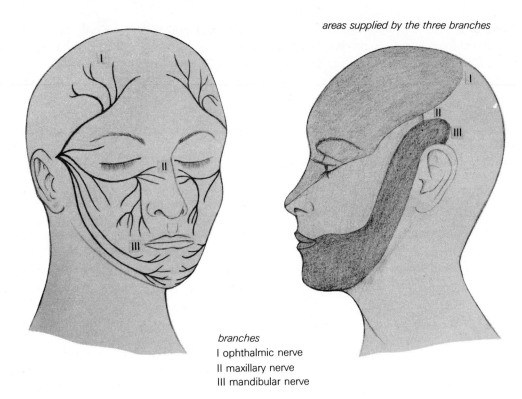

branches
I ophthalmic nerve
II maxillary nerve
III mandibular nerve

Trigeminal (fifth cranial nerve or tri facial)

coughing and vomiting. The pons lies above the medulla and is composed of white matter as well. It regulates respiration and is the origin of the fifth and eighth cranial nerves. The diencephalon and midbrain (mesencephalon) are found between cerebrum and pons.

The spinal cord   The spinal cord extends from the brain down through the neural canal as a continuation of the brainstem. It contains nerves for sensory, motor and reflex functions. The white matter in the spinal cord is on the outside and the grey matter inside.

The cranial nerves   Twelve pairs of cranial nerves arise from the brain reaching their destinations in the various parts of the head, face and neck by means of small openings in the skull. They are named according to their distribution or function and are sensory, motor and mixed nerves:

olfactory, first cranial nerve – located in the nasal mucous membrane; function: sense of smell,

optic, second cranial nerve – behind the eyes; function: vision,

oculomotor, third cranial nerve – extends to the external eye muscles; controls movement, size of pupil,

trochlear, fourth cranial nerve – ends at the upper eye muscle; controls movement,

trigeminal, fifth cranial nerve – has three branches:

ophthalmic, maxillary and mandibular. It originates at the pons and carries impulses from the head and face to the brain; controls chewing (muscle of mastication), sensations of face, head and teeth,

abducens, sixth cranial nerve – a motor nerve extending to the eye muscles; controls abduction of eye,

facial, seventh cranial nerve – has motor fibres to the superficial face and scalp muscles and sensory nerve fibres to the tongue; controls facial expression, taste,

acoustic or auditory, eighth cranial nerve – has two sensory divisions reaching the ear:
1 the vestibular maintains body balance and
2 the cochlear whose function is the sense of hearing,

glossopharyngeal, ninth cranial nerve – has sensory and motor nerve fibres and extends to tongue and sinus, sense of taste,

vagus or pneumogastric, tenth cranial nerve – contains motor and sensory fibres. Motor nerves reach heart, respiratory and digestive organs and sensory nerves, respiratory and digestive organs,

accessory or spinal accessory, eleventh cranial nerve – has motor fibres to trapezius and sternocleidomastoid muscles,

hypoglossal, twelfth cranial nerve – supplies motor fibres to the tongue.

Nerves of the face The trigeminal, the fifth and largest cranial nerve, originates from the pons and leaves the skull in front of the ear. This nerve separates into three main divisions, the ophthalmic, sensory nerve; maxillary, sensory nerve; and mandibular, sensory-motor nerve, branching out to cover the major area of the face. The ophthalmic subdivisions and the areas affected by them are:

supra-orbital nerve – eyebrows, upper eyelid and forehead,

supra-trochlear nerve – bridge of nose,

infra-trochlear nerve – skin and mucous membrane of nose,

lacrimal nerve – tear glands and upper eyelids,

nasal nerve – lower part of nose.

The maxillary subdivisions and the areas affected by them are:

zygomatic nerve – upper cheeks, temples and sides of forehead,

infra-orbital – mouth, nose and skin of lower eyelids.

The mandibular subdivisions and the areas affected by them are:

anterior portion – skin of cheeks, muscles of mastication,

posterior portion – skin from temple to skull, external ear, teeth and chin (mental nerve).

The seventh cranial nerve originates from the pons and emerges from the skull in front of the lower part of the ear. Its branches control the facial expressions. The names and areas affected are:

posterior auricular nerve – muscles at the lower part of the skull,

temporal – muscles of the temple, eyelids, brows and upper cheeks,

buccal – muscles of the mouth,

mandibular – chin,

cervical – neck muscles.

Thirty-one pairs of spinal nerves leave the spinal cord and are distributed to muscles and skin of the body. Eight of them, the cervical nerves, innervate the back of the head and front of the neck.

The nerves of the arm and hand are:

ulnar – supplies the arm at the side of the little finger and some hand muscles,

median – supplies front of forearm, palm of hand, thumb, index and middle finger (digital nerves). Ulnar and median are branches of the brachial plexus:

radial – supplies triceps, forearm and hand,

medial – supplies inner arm surface.

The nerves of the leg are:

sciatic nerve – the largest nerve of the body, runs down the back of the thigh. The branches of the sciatic nerve are spread over the thigh, lower leg, foot and skin of the leg. The lower part of the nerve is the tibial nerve with a side branch above the knee bend to the shin, the common peroneal nerve. The tibial supplies the calf and its skin and the sole of the foot.

The autonomic nervous system The nerves of the autonomic nervous system derive from the brain and spinal cord. They regulate the functions of the inner organs and control the movements of their muscle walls and the secretions of the endocrine glands. Branches of this system are sent to the skin to supply the capillaries, exocrine glands and arrector pili muscles. The actions influenced by the autonomic nervous system are involuntary in that they are independent and outside the control of the will. For the function of an organ, a positive and a negative stimulus is required, to accelerate and to moderate. The nerves which quicken the heart beat are called sympathetic nerves and those slowing down the heart beat are the parasympathetic nerves.

THE SENSE ORGANS

The five sense organs are the eyes, ears, tongue, nose and skin. The skin, as the sense organ of touch, is discussed in a separate chapter.

The eye

The eye is a delicate organ and is protected by the bones of the orbit and a pad of fat behind it. If the fat diminishes through sickness or old age, the eyes sink, causing a hollow-eyed appearance. The eyelids, eyebrows, lashes and lachrymal glands are the eyes' protection against penetration of objects or of too much light. The conjunctiva, a mucous membrane, covers the front of the eyeball and lines the eyelids.

The eye is the organ of sight and serves to receive light impressions reflected from objects in the environment. The impression passes to the retina and via the optic nerve to the brain, where a picture is formed.

**The outer coat of the eye, the sclera, is made of tough, white opaque connective tissue. The front part of the sclera is the transparent cornea, which lies over the iris.

The **middle coat or choroid**, of which the iris is a part, is coloured. It contains blood vessels and a large amount of pigment. The dark colour of the choroid prevents the reflection of the rays which enter. The pupil is the small round opening in the centre of the iris. The muscles of the iris control the amount of light entering by adjusting the size of the pupil. Behind the iris lies the lens, which bends the rays so that they may be focused on the retina. The shape of the lens can be changed to allow objects to be seen clearly at different distances.

The **inner eye-coat, the retina**, contains the nerve endings, which are stimulated by light rays. An upside-down image of impressions received is formed here and turned up automatically by the brain. Right at the back of the eyeball near the centre of the retina lies the area of the most distinct vision, the so-called yellow spot.

The ear

The ear, the organ of hearing, is constructed to combine two functions:
1 to receive waves of sound, transmitting them to the brain,
2 to assist in maintaining balance.

The **trumpet or auricle** is made of cartilage and is the visible part of the ear. The inner, more essential structures lie sheltered by the temporal bone and are divided into three sections: the external, middle and inner ear.

The **external ear** is a short, twisted canal leading from the outside to the drum which separates it from the middle ear. Hair and wax excreted by the ceruminous glands serve as a protection against the penetration of matter.

The **middle ear** is a small cavity containing three aural bones which are called (according to their shape): hammer, anvil and stirrup. The external wall of the chamber is covered by a membrane called the eardrum (tympanic membrane). The internal wall opposite holds small oval and round windows, the fenestra ovalis and the fenestra rotunda. An airduct enters the cavity allowing air from the nose to enter the middle ear to equalize the balance of atmospheric pressure on both sides of the drum.

The **inner ear** is also called the labyrinth because of its complicated arrangement of bones and membranes. It is filled with fluid in which the nerve endings of hearing and balance float. Some of these nerve endings are stimulated by sound waves and others by pressure. The latter assist in controlling balance.

Receptors of taste

The receptors of taste (gustatory sense organs) or taste buds are distributed over the tongue in various areas for different sensations. Only four tastes are recognized: sweet, salty, sour and bitter; all other flavours are perceived merely in combination with smell.

Receptors of smell

The receptors of smell or olfactory sense organs are in the mucous membranes of the upper part of the nasal cavity. In order to observe delicate odours, the air has to be drawn in deeply to reach the receptors. They are extremely sensitive and tire easily so that an odour first perceived is no longer noticed after some time. The sense of smell plays an important part in life. An odour can be stimulating, repellent or attractive, and influences the subconscious which may reflect on actions.

THE CIRCULATORY SYSTEM

The body needs a well-functioning transportation system to supply all body cells with nourishment and oxygen and to carry away waste and carbon dioxide, the end-products of cellular metabolism.

This requirement is met by the circulatory system, comprising the blood, heart, blood vessels, circulation and lymphatic system.

The blood

The blood transports hormones, enzymes and antibodies to fight harmful organisms. It regulates the body's temperature and fluids. The regulation of body temperature is performed mainly by the capillaries on the body surface, which can expand to give off heat or contract to retain it. Body fluid is excreted by means of the capillaries and sweat glands through perspiration. The blood acts as a buffer to maintain the pH balance of body fluids in cooperation with the lungs and kidneys.

Blood is composed of blood plasma and blood cells. The plasma is a straw-coloured liquid containing approximately 85 per cent water. The remaining percentage is made up of nutrients, metabolic waste products, gases, mineral salts, enzymes, hormones, albumin, globulins and fibrinogen. The blood cells are red corpuscles, white corpuscles and blood platelets.

Red corpuscles, or erythrocytes, are formed in the red bone marrow and are the most numerous component of the blood. Each cell has the shape of a small disc, concave on both sides. Erythrocytes consist of a substance called haemoglobin, an iron-containing protein, and are responsible for the red colour of the blood. They transport oxygen from the lungs to the body cells and carbon dioxide away from the cells to the lungs. Erythrocytes are continuously renewed in the bone marrow and broken down in the liver and spleen. The colour matter is chemically changed and excreted as bile pigment. The iron is re-used to build new blood cells.

White corpuscles or leucocytes are larger in size than erythrocytes. They are produced in the spleen, lymph nodes and red bone marrow. Their function is to defend the body against micro-organisms and other harmful factors in order to protect it against diseases.

Platelets or thrombocytes are the smallest of the three blood cells. They are also formed in the red bone marrow. Their task is to initiate blood clotting to prevent haemorrhage. Blood clotting is a complicated process. In case of injury, fibrinogen is converted by action of thrombin into fibrin, forming a network of fine fibres over the wound in which the cells are caught. The resulting clot prevents further loss of blood.

The heart and blood vessels

The heart is a muscular organ, approximately the size of a closed fist, and is located in the thorax immediately above the diaphragm. Two-thirds of the heart is on the left side of the body midline. The heart has an outer, loose-fitting, sac-like covering, the pericardium, made of a fibrous layer at the outside and a double inner serous layer with a lubricating liquid in between. This structure allows the heart to move freely without friction with its surroundings. Cardiac muscles form the wall of the heart, the myocardium, lined by the endocardium, a delicate layer of tissue. The heart is divided into four

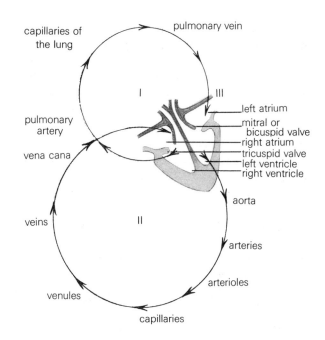

I PULMONARY CIRCULATION
II SYSTEMIC CIRCULATION
III HEART

Scheme of the blood circulation

chambers, the right and left atria or auricles above and the left and right ventricles below. The walls of the ventricles are thicker than those of the atria as they have to contract and pump the blood out into the blood vessels. Valves at openings between atrium and ventricle, and where arteries leave the ventricles, permit blood flow only in one direction. A cardiac cycle is a complete heartbeat including contraction and relaxation of both atria and ventricles. The atria contract, simultaneously squeezing the blood into the ventricles; they then relax. During this time the ventricles, on their part, contract, pumping the blood into the arteries before they relax as well.

Blood vessels There are three kinds of blood vessels: arteries, capillaries and veins. Arteries distribute the blood from the heart to the body cells. The main artery or aorta leaves the heart to branch out in smaller arteries and arterioles which finally end in a network of minute vessels, the capillaries, throughout all tissues. Capillaries become venules, eventually enlarging to veins and are united in the main vein or vena cava, which collects the blood to transport it back to the heart.

Arteries are thick-walled, muscular vessels. Veins have thinner, less elastic walls than arteries. They

31

contain valves to prevent back-flow of the blood on its return to the heart. Capillaries have thin, porous walls through which nourishment is given to the cells and waste products are collected from them. This movement of fluids through the walls of the vessels is called osmosis. Arteries are located in the deeper parts of the body tissue for protection, whereas veins are closer to the outer surface. Arterial blood is bright red owing to its oxygen content, and venous blood is bluish-red due to the presence of carbon dioxide. The exceptions are the pulmonary artery and vein in which it is reversed.

The blood is constantly flowing in a closed circuit from the heart through the vessels and back again to the heart. It is distinguished between two circulatory systems, the pulmonary and the systemic.

Pulmonary circulation During pulmonary circulation the blood flows from the right ventricle via the pulmonary artery to the lungs, where an exchange of gases takes place. By exhaling, carbon dioxide is given away; by inhaling, oxygen is absorbed into the blood. The blood, enriched with oxygen, returns to the left atrium of the heart by means of the pulmonary vein.

Systemic circulation In the systemic or general circulation the blood, after returning from the lungs, passes from the left atrium to the left ventricle. It is pressed out into the aorta and sent through arteries, arterioles and capillaries to all body parts. It then travels through venules and veins to the vena cava and back to the right atrium of the heart. From the right atrium it passes to the right ventricle in order to be transported into the lungs, thus closing the cycle.

The main arteries of the head and neck

The common carotid artery is located at both sides of the neck and has two branches.

1 The internal carotid artery which supplies the brain, forehead, part of the nose and eye.

2 The external carotid artery which supplies the neck, tongue, ear, scalp and face. It ascends up the neck to the lower part of the ear and from there branches out into the following:

    a the posterior auricular artery, which supplies the scalp and part of the ear,
    b the occipital artery which supplies the scalp at the back of the head,

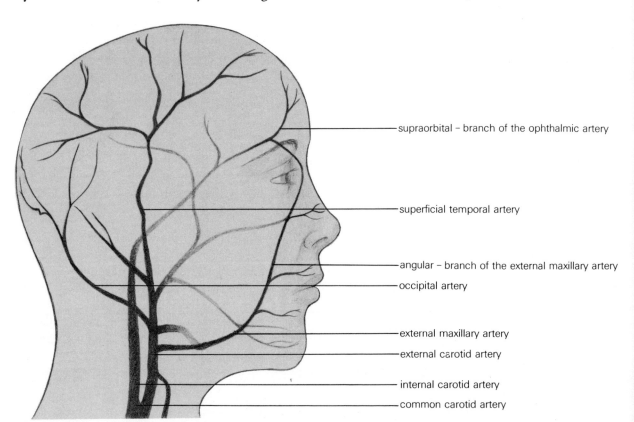

supraorbital – branch of the ophthalmic artery

superficial temporal artery

angular – branch of the external maxillary artery

occipital artery

external maxillary artery

external carotid artery

internal carotid artery

common carotid artery

Main arteries of the head

c the superficial temporal artery has the following branches:

    the frontal artery – to the forehead,
    the middle temporal artery – to the temple and eyelid,
    the transverse artery – to the masseter
    the parietal artery – to the crown and side of the head,

d the external maxillary artery supplies the chin with the following branches:

    submental artery – to the lower lip,
    inferior labial artery – to the upper lip and nose,
    superior labial artery, and angular artery – to the sides of nose and to bridge of nose.

3 The opthalmic artery reaches with branches, called the supraorbital branch and the frontal artery, to the forehead.

The main arteries of the arm and hand

1 The innominate artery – a short artery and largest branch of the aorta; arises from its arch and continues in the right subclavian artery.

2 The axillary artery originates from the subclavian and ends in the brachial artery which supplies the upper arm.

3 The radial artery supplies the thumb-side of the forearm and the ulnar artery the little finger side of the forearm. They send numerous branches to the hand and fingers.

The main arteries of the leg and foot

The deep femoral and femoral supply the thigh. The popliteal, a continuation of the femoral, has three continuations in the lower leg: the anterior tibial, peroneal and posterior tibial, with terminal branches supplying the foot and toes.

Veins

There are two types of veins, deep and superficial. The deep veins are located close to arteries and are named by them. The superficial veins are those that can be seen through the skin.

The main veins of the head and neck

The internal jugular vein is a deep vein on the right and left side of the neck; the external jugular vein is a superficial vein at both sides of the neck, which

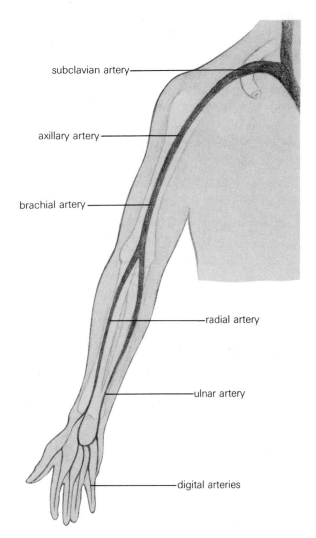

Main arteries of the arm

receives the blood from the superficial veins of the face, scalp and neck; the anterior facial vein collects the blood from the vessels of the face and pours it into the external jugular vein.

The deep veins of the forearm

The radial and ulnar veins collect the blood from the hand, and empty it into the brachial vein which enters the axillary vein, continuing in the subclavian vein.

The two main superficial veins of the arm

These are the basillic vein (little finger side) and the cephalic vein (thumb side). They also collect the blood from hand and arm and pour it into the axillary vein.

The main veins of the leg

The anterior and posterior tibial and popliteal are deep veins, ending in the femoral; and the superficial veins, the small and great saphenous veins. They return the blood from the feet, lower and upper leg.

The lymphatic system

The lymphatic system comprises the lymph, lymph vessels and lymph nodes and is part of the circulatory system.

Lymph is a watery, colourless fluid deriving from blood plasma filtered out through the walls of the capillaries. It fills the spaces between the body cells as tissue fluid (interstitial fluid) supplying them with nourishment in areas where the capillaries do not reach. The fluid is transported back to the blood stream by a drainage system starting between cells as small lymph capillaries which have blind ends. They merge into the lymphatics, larger channels widely spread throughout the entire body. Lymphatics are well equipped with valves to prevent backflow. Lymph moves slowly and on its course passes lymph nodes or glands. These function as a filter, to retain pus and bacteria as a defence against infection and to prevent damaging micro-organisms from entering the body's interior. They are also responsible for the formation of lymph cells called lymphocytes, monocytes and plasma cells.

Lymph nodes are small, oval-shaped structures, generally arranged in a group, e.g. in the axilla, bend of the elbow, neck, mouth and groin.

Lymph vessels become gradually larger until they end in the thoracic duct and right lymphatic duct from where lymph re-enters the blood in the vena cava.

THE ENDOCRINE GLANDS

The endocrine system is composed of ductless glands. Instead of being carried to the body parts by means of a duct, their secretions are absorbed directly into the blood stream and lymph which take over the task of their distribution. These internal secretions or hormones are catalysts, chemicals that initiate and accelerate a chemical reaction. They together with the nervous system enable us to adapt ourselves successfully to our changing environment.

Hormone secretion occurs through the gland tissue into the close-by vessels. Thus the hormones reach the organs and the target cells in which they are destined to cause a specialized reaction. The significance of the hormones is not realized and generally not noticed until it comes to disturbances in the endocrine system. The activity of the endocrine glands is a complicated teamwork in which each gland depends on the other and affects the other. The fact is of importance for a healthy balance within the bodily system, as well as for recognition of the origin of any irregularities in the interaction.

There are two glandular states which may result in disease in the human body: overproduction of a hormone by hyper-functioning and underproduction of a hormone by hypo-functioning. These deviations bring about changes which differ in an adult or a child.

The endocrine system is supervised by a master gland, the pituitary body or hypophysis cerebri, which exercises a great influence over all other glands. Apart from the mutual connections within the system, there is a complicated, close interrelation with the nervous system. The names of the glands according to their location are:

pituitary gland (hypophysis cerebri),
pineal gland (ephiphysis cerebri),
thyroid gland,
parathyroid gland,
thymus,
adrenal glands,
islets of Langerhans (pancreas),
ovaries – placenta,
testes.

The pituitary gland

The pituitary gland, or hypophysis cerebri, is found at the base of the brain, protected by the cranial cavity. It is smaller than all other glands and actually consists of two separate lobes with different functions, the anterior and the posterior lobe. The anterior lobe secretes seven hormones and the posterior lobe approximately two.

The hormones produced by the anterior gland influence body growth, skin pigmentation and development of breast milk after childbirth. They also control the thyroid gland, adrenal cortex and sex organs.

If the growth hormone somatotropin is secreted in excess during childhood, the bones grow too rapidly, bringing about gigantism. The opposite occurs in the case of a growth hormone deficiency during this time of life; the child does not grow adequately, resulting in dwarfism. In adults, the over-secretion of this hormone produces enlarged hands, feet, cheeks and jaws, together with an over-growth of the fatty tissue; this disease is called acromegaly. Contrary to it is Simmonds' disease, a premature aging, caused by a deficiency of the somatotrophic hormone in an adult.

The posterior lobe of the pituitary gland produces an antidiuretic hormone which controls the amount of urine excreted by the kidneys. The lobe's hormones regulate blood pressure, and also influence peristalsis and the contractions of the uterus during child-birth.

The pineal body

The pineal body, or epiphysis cerebri, is an endocrine gland present in the cranial cavity behind the mid-brain at the third ventricle. The epiphysis is a gland of childhood, which starts to degenerate slowly from the age of seven years until only a fibrous tissue remains in an adult. The functions of the hormones secreted by this gland are not fully known. They presumably have a part in regulating the sex gland activity and influence skin pigmentation.

The thyroid gland

This consists of two fairly large lobes located at the sides of the trachea below the larynx. These lobes are connected across the front of the trachea by a third portion, the isthmus, giving the gland the shape of a horseshoe. The thyroid gland secretes two hormones containing iodine of which the main hormone is thyroxine. It is the only endocrine gland that stores its hormones.

The primary actions of the thyroid hormones are to regulate the rate of metabolism and growth of the body. Hypersecretion by an overactive gland leads to an increased metabolism; hyposecretion produces too little thyroxine and results in a decreased metabolism. The symptoms of over-secretion are nervousness, high metabolism, loss of weight, heart trouble, bulging eyes and exophthalmic goitre (i.e. Grave's disease or Basedow's disease).

Hypo-function of the thyroid gland in an adult leads to myxoedema. This disease is characterised by a low metabolism, collection of fluid in the subcutaneous tissue, weight gain, disturbances of skin and hair, and reduced mental and physical vigour. A deficiency of the hormone before birth or in the first years of life leads to cretinism.

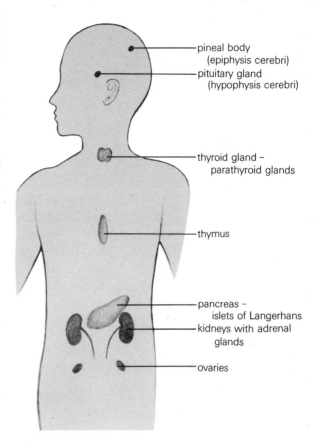

Endocrine glands

pineal body (epiphysis cerebri)
pituitary gland (hypophysis cerebri)
thyroid gland – parathyroid glands
thymus
pancreas – islets of Langerhans
kidneys with adrenal glands
ovaries

The parathyroid glands

These are small round organs attached to the back surface of the thyroid lobes, generally a pair at each lobe. These have the task of regulating the calcium and phosphorus metabolism. The maintenance of the calcium level in the blood is very important for health. If the parathyroid glands have been removed or are not functioning properly owing to sickness, the result is a greater neuro-muscular irritability, sometimes to a degree to produce spasms and con-vulsions (tetany). If the calcium concentration in the blood is increased by hyper-function of the parathyroid glands, painful growths in bones and decalcification of bone tissue occur.

The thymus

This is situated in the upper part of the chest cavity and extends up to the lower neck. This gland develops and reaches its largest size compared to the rest of the body during the first two years of life. At puberty the thymus has arrived at its absolute size, and from then on it gradually shrinks until it is hardly recognized in old age. It is apparent that the thymus plays a part in building up the body's resistance to infections.

The adrenal glands

These form a cap over the top of the kidneys. They consist of two parts: the outer capsule, or cortex, and the inner substance, or medulla. The adrenal cortex and the medulla cortex function as separate endocrine glands, each in itself producing different hormones.

The adrenal cortex, which has three different cell layers, secretes three hormones.

1 Glucocorticoids, which are mainly cortisol and influence all body cells. They promote normal protein, carbohydrate, and fat metabolism and assist the body to endure stress. Chronic excess of glucocorticoids results in redistribution of body fat, which is removed from the extremities and allotted to the face, shoulders and trunk. This over-growth of the fatty tissue is known as Cushing's syndrome.

2 Mineralocorticoids, which are mainly aldosterone regulate the mineral metabolism and maintain fluid balance in the human body.

3 Small amounts of female and male hormones in both sexes, which seem to be of no significance if they are produced normally. A disorder of the adrenal cortex, however, might cause excessive secretion of one part of those hormones, the androgens, having a masculinizing effect on a woman, e.g. increased hairiness and voice change. Androgens stimulate the sebaceous glands in a woman causing oily scalp and skin. They enhance facial hairgrowth after menopause resulting in longer, coarse hair on upper lip and chin. Both phenomena are evident during a time in a woman's life when the female hormones are imbalanced.

The adrenal medulla, the inner portion of the adrenal glands, produces adrenaline (epinephrine) to 80 per cent. It assists in meeting stress situations, and affects the non-striated and cardiac muscles.

The pancreas

This is a lengthy body which lies behind the stomach. It produces digestive ferments and in the cells of the pancreas, called the Islands of Langerhans, insulin is produced. Insulin has the task of furthering the storage of glucose as glycogen in the liver. It regulates the carbohydrate metabolism and decreases the blood sugar at the same time. If the functions of the pancreas are disturbed there is an inadequate secretion or utilization of insulin, and the blood sugar is increased with diabetes as a consequence. Diabetics have a greater incidence of foot disorders together with more susceptibility to infection. Skin injuries have to be avoided.

The ovaries

These are two oval, almond-shaped glands situated in the pelvic cavity on both sides of the uterus. They develop and begin functioning when a girl reaches puberty, at approximately 11 to 13 years, bringing about mental as well as physical changes. The ovaries produce female hormones: oestrogens and progesterone. Oestrogens promote the development of the breast during adolescence and pregnancy and play a part in the formation of the ovum, which is expelled by one of the ovaries every 28 days. The activity of the ovaries slows down and ceases during menopause. Oestrogens let liquid collect in the tissues before menstruation, leading to temporary weight gain and a bloated sensation. A slowing down of the production of oestrogens in later years reflects on a woman emotionally, on her skin, hair, bone tissue and blood vessels.

Progesterone is a hormone produced by the corpus luteum which makes the endometrium, the lining of the uterus, grow before menstruation and during pregnancy. The corpus luteum develops from a follicle of the ovaries after a ripened ovum has been discharged. During pregnancy the placenta acts as a temporary endocrine gland, secreting oestrogens and progesterone. The formation of milk in the breast after childbirth is influenced by progesterone.

A minimal imbalance in the amount of oestrogens and progesterone can cause poor distribution of fats and water in the female organism. This leads to local lumpiness in the subcutaneous connective tissue, particularly in the upper arms, hips and thighs. This so-called cellulite can be very painful, as well as the cause of an aesthetic problem.

Cells of the testes secrete testosterone, the main male hormone. Female and male hormones are found in both sexes.

THE RESPIRATORY SYSTEM

The cells of the body tissues require oxygen for their metabolism. The erythrocytes carry oxygen from the lungs to the cells and convey carbon dioxide back to the lungs from the cells. The respiratory system, in co-operation with the circulatory system, makes possible the exchange of gases among air, blood, and cells. The main organs of respiration, the lungs, are situated in the thorax, and are linked to the outside by several passages through which the air is inhaled and exhaled. They are the nose, pharynx, larynx, trachea and bronchi. If the functioning of this system is interrupted in any way, death occurs after a short time.

In a respiratory cycle the air is inhaled into the nose, a structure made up of bony walls and cartilage and consisting of a small external and larger internal portion. The septum, a thin bone partition, divides the nose into two channels and cavities. The air entering the nostrils is warmed, moistened by the mucous membranes, filtered of impurities by bristly hair and chemically examined. The olfactory receptors or sense of smell are located in the mucous membrane of the upper part of the nose passage. The air passes to the pharynx or throat, which is connected to both nose and mouth. In case the air passages of the nose are plugged, the mouth takes over. However, mouth breathing lacks filtering and warming up as performed by the nose channels.

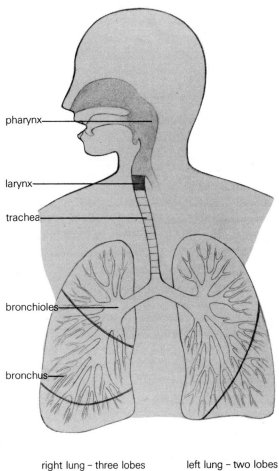

The respiratory system

The pharynx

This serves as passageway for nourishment and air before they reach their relevant tubes – food, the oesophagus; air, the trachea. Prior to entering the trachea, the air passes the voice box or larynx, a box-like structure made of cartilage, located in the upper portion of the neck. Vocal cords are stretched across the larynx producing sounds when air is pressed through them. Vowels are formed in connection with the pharynx changing its shape. The epiglottis, a cartilage lid, closes the opening of the larynx during the process of swallowing so that food cannot enter the trachea.

The trachea, bronchi and alveoli

The air continues its course into the windpipe or trachea, a tube of smooth muscle walls, supported by cartilage rings are lined by ciliated epithelium. From here it passes down into the bronchi or bronchial

tubes, a main tube to each lung. They divide and ramify into smaller and smaller tubes until each ends in a group of minute air sacs called the alveoli.

The lungs

The right and left lungs are spongy organs situated within the chest cavity or thorax. Their base rests on the diaphragm, the muscular partition above the abdomen, while their upper portions reach the neck behind the clavicles. Numerous capillaries are found between the air sacs into which the inhaled air penetrates. The entire structure is held together by elastic tissue and covered on its outside by a serous membrane called the pleura. The pleura has a double layer lubricated by fluid to prevent friction with the chest walls.

The muscles of respiration

The muscles of respiration are the diaphragm and the intercostals, the muscles of the chest walls. In inhaling, the floor of the chest or diaphragm flattens

37

out, and the intercostal muscles contract to raise the ribs and allow air to enter the lungs. In exhaling the diaphragm and chest muscles return to their normal position and exert pressure on the lungs. The lungs act as excretory organs by exhaling carbon dioxide and water. The process of breathing is inspiration and expiration.

An adult breathes normally about 16 to 18 times a minute. Physical work and exercise increase energy consumption and the body demands more oxygen to produce this energy. Costal or shallow breathing is characterized by the outward movement of the thorax without action of the diaphragm. Abdominal or deep breathing with action of the diaphragm accomplishes a greater exchange of gases.

THE DIGESTIVE SYSTEM

The digestive system carries out the vital function of breaking down the food mechanically and chemically, so that it may be absorbed and utilized by the body cells. Nourishment is converted into soluble matter and mixed with the digestive secretions of the salivary glands, gastric glands, liver, pancreas and intestinal glands. The alimentary tract or canal consists of the following organs: mouth; pharynx, oesophagus, stomach, small intestine and large intestine.

The mouth

The first step in digestion takes place in the mouth or buccal cavity, the beginning of the long gastro-intestinal tract. Here food is broken down mechanically by the teeth. After the first set of teeth has been shed from the age of about 6, there are 32 permanent teeth: 4 incisors, 2 canines or cuspids, 4 premolars and 6 molars per jaw. The crown of the tooth lies above the gum and the root lies below. A tooth is made of a hard substance called dentine, covered with enamel at the crown and cementum at the root. The inside of the tooth is hollow and contains pulp. Capillaries and nerves enter the tooth cavity by means of the root canals.

The tongue, a muscular structure covered by a rough mucous membrane, is attached to the floor of the mouth. It assists in chewing, swallowing and speech, and represents the sense organ of taste with the taste buds in its small elevations, the papillae. The ducts of the salivary glands are found around the mouth. They secrete saliva, a watery fluid containing the enzyme

ptyalin which changes starch into disaccharide. After mastication and the start of chemical break-down, the food passes from the mouth cavity into the pharynx and oesophagus leading through the diaphragm into the stomach. The oesophagus has a muscular tube-like wall lined by a mucous membrane.

The wall of the oesophagus contracts and relaxes, assisting the food to glide down into the stomach through the cardiac sphincter.

The stomach

The stomach is a lengthy, pouch-like organ in the upper left portion of the abdomen under the liver and diaphragm. The food stays in the stomach for several hours and is mixed by the muscle contractions of the stomach walls. The acid gastric juice, from the glands in the stomach's lining, contains pepsin, lipase and hydrochloric acid. It is added to the food and partly digests protein. It acts simultaneously as a disinfectant, killing bacteria swallowed with the nourishment, and plays a part in the absorption of vitamin B_{12} which is required for the formation of red blood cells in the bone marrow.

The small intestine

The food is next pushed through the pyloric sphincter into the small intestine. This 4 to 6 m long tube is the actual place of digestion. Its membranes contain the intestinal glands which secrete mucus and digestive enzymes to complete the break-down of carbohydrates into glucose, and protein into amino acids.

Pancreatic juice from the pancreas enters the small intestine in its first division, the duodenum. The digestive enzyme requires the presence of bile from the gall-bladder to emulsify fat, before it can become fully active. The end product of digestion is absorbed by the villi, the numerous finger-like processes projecting from the lining of the small intestine. Through the villi, the food substances pass into lymph vessels called lacteals and capillaries to the portal vein. Where the small intestine joins the large intestine a worm-like structure, the appendix, branches out. Its function is unknown. After absorption of the liquids, bulk and waste of the digestive process are eliminated from the colon via the rectum.

The three steps in the body's food supply are: ingestion, digestion and egestion.

The pancreas

This is a fish-shaped gland situated behind the stomach. The two secretions of the pancreas are pancreatic juice and insulin. The pancreatic juice, as mentioned before, plays an important part in digestion; insulin is essential for the cells' sugar metabolism.

The liver

This is the largest gland of the body, located in the upper right-hand side of the abdomen immediately under the diaphragm. It has a diversity of tasks: storing iron, vitamins and glycogen, assisting in the formation of antibodies to fight infection, excreting bile and urea, and producing heat. The bile manufactured by the liver is stored in the gall-bladder which lies on the under surface of the organ. It passes through a duct into the duodenum to help in digestion.

THE EXCRETORY SYSTEM

The excretory organs eliminate the end-products or waste of the body's metabolism. A failure of these organs, or retention and accumulation of these substances, brings about ill health and endangers life. The system includes the skin, the lungs, the large intestine and the kidneys. These organs, with the exception of the urinary system, have been dealt with in their capacity as excretory organs in foregoing sections.

The urinary system

The urinary system, together with the remaining excretory organs, controls the fluid balance of the body. The system consists of the following structures: the kidneys, ureters, bladder and urethra. The kidneys are two bean-shaped organs lying at the lower end of the spinal column at the back of the abdomen. For their protection and to keep them in position, they are embedded in a heavy pad of fat. Each kidney has a central hollow portion, the medulla and cortex. The major part of the kidneys is made up of nephrons, microscopic urine forming units regulated chiefly by two hormones, aldosterone of the adrenal glands and antidiuretic hormone of the pituitary gland.

The blood circulates through the kidneys giving up fluid and various metabolic end-products. These substances are excreted as urine which is made of 95 per cent water, urea, uric acid and ammonia (nitrogenous wastes from protein foods), mineral salts and toxins (bacterial poisons).

A fine muscular tube, the ureter, is attached to each kidney leading down into the pelvis where it enters the bladder. Urine is stored in the bladder and expelled from the body by means of a passageway, the urethra.

An insight into skin disorders

Contents

Dermatology is the specialized medical field dealing with the skin and its diseases. Before getting acquainted with some of the disorders it is necessary to understand that skin diseases are more than just symptoms appearing on the outside; most of them are a reflection of internal sickness, such as infections, deficiencies and other physical disturbances.

The only part of this extensive field to be discussed here will be the symptoms visible to the aesthetician. The intention is to guide her to recognizing the presence of a disorder and to encourage her to recommend her client consults a skin specialist. It is important to make the aesthetician realize that she must not trespass into a field beyond her abilities and competence.

HEALTHY SKIN

Before going into the different skin disorders, a definition of a normal skin has to be given. This is a healthy skin, velvety-smooth with fine pores and a well-balanced moisture and oil secretion. There should be no warts, hair overgrowth or colour marks. Usually this is a young skin, for we must never underestimate age in its influence on the whole body system. But even in youth this so-called 'ideal' picture is not always the rule. Minor faults of beauty such as freckles, comedones, spots and milia are more common than an immaculate complexion. The majority of people have a combination skin, with its typical T-zone (forehead, nose and chin oily, temples and cheeks dry or normal). A tendency to dryness progressing with age should not cause concern unless it reaches extremes and is accompanied by flakiness. Obviously under those circumstances the doctor has to be consulted.

Because acne and rosacea can be improved in appearance by proper care, they are described under 'Skin Types'. There is an hereditary predisposition to the two conditions, and seborrhea is generally involved.

ACNE

Acne vulgaris (acne juvenilis) is not contagious, but through infection lesions that did not originally contain pathogenic bacteria can develop into cysts, leaving pitted scars after involution. Touching with unclean hands has to be avoided and extreme cleanliness is indicated. Although acne is still not fully understood, antibiotics (tetracyclines) have been a major advance in treatment. Ultra-violet light also benefits acne skin. The male hormones, androgens, stimulate the sebaceous glands; to counterbalance them the doctor can prescribe female hormones to women.

Other varieties of acne are:

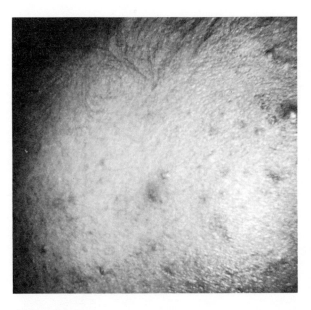

Acne vulgaris

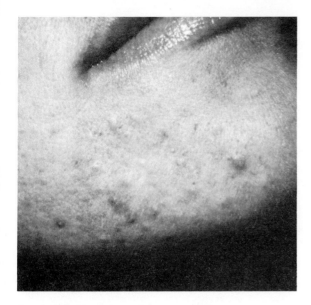

Acne vulgaris

Acne picea

This is caused by inferior cosmetic preparations, contact with tar, other raw materials and their fumes. The skin directly influenced by these substances shows numerous comedones.

Acne varioliformis

This is named after variola or smallpox, as its appearance reminds one of the disease. Small blisters filled with an opaque liquid are found, generally at temples and hairline. A crust forms leaving a scar after healing. In this disease comedones are absent.

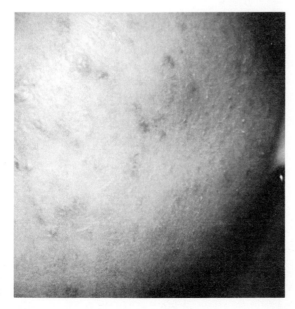

Acne vulgaris

Acne conglobata

This is a form of acne marked by the presence of comedones, pus formations and severe scarring.

ROSACEA

This is a disorder of middle age usually found on the nose and upper cheeks. If neglected it can appear on chin and forehead as well. Telangiectasia and lumps are found in the areas. The growths can disfigure the nose reaching a bulbous enlargement, the so-called rhinophyma. The blood circulation slows down in the expanded capillaries giving their locations a bluish-red look. Single capillaries can be surgically removed by coagulation. Several factors play a part in the development of this disorder: seborrhea, endocrine changes, irregularities in the gastronomic system, liver sickness and the misuse of stimulants.

DERMATITIS AND ECZEMA

These are very common inflammations. They include a large group of skin disorders which appear in various forms. The cause, in many cases, is hard to determine, and the designations of dermatitis or eczema are used in a broad sense also for skin eruptions where an exact diagnosis cannot be made.

Dermatitis

A dermatitis might be caused by outside influences such as chemicals. The skin must be primarily disposed to react accordingly; that is, skin responds with an inflammation to contact with certain matter in the external environment. Hypersensitivity to a stimulus can also be effected from inside through the intake of a nutrient. Exposure to ultraviolet light might cause a dermatitis in which the skin becomes red, swollen and blisters form. If the skin responds with an inflammation to something from outside, the appearance is local; inflammation is only present in those areas where the skin has been in contact with the irritating substance. It soon regains its normal appearance when no longer under the influence of the stimulus. If a person is constantly in contact with the irritant, he may develop a general hypersensitivity to the primary and related substance. This way the hypersensitivity, named allergy, might develop into an eczema which then also appears on skin untouched by the irritant, and if no longer in contact with it. This refers only to a small part of eczemas, the origin of many of them cannot be detected. However, not all skin irritations are, or will result in, an eczema.

Eczema

An eczema is an infection or inflammation of the skin brought about the same way as dermatitis, from internal or external stimuli. Although an eczema is a dermatitis, a dermatitis is not an eczema.

An eczema can cause reddening of the skin, swelling, oedema, blisters and discharge. The latter can be seen after the blisters burst. The secretion of the erosions hardens, forming scabs. When healed the skin has a scaly look. Often the skin becomes thicker in the areas of the eczema and shows a coarse design of squares if the eczema has been there for some length of time. An eczema easily becomes infected when scratched or rubbed.

As there is such a great variety of eczemas and the reasons for them are so numerous, they belong in the care of an experienced skin specialist.

SKIN DISORDERS DUE TO PHYSICAL AGENTS

Skin diseases brought about by environmental factors as discussed in foregoing sections are in part due to chemicals. As the skin is also exposed to temperature extremes, these too may be the reason for skin disorders. Over-exposure to heat or cold causes skin damage, allergic responses and may even further an individual anatomical characteristic. Overheated rooms, dry air and low humidity add to the sensitivity of the skin.

Freezing

The length of exposure of skin to cold decides the severity of the consequences. We distinguish among three degrees of freezing. First there is a light redness which hurts and itches as it disappears. After a longer exposure the skin may turn white and numb, with swelling, blisters, and oedema. Frostbite, or chilblains may result. In the most severe degree of freezing, the cells die off and the tissue turns black as gangrene sets in.

For the first two types of freezing, temperatures below the freezing point are not necessary. Wintry, low temperatures combined with dampness and wind may produce these effects on the skin. Frostbite and chilblains are generally confined to hands and feet, though occassionally the nose or ears are affeced.

During exposure to cold, the capillaries regulate the body temperature by contracting to avoid heat loss.

If they lose their elasticity through cold damage they expand after freezing and are unable to regain their normal shape. For this reason, freezing looks white at first and becomes bluish-red later on. Finally a complete local standstill of circulation takes place.

Frost damage might cause a chronic condition, due to minor repeated exposure to cold over a length of time. This is found frequently in women whose legs are of a bluish-red colour, and often goes together with a higher sweat secretion. This, and bluish or red hands are usually a sign of poor blood circulation in the extremities. To avoid more serious consequences, legs, feet and hands have to be kept warm.

An allergic reaction to cold is urticaria, generally limited to those body parts which have been directly exposed to low temperature. Urticaria are itchy elevations which disappear after a short time.

Heat

Skin disorders due to heat can have a local or a widespread effect. The time of exposure does not play as significant a part as it does with cold. The height of the temperature is decisive, as protein, including the protein in the skin, reacts to heat by coagulation. Several degrees of burning are distinguished, depending on the intensity of the heat source as well as the dimension and depth of the affected skin portion.

Swelling and reddening are the initial signs, to which blisters of different sizes are added in the next stage. The blisters contain a clear, serous liquid. The following degree is characterized by scabs made of dead cells. Burning might be superficial or deep, depending upon whether the skin has been destroyed to the papillary layer or beyond, and whether the underlying layer has been burned as well. The most severe burn is a destruction and complete carbonization of the skin, inclusive of its associate organs.

The scars resulting from burns are frequently deforming and represent a cosmetic problem. A plastic surgeon should be consulted as to how far the appearance of the skin can be improved.

Heat hives are a rash on body parts exposed prolongedly to high temperatures, usually found only on persons susceptible to such outbreaks. If no longer under the influence of the cause the condition fades, leaving pigmentation.

A heat rash known as prickly heat (miliaria) appears as a rule on covered body portions in warm, damp climates. It is accompanied by itching and burning sensations and is brought on by blocking of the sweat ducts, interfering with the regulation of body temperature.

Sunburn and skin conditions due to ultra-violet rays

Sunburn (erythema solare) is not a true burn, but a reaction to ultra-violet rays. The damaging effect of a burn would be immediately apparent, while that of ultra-violet rays is noticed only several hours later. Susceptibility to the rays varies. Fair people with blue eyes are more quickly and intensively influenced. They have less skin melanin, and they may develop freckles whereas a darker skin tans evenly.

There are a number of preparations on the market which will preserve an untanned skin or reduce and lessen the intensity of freckles. Research into the reaction of ultra-violet rays on the human skin led to the development of sun screens and blocks. They (as their name indicates) either block the rays completely from reaching the skin, or filter out the undesired rays (see: Light in chapter on Physics). Substances incorporated into the oil in water or water in oil emulsions for this purpose are: para amino benzoic acid (PABA), benzophenone, titanium and zinc oxide; the latter two are heavier agents. A good, covering foundation alone can serve as an effective protection.

Preparations with an addition of tannin simultaneously reduce the skin's sensitivity and counteract inflammation. Because of these properties they are suitable for an already-irritated skin, but in the long run could be drying and should not be applied over any length of time on a fine-textured skin. Talcum powder or a compress made with strong black tea or diluted boric acid are old, home remedies that will soothe a light sunburn.

Sun exposure can bring about undesired side-effects like colour changes and hypersensitivity to those on medication.

Damage through overexposure The body must adjust itself slowly to ultra-violet rays from the sun or from a lamp, in order to build up the necessary resistance. Burning, peeling, and an uneven tan are not beneficial for health or beauty. To prevent conjunctivitis, the eyes need protection with sunglasses, or with cotton balls held in place with cream over the closed eyes.

Overexposure to sun causes chemical and metabolic changes which can further or initiate certain diseases. Excess exposure to ultra-violet rays without head protection can induce a sunstroke with its symptoms of headache, dizziness and vomiting.

Permanent damage may result from repeated and constant over-exposure over long periods to sun, especially to individuals with fair skin. Telangiectasia, early atrophy and dryness may be experienced. To protect itself, the stratum corneum builds up so that keratosis is not uncommon. The complexion looks thick and ragged, the so-called sailor's or farmer's skin.

Allergic conditions In contrast to sunburn, there are allergic reactions to ultra-violet rays. These differ according to skin response, and may take the form of papules, oedema or other lesions, for example solar urticaria.

X-rays and radium Although ultra-violet rays can be harmful, rays from X-rays and radium may injure the skin permanently. In most cases, the effects of sunlight are temporary and the skin soon regains its normal appearance. The reactions to X-rays and radium may look, to a certain extent, like those to ultra-violet rays, but if once initiated, their skin damage cannot be annulled. Small doses of X-rays lessen the activity of the sebaceous glands which is to be desired in some disorders. This can be accompanied by pigmentation, which eventually fades when the skin is no longer exposed to the rays.

HYPERKERATOSIS – CALLUSES

A hyperkeratosis is a disorder leading to an abnormal thickening and hardening of the skin. The resulting horny layer may develop into a considerable build-up. This formation may be seen on the whole body or be limited to certain parts. Causes range from serious disorders, to toxins and mechanical influences. The simple callus is a local hyperkeratosis, representing a protection of the skin to prevent damage.

A hyperkeratosis of the palms and soles

This belongs to the inherited disorders or is due to aging. Elderly persons of fair complexion are prone to a senile hyperkeratosis, in particular after repeated and prolonged over-exposure to sun. This appears as a brownish, wart-like elevation on the uncovered skin portions. Seborrheic keratosis is a similar phenomenon in middle-aged or elderly people on the body. Intake of toxic matter like arsenic over a long period of time can also cause a hyperkeratosis, as can a vitamin deficiency.

Calluses

These, as a reaction to continuous mechanical stimuli, are mainly found on hands and feet. Poorly-fitted shoes often cause the formation of calluses and corns. Calluses on feet can grow into a considerably thick layer which can disappear if the pressure that caused them is no longer present. They are generally seen on heels, bunions, soles and toes. The horny layer can be removed by rubbing with an anti-keratotic substance or with a pumice stone.

The corn or clavus

This represents a different type of callus. It forms where the skin is close to a projecting bone, as in the case of the toes. A corn is round and varies from an ordinary callus insofar as it has a prolongation or root extending from the centre into the tissue below. This root does not necessarily disappear after the cause of the corn is gone. Therefore, the corn should be removed by a trained person. In some cases, a corn plaster can help to bring relief. This plaster contains a combination of salicylic acid, phospherous and other chemicals to soften the horny substances so that the corn can be lifted out after a hot foot-bath.

DISORDERS OF THE VASCULAR SYSTEM

Varicose veins

Varicose veins (varices) have several causes. They are found in some families as an inherited trait. They are mainly present in women but can be seen occasionally in men. The hypothesis is a weakness in the connective tissue, with a poorly developed musculature of the venous walls.

An indication that hormones are influential in the development of varices is seen in the fact that they often appear or become worse during and after pregnancy.

Varicose veins are bluish lines, thin or thick, straight or winding. They are more often present on the calves than on the thighs. In serious cases they become very obvious and thick, bulging out in places. They resemble knots and can have a considerable diameter.

There are two kinds of veins in the legs – the superficial veins and those in the deeper tissues. As long as the back flow in the varicose veins is not disturbed, and the valves which regulate the transport of the venous blood to the heart have not been damaged, they do not cause any inconvenience. Under these circumstances, they only present a cosmetic problem. They can be surgically removed to improve the appearance of the leg.

If the back flow of the blood is not normal and the veins have to handle an increased amount, their walls are weakened. This condition is bound to influence the legs more than any other part of the body because of the action of gravity. The greater amount of venous blood flows through the deeper veins; the surface veins contain only one-tenth of the entire returning blood.

If a thrombosis or an inflammation of the leg veins occurs after illness or accident, destruction of the valves or dislocation of the veins themselves may take place. The blood congests and the capillaries on the surface expand as they are firmly filled. This occurs mainly at the calves where the capillaries are more obvious. It may lead to an extravasation of blood in the tissue around the vessels, when the leg swells and redness can be seen. After a time the colour changes through the presence of the pigment and becomes yellowish-brown. This area then enlarges to cover a considerable portion of the calf or ankle. In order to absorb this chronic oedema the body forms new tissue around and over it which is hard and firm.

Varicose veins are liable to haemorrhage, inflammations and mechanical injuries. The hard tissue over the oedema heals poorly and is extremely susceptible to infections.

Telangiectasia

This is a dilatation of the capillaries, often seen with rosacea. If it occurs in a dense network of vessels giving the impression of a dark pink area, it is also called couperose.

COLOUR CHANGES OF THE SKIN

An abnormal colour change in the skin is based on various factors. Hyperpigmentation and depigmentation depend upon the amount of blood in the capillaries and the deviation of the colour matter.

A lack of haemoglobin, red corpuscles or both, results in a pale complexion. This disorder, an anaemia, is noticed from the skin and mucous membranes which, in extreme cases, look almost white. The mucous membranes under the eyes clearly show an indication if the haemoglobin or red corpuscle content is below normal. Blushing and turning pale are signs of changes in the amount of blood present in the face capillaries. Temperatures also cause the skin to become red or pale. Blushing or turning pale as a sign of fear, shock and other reactions, is caused by nerve stimuli.

In old age, when high blood pressure often increases the amount of blood passing through the arteries, the complexion can appear flushed. Heart disease or other illnesses make lips, face and hands seem bluish-red owing to a lack of oxygen in the blood.

Cold temperatures let the extremities become bluish or red, as discussed under skin disorders due to physical agents.

Pigmentation of the whole body skin in relation to racial background is an inherited characteristic. The darker the skin the more pigment is present. In deeper shades, melanin is found in the stratum basale and the higher layers of the epidermis closer to the surface, e.g. the stratum spinosum. In a light complexion the colour matter is concentrated in the bottom layer of the epidermis.

Hyperpigmentation

As a disorder, this is an abnormal process taking place in the body pigment. A hyperpigmentation might cover the complete body or be limited to certain areas.

Freckles (ephelides) are small yellow-brown spots, a sign that some parts of the skin have more pigment than others. Their favourite locations are nose, forehead, cheeks, arms, hands, shoulders and back. In summer, ultra-violet rays intensify the colour of the freckles while in winter they have a tendency to fade. There is no means of making freckles disappear completely, but they can be made paler by bleaching or peeling of the skin. They will always appear again after a certain length of time if the skin is exposed to ultra-violet light.

Lentigines are small yellow-brown spots, mentioned also under nevi. A pigment concentration present at, and shortly after, birth produces the so-called nevi spili.

The blue nevus (nevus coeruleus) is a single blue-black cell nevus which is on the skin at birth or appears during the first years of life. In old age, dark pigment marks are seen on hands, arms and face. They are sometimes the beginning of a senile hyperkeratosis.

Chloasma (chloasma uterinum) is found on the forehead, temples and cheeks. This hyperpigmentation has a light to deeper brownish colour and is a phenomenon of pregnancy, fading shortly after the baby is born. In a few cases it is quite tenacious, remaining on the face for a considerable length of time. The showing of the chloasma during this period indicates that it is influenced by the endocrine system and its hormones. Chloasma uterinum is also seen on women taking hormones. Chloasma virginum, yellow-brownish patches, is due to a disorder of the internal organs.

Other causes Vitamin deficiencies, such as pellagra, caused by the lack of nicotinic acid, can show a hyperpigmentation on the affected portions after healing. Pigmentation from ultra-violet rays, radium and X-rays has been dealt with under skin conditions due to ultra-violet light.

The skin can react to continuous pressure and heat by producing pigmentation for protection. Eau de Cologne or perfume applied with consequent exposure to ultra-violet rays can induce photo-sensitivity, and lead to skin inflammation followed by a lasting pigmentation called Berlock dermatitis.

Depigmentation

The opposite of hyperpigmentation is decolouration of the skin.

Albinism is a disorder in which the pigment matter is missing completely. Albinism is present from birth and appears in different degrees; in some cases the iris of the eyes is light blue or, if the retina is without pigment, the iris may be red.

Vitiglio An acquired loss of skin colour is vitiglio. Generally seen in face, neck, hair and hands it may slowly cover the entire body, leaving white, irregular patches.

Leukoderma is a disorder with an absence of pigment in some skin areas. These patches have little tendency to enlarge.

Other causes Depigmentation of skin portions can be seen after healing of certain diseases. The nevus achromicus has the same characteristics as the coloured nevus, only its pigmentation is missing.

Chemicals and metals carried to the skin through the body system or forced into it from outside can also create a disturbing cosmetic problem. Drugs containing gold or silver make the skin look greyish when particles of the metal are deposited in the dermis and epidermis. There is hardly anything that can be done to improve this condition. The same is true of tattoo marks. The colouring matter tatoos place in the deeper layers of the skin generally cannot be removed without leaving a scar.

Metal splinters under the skin can often be successfully removed by an experienced doctor.

SKIN DISEASES OF UNKNOWN CAUSES

A skin disease almost as common as eczema is psoriasis, the origin of which is not known. It is characterized by patches of dull red with white silvery scales. These lesions are very itchy and, if a scale has been removed by scratching, a minute drop of blood is seen. Psoriasis usually appears on the elbows, knees, lower back and scalp, but is also seen on other body parts. The growth of head hair is not impeded by psoriasis.

Lesions shaped like a butterfly and extending over the nose and upper parts of the cheeks constitute lupus erythematosus. This disease is sometimes evident after a serious sunburn and may become chronic. It is among the skin diseases of unknown cause. Medical attention is required immediately as the first symptoms become visible.

Pityriasis rosea, generally seen in young adults, is characterized by pinkish spots. It is non-contagious and usually disappears after a few weeks.

DISORDERS OF THE SWEAT GLANDS

The human skin has two kinds of sudoriferous glands, the apocrine and the eccrine sweat glands. The apocrine glands are the larger of the two and excrete a liquid which has a slight odour. The odour of fresh sweat is weak and not disagreeable, but an unpleasant smell results from its decomposition by means of bacteria. The apocrine glands are located chiefly in the axillae. The eccrine glands excrete a liquid consisting of approximately 99 per cent water, in addition to other inorganic and organic matter. They are distributed to all body regions and are numerous in the palms of the hand, footsoles and underarms.

The chemical reaction of the fresh sweat is acidic. After being decomposed the liquid reacts in an alkaline fashion.

Hyperhidrosis

Hyperhidrosis means an abnormal, excessive perspiration which can be either local or general. The localized form of this disorder is mainly concentrated on palms, footsoles and axillae. In most cases, the cause of this symptom is a nervous condition and it does not represent a serious problem. When the skin of the whole body excretes high amounts of sweat at temperatures where humans do not normally perspire to any large degree, the condition is called a general hyperhidrosis. Because of the varying distribution of the sudoriferous glands, some body regions have a higher rate of excretion than others.

Tuberculosis and other systemic diseases, general physical weakness, nervous or psychological conditions and heart disorders may all cause a hyperhidrosis. Chemicals in drugs and stimulants also increase sweat excretion.

Localized perspiration

This is only of interest from the cosmetic aesthetic viewpoint. Preparations to fight unpleasant sweat odour neutralize the liquid before it turns alkaline so that bacteria cannot interfere. For local treatment astringents, diluted tannic acids, aluminium salts ($AlCl_3$ or $Al_2(SO_4)_3$) and formaldehyde in preparations with pH 4 to 4.5 are recommended.

The apocrine sweat glands develop during adolescence and vary in persons and sex. Women excrete more liquid from these glands than men.

Hair in the armpits assists in the evaporation of sweat. If this natural regulatory medium is removed, adequate disposal of the liquid cannot take place. Talcum powder may compensate in part for the missing hair.

Axillary tissue is fine and sensitive. To avoid irritation, chemical hair removers and deodorants must be tested for possible reactions before application to the skin.

If this tissue is damaged by chemicals or cuts, inflammations or serious infections may result.

Anhidrosis

This is the opposite of a hyperhidrosis – an abnormally low sweat excretion. In this congenital condition the skin is dry and sometimes rough as its natural source of moisture is insufficient.

TUMOURS

We distinguish between two kinds of new skin growths, the good-natured or benign and the malicious or malignant. Whether good-natured or malicious they belong in the hands of a skin specialist.

Tumours are new skin growths formed by a cell unit that is not following the regular pattern of rebuilding body cells. All cells in the human body, whether they are bone, cartilage, fat, skin, gland, muscle or any other, have the ability to form new growths called tumours, containing either cells like the mother cell or cells of different shapes. The good-natured growths are surrounded by a capsule separating them distinctively from the surrounding tissue. The malignant tumours penetrate their environment with branches in a destructive manner. They have the ability to form daughter cells which are carried by means of blood and lymph to all body parts to form new tumours.

Some skin growths have the tendency to become malignant although they are benign at the time of their appearance. These are classified as pre-malignant in contra-distinction to the malignant tumours. They might be the preliminary step to a cancerous growth. Skin damaged by excessive quantities of ultra-violet rays, skin scarred by infections or burns or other causes is more vulnerable to malignant degeneration.

BENIGN TUMOURS

Fibroma

These harmless growths are made up of skin fibres, lymph and blood vessels. They are of skin colour and may either be flat or have a tiny stem and can grow to the size of a pea. Fibromas are found on the body or head where they often come up on eye lids. Fibromas in the shape of a thick thread may develop on the neck, bust or under arm and sometimes become quite numerous. An oval-shaped fibroma, hard to the touch and pink in colour, is located on arms and legs.

Lipoma

A lipoma is a soft tumour of fatty tissue under the skin. It is sharply outlined and does not cause any changes of the skin.

Keloid

A keloid is a flat skin elevation, irregular and extending into the surrounding tissue. It might appear on a young person on the skin over a bone but generally is seen after burning or corrosion.

Keloids following skin injury such as post-operative trauma can be removed by excision of the scar, succeeded by radiation therapy. Results are good if radiation is undertaken immediately after excision of keloids.

If the lesion exists longer than six months, radiation without re-excision is not as successful.

Nevi

Nevi are skin malformations caused by a disturbance during the embryo stage. They may develop later in life or show right at birth. One form of nevus is the nevus papillomatosus which looks like a wart or knot. Generally present at birth, or developing in the first years of life, it is an elevated, light to dark-brown area.

At birth or during the first years of life we also find pigment marks (nevi spili), light brown pigmentations mostly seen on body, legs and arms.

Lentigines, small yellow-brown spots, appear on different body parts, at times distributed all over. In the latter case one speaks of a lentiginosis.

A firemark (nevus flammeus) is an irregular red mark sharply outlined against it surroundings. It is present at birth and enlarges proportionately to body growth. Firemarks are of a harmless nature but can be disturbing cosmetically. They are not easily influenced or removed. One kind present at birth, generally in the middle part of the body, disappears in the first years of life. A reddish-blue nevus, small as a pin head, sometimes develops later in life.

The favourite areas for spider nevi (nevus araneus) are the upper body half, arms, neck and face. A small, light to bluish-red spot centres fine extensions resembling spiders' legs. Liver ailments can cause spider nevi on body skin. They may also appear during pregnancy.

Hair nevi, as the name indicates, are covered with hair-like fur, and are very disturbing in as much as they are hard to disguise. A similar kind, but with the distinction of being a small hairy tumour, is the cell nevus.

Xanthelasma

This is a whitish-yellow, low skin elevation caused by cholesterol collection in the skin tissue. It is commonly found around the eyes on the inner half of the eyelid. It can be removed by a doctor under local anesthesia. It is advisable to make sure that there is no diabetes.

Milia

A milium is a concentration of horny matter originating from sebum resembling a hard pearl. Sub-epithelial, whitish-yellow, of the size of a pin head or larger, it is often seen close to the eyes on the upper cheeks.

PRE-MALIGNANT TUMOURS

Old age wart verruca seborrheica

As indicated, this wart is seen only in old age, on the face and on the body. It is flat, soft, round or oval in elevation, yellow or brown in colour. This wart is seldom malignant.

Atheroma

This round cyst or tumour mainly develops on the head. It evolves in advanced age, accumulating dead cells and fat. As it can become malignant, the atheroma must be removed.

Lymphangioma

A lymphangioma may be present at birth or may become evident in youth. This lymph cyst is sized from a pin head to a pea with a round surface of skin colour or yellow-red. It looks like a little lump or blister and appears on shoulders, neck and face, arranged in groups or rows.

Angioma

An angioma is a blood vessel tumour which can grow in size. If present at birth, it has the tendency to disappear in the first years of life; otherwise it can be removed by the doctor. It may come up in middle-age in small size and greater number. The angioma is harmless and becomes malignant only in rare cases.

Nevi which change in colour, shape or form may develop into malignant tumours. The doctor must be consulted as soon as possible if such a deviation is noticed.

The senile keratosis is seen on the face, hands or other uncovered parts of the body. At the beginning, a brownish-red pigmentation is noticed. Later the skin thickens to form the hyperkeratosis which may become a malignant growth. A degeneration of the horny skin layer is the cutaneous horn which resembles a wart with a round, yellowish-brown elevation. This form of a hyperkeratosis may also develop into a carcinoma.

MALIGNANT TUMOURS

Malignant tumours of the skin are those which characteristically form metastasis at a distance from the initial location.

Basal cell epithelioma is the least life-threatening skin cancer. Its favourite locations are on the upper part of the face around nose and cheeks. This tumour can either originate from a benign growth or appear without the prior presence of a lesion. It can start out as a small, slowly growing lump, a firm, rounded, skin-coloured elevation. When becoming larger the centre forms a pustule and sinks in, forming a light ring at the border. Basal cell epithelioma rarely multiplies but is very destructive to the surrounding skin tissue.

Malignant melanoma is the most virulent of all skin tumours. It is nearly always blue-black in colour and forms a small, rounded lump. This tumour forms metastasis in the inner body organs which can lead to a very serious condition.

DISORDERS DUE TO MICRO-ORGANISMS

Bacteria are single cells, which carry out all reactions associated with life. In order that they may be able to accomplish an exchange of food and waste products by osmosis, their nourishment must be in fluids.

A bacterium (microbe, germ) is a minute organism which divides by amitosis along the short axis of the cell. There are about 2000 different kinds of bacteria of which approximately 100 are disease-producing or pathogenic. The remaining majority are non-pathogenic and play an important part in various processes of nature, such as chemical decomposition of dead matter or waste products. They are helpful to all living humans, animals and plants. Bacteria are widespread in nature, being found in water, in food, on the human skin, in the intestines and in the soil.

Bacteria can be distinguished according to their three basic shapes:

rod shaped – bacterium (plural bacteria), bacillus (plural bacilli),

spherical – coccus (plural cocci),

spiral shaped – spirillum (plural spirilla), vibrio, spirochete.

Cocci sometimes form a chain when they are known as streptococci, or cling together in a pair as diplococci. They are also arranged in clusters as staphylococci. A similar tendency may be found in bacilli, fashioning diplobacilli and streptobacilli.

Spirilla and many bacilli are mobile in liquids. They move with one or more hair-like appendages, the flagella or cilia, which derive from the cell wall.

Certain bacteria have the ability to form spores by surrounding themselves with a resistant capsule. Most of these are non-pathogenic bacteria. Spore formation seems to be an inactive stage these species undergo when outside conditions are favourable. Spores are especially adept at withstanding chemicals, dryness and heat. An active, vegetative period follows spore formation and reproduction starts again.

To be able to multiply rapidly, the bacterium requires suitable temperature, moisture, oxygen, little or no light, and an adequate degree of alkalinity or acidity in its environment. Saprophytes obtain their food from dead organic matter. Parasites take their nourishment from living matter. Bacteria have the ability to adjust themselves to their surroundings, though cold interferes with their growth.

Ultra-violet rays, high temperatures and certain chemicals are destructive to bacteria. Bacteria may penetrate the human body through injuries, as well as by entering the mouth, nose, ears or eyes.

The pyodermas include infections of the skin by pus-forming micro-organisms, e.g. the staphylococcus. The bacterium enters the skin through injuries which may not even be visible to the human eye. Reduced resistance to harmful bacteria may follow an inflammation.

Folliculitis

This is a superficial infection around the hair follicle. If not carried forward to other skin portions it heals after the pus has been excreted.

Folliculitis barbae is an infection in the hair follicle of the beard. It commences with redness around the hair and develops into small pustules. It is found on the upper lip, chin or cheeks.

A minor injury or abrasion to the axilla can result through bacteria in an abscess of the apocrine glands. This painful red, hard lump opens after a time, excreting pus. An inflammation of this area should always be under a doctor's care to avoid further damage.

Boils

A boil or furuncle begins with a red, very painful lump extending deeply into the tissue. A yellow centre, a core, is formed from which pus is drained. A boil leaves a scar after healing. Boils and furuncles are often found in poorly-nourished individuals. Preferred sites seem to be the back of the neck, seat, ankles and wrists. Boils, in particular those occurring on the upper lip, or in the nose, are a severe condition; as they are close to the eyes and the brain. The infection may spread by means of the venous system up the nose. A carbuncle is an extended infection with a number of hair follicles involved. It too is frequently seen at the back of the neck. The inflammation is accompanied by a general indisposition, fever and shivering.

A sty

A sty (hordeolum) is a small lump. It is an infection of a gland at the edge of the eyelid, which disappears after the pus has been released.

Paronychia

This is an infection of the tissue around the nail, and is generally caused by injury to the cuticle. A red swelling first becomes apparent, later turning into a white pus-containing ring.

Angulus infectiosus

This is an infection of the corners of the mouth or is a sign of deficiency of vitamins B and C.

A phlegmon

This is an acute, subcutaneous, pus-forming infection of the skin, and has a red, painful and swollen surface.

Impetigo

This occurs commonly in children, induced by pus-forming bacteria, by streptococci and staphylococci. Blisters are present which quickly become pustular. After rupture, a light yellow-brownish crust is seen, surrounded by erythema. If scratched, the skin demonstrates redness with a tendency to bleed. Impetigo mainly affects the face and hands but can be carried forward to other body parts. It is highly contagious and to avoid infection of others requires immediate doctor's care.

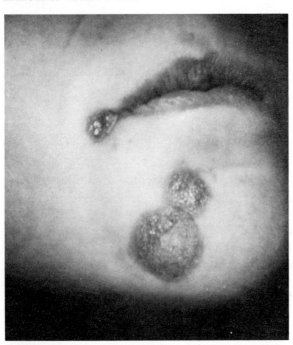

Impetigo

Erysipelas

This is an acute, rapidly-spreading infection accompanied by fever, headache and nausea. A red, raised erythema appears enlarging quickly at its border which shows a distinct outline against surrounding skin. Erysipelas is generally found in the face but also can occur on other body parts. It starts from a scratch or minor injury which becomes infected by streptococci.

Numerous serious skin diseases caused by infections are not accompanied by a pyoderma. Some of them are mentioned here as far as they are of interest in the scope of this book.

Skin tuberculosis

This is caused by the same bacillus as tuberculosis of the inner organs and has different cutaneous expressions.

Lupus vulgaris, the most frequent kind of skin tuberculosis, may be found on all body parts but generally is present in the face because the mucous membranes are less resistant than the skin. The first evidence is a small red-brown macule which is softer than the surrounding tissue. The disease spreads and extends deeper into the skin, becoming devastating. In the centre of the lump a pustule may develop. After healing, scars are left on the skin. To avoid further harm to the skin texture, the disease should be treated by a physician as soon as it is noticed.

Tuberculosis verrucosa cutis can be mistaken for an ordinary wart. The skin build-up is yellow-brown or brown in colour, and the border shows a reddish ring. Warts should in all cases be brought to a doctor's attention.

Tuberculosis of the skin goes together with tuberculosis of the inner organs. The bacillus is carried to the skin by means of the blood vascular system. Bluish, brown-red macules frequently appear on the extremeties as well as on the trunk. Tuberculosis, of the lungs particularly, is highly contagious and easily affects those coming into contact with the patient.

Syphilis

This belongs to the venereal diseases, but because it appears in different forms on the skin it is important too as a skin disease. This serious illness is caused by a spirochete, spiral-shaped body, the treponema pallidum. It is a contact disease generally carried forward to the mucous membranes or lesions in the skin. It affects the whole body and its organs. Syphilis is acquired through infection or can be congenital. Three stages of this disease are distinguished.

The early stage can be seen approximately 3 weeks after infection. At this point, a small, hard, painless lump develops at the location of communication. It secretes moisture and heals after 7 to 10 weeks, leaving a round pigment spot. The person suffers from headaches, aching muscles and joints, as well as swelling of the lymph nodes. If untreated, eruptions become visible all over the body, vanishing after a few weeks. The rash consists of red-brown macules which are painless and without inflammation. These eruptions are repeated during the second stage that may go on as long as 5 years. After healing of the rash, light spots often remain on the skin. These are generally noticed on the chest, upper arms and back.

Following these years, if the disease has not been treated, a third stage commences. This is marked by serious changes in the body organs and deterioration of the arteries, bones and nervous system, with consecutive strokes, severe disorders of the spinal cord or brain damage.

The first two stages of the syphilis have a good chance of being cured, but in the third stage the damages can be annulled only in part.

VIRUSES

Viruses are considered to be parasites, since they need living tissue in which to dwell and multiply. They are agents of infectious diseases. A cell attacked by a virus may sustain injury or be completely destroyed. A pathogenic increase of cells can be brought about by certain viruses, and virus lesions in the skin may have a piling-up of skin cells as a consequence.

Viruses are the smallest living bodies and have the ability to pass through filters which would retain bacteria. They are responsible for pathological symptoms in plants and animals, as well as highly communicable, serious and dangerous diseases in humans. Viruses are distinguished according to their different sizes or shapes. Some of the best known viral diseases are measles, smallpox, mumps, influenza, yellow-fever, pneumonia and rabies. The virus host, i.e. the human being, spreads the disease by direct or indirect contact with others, as well as by throat excretions and faeces. Some viruses are carried to man by insects such as fleas, lice and mosquitoes. Rabies is communicated by an animal bite or scratch. Human viral diseases are rarely transmitted by food or drink.

Immunity to a virus is obtained after one attack of the disease, during which antibodies are formed in the system to fight the respective organism. The purpose of vaccination is to bring a virus into the body to an extent insufficient to cause the disease but sufficient to produce antibodies to counteract it.

Herpes zoster

This is a virus infection seen on different body parts and is accompanied by considerable nerve pain. The skin turns red and small blisters filled with a milky liquid develop. After about a week the lesions crust and healing begins. Herpes zoster is also known as shingles.

Herpes simplex

This is the cold sore or fever blister, and is an acute eruption of a group of small blisters on the mucous membranes of the lips and nose; it can also be seen on the skin. The clear liquid of the blisters dries out after a few days so that a scab can be formed. In about a week this falls off, leaving a reddish spot. The skin soon regains its normal colour.

Molluscum contagiosum

Certain viruses bring about warts or wart-like skin growths. The molluscum contagiosum is a virus disorder formed by degenerated cells. It is a skin-coloured growth up to the size of a pea.

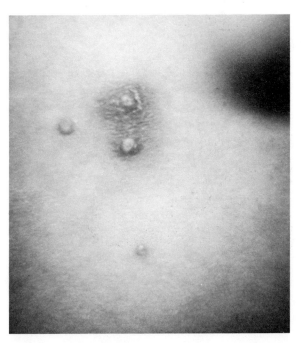

Molluscum contagiosum

Verruca vulgaris

The ordinary wart has a yellow-brown or darker prickly surface. Typical locations are hands and feet, particularly on the fingers in the nail fold. On the footsoles, it can become very painful as it grows into the tissue under constant pressure. Warts must be removed by a doctor.

51

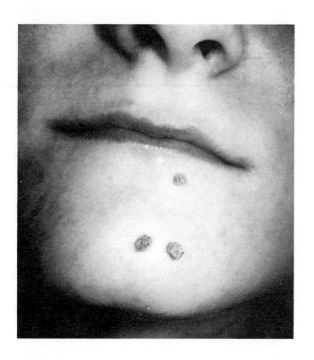

Verrucae planae

Verrucae planae

Flat warts are often seen in young people on the hands, arms, face and head. They are skin-coloured. This wart sometimes spreads, with the back of the hand being its favoured place. In many cases, it disappears by itself without treatment.

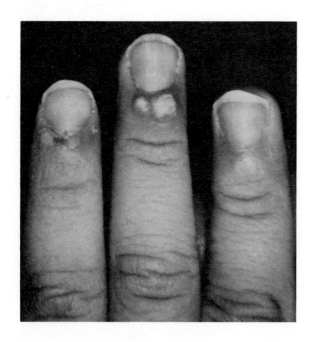

Verruca vulgaris

FUNGI

Fungi belong to the plant kingdom but as they do not contain chlorophyll, they are dependent upon other matter for their existence and are classified as parasites. There is a great variety of fungi that cause diseases of the skin, nails and hair wherever they find the environment suitable for growth and multiplication. Some stay on the surface, while others penetrate deeply into the tissue accompanied by inflammations. Some fungi are more communicable than others.

Fungi are found in single or multi-cellular form. They spread rapidly, forming mycelia under favourable conditions of temperatures and dampness. Reproduction of fungi is by means of spores.

Athlete's foot

A very common fungus infection between the toes and on the footsoles is the so-called athlete's foot. This disease is highly contagious and tenacious. Cold temperatures in winter sometimes bring it to a standstill, only to be followed by a new, heavier outbreak in the heat and moisture of a warmer season. The name athlete's foot indicates in itself that the disease is frequently communicated in public sports facilities like swimming pools. It is widespread in over-populated areas. At the beginning of this fungus infection small blisters form containing a transparent, yellowish liquid. On bursting, they cause a very painful wound. The disorder develops in different ways, with blisters sometimes turning into a pustule or becoming quite large, or drying out so that the skin starts to peel. In the treatment of athlete's foot it is very important to disinfect shoes and stockings continuously to avoid renewed self-infection. This fungus can also affect fingers and palms of the hand.

Tinea capitis

Ringworm of the scalp is more common in children than adults. It is highly contagious and brought about by contact with different agents in the child's environment, particularly animals. The hair falls out in patches, leaving a bald circle, the disease tends to progress slowly, with scales possibly developing into an abscess.

Tinea barbae

This is a fungus infection of a man's beard, and can also spread by contact with animals. Blisters and pustules are present on the affected skin.

Tinea corporis

Another type of ringworm, which is seen mainly in children and appears assymmetrically in varying sizes on the body. It is reddish, scaly and sometimes complicated by blisters.

Tinea versicolour

A superficial and harmless fungus disease is tinea versicolour. The skin areas affected by this fungus are slightly inflamed, pigmented and scaly. They tend to be more deeply coloured in summer than in winter, when they may fade almost completely.

Cutaneous moniliasis

Appearing on overweight women, this is a reddish, slightly-inflammed area under the breast, arms and other body parts where the development of the fungus is promoted by a warm, moist atmosphere.

Moniliasis has one of its manifestations in paronychia, a red, tender swelling around the nail which interferes with its proper development. The surface of the affected nail shows irregularities. Another disorder through fungi is penetration of the fungus under the nail plate (Onychomycosis). The nail looks yellow-brownish, and thickens and splits easily at the free edge. Curing this disease requires great perseverance and the doctor's treatment must be followed faithfully until a new, healthy nail has grown out.

ANIMALS

Animal parasites also cause diseases of the human skin. Among the most common are *scabies, pediculosis* (lice), fleas and ticks.

Scabies

This is a highly contagious disease originating from the 'itch mite'. After communication of the disease, an incubation time of 4 to 6 weeks precedes its actual outbreak. The female mite digs small passages into the epidermis, leaving eggs and waste products behind. This causes extreme itching especially at night. Scabies are seen on hands, wrist, elbow and in the axilla, and if neglected can spread all over the body. The disease is transmitted by infected persons as well as by bed linen.

Head louse

The *pediculosis capitis* or head louse, is an animal parasite found in human head hair, mainly on the back of the scalp. The eggs are light, small bodies, called nits, and are attached to the hair close to the scalp. The bite of the louse causes an itchy sensation of the skin. Lice are found more often in children than in adults. *Pediculosis pubis* attacks the body hair, including eyebrows and lashes. This louse is bigger than the foregoing parasite, and its bite leaves a small, bluish spot. *Pediculosis corporis* attacks the body skin. The nits may be present in the clothing of unclean persons.

Ticks

These are related to mites. They are blood-sucking acarid parasites that transmit infectious diseases.

Fleas

Fleas are known carriers of the diseases such as the plague and typhus. Their bites are expressed in an erythema centered by a minute wound. Flea bites may follow a skin eruption and are usually found on the leg. The parasite does not live on its host. It attacks mainly at night.

DISEASES OF NAILS AND HAIR

Nails

The nails can undergo various changes in colour, consistency, surface and shape.

Changes in colour Together with the inheritance of a dark skin colour comes a darker nail caused by the presence of melanin in the cells. In this normal condition, the shade varies according to the amount of melanin.

Chemicals can stain nails temporarily or permanently until the nail has grown out. The pathogenic changes include a brown or yellow nail body caused by fungus infections.

White spots and stripes in nails are thought to be a sign of air between the horny cells. The entire nail may even become white. There is no cure for this phenomenon, which is given the name of leukonychia. The white disappears with the out-growing nail.

Changes in consistency, surface and shape In an onycholysis the nail body separates in part or completely from the nail bed. Reasons range from injury through manicuring to the use of alkaline soaps, contact with damaging chemicals or even a physical disorder. One or more nails can be affected by onycholysis.

Onychorrhexis is the term for a dry, thin nail which frequently has longitudinal ridges. This nail tends to break at the free edge. It is seen in elderly people, but a thin, brittle consistency of the nail may also be inherited, or may be caused by lack of calcium and vitamin A. Chemicals such as those found in detergents also contribute to this condition of the nail.

A thickening of the nail body may result from increased keratin production after injury, from psoriasis or from eczema at the fingertip. This disorder is known as onychauxis.

Transverse lines in the nails can be a consequence of a matrix injury as well as the expression of a systemic disease. These lines, called Beau's lines, disappear when the nail has grown out far enough to reach the free edge.

The shape of the nail is usually inherited. However, continuous nail-biting or onychophagia can result in a small nail with a receding free edge and a wide fingertip.

The spoon nail or koilonychia, representing a nail with an indentation in the centre, can originate from an injury of the nail body or may be associated with a disorder such as anemia.

A chronic thickening of the nails, together with an enlargement of fingertips and toes, is known as clubbed fingers. The nails may also be more curved than normal. This disorder is based on a systemic disturbance.

Infections of the nail bed, grooves and walls by pus-forming bacteria are very painful. They may cause temporary or lasting damage of the nail body. These infections are often the consequence of cuticle injuries through manicuring or handling of implements in everyday life. Minor injuries should be disinfected to avoid inflammation.

Ingrown toenails, a frequent complaint, are nails growing curved or may be brought about by improper clipping. Pressure is released by removal of the pain-causing nail parts.

Hair

Hair and nails, being the appendages of the skin, can be affected simultaneously by diseases that involve the skin. However, some disorders are characteristically limited to the hair or nails.

Abnormal hair growth in women is sometimes present on the face, appearing mostly on the upper lip, chin and occasionally at the sides of the cheeks. There may be only single hairs scattered over these areas, but there are cases when the growth becomes dense, resembling that of a man's beard. Hair on a woman's chest, breasts and lower back is not uncommon. This excessive hair growth, hirsutism, is the manifestation of a disorder in the endocrine system. A symptom in which the hormonal balance in the female body plays a part is the appearance of facial hair or heavier growth during menopause.

A certain amount of hair on the forearms and legs is normal for all women, but if it increases and becomes darker, it is more apparent. This condition, called hypertrichosis, is common in dark-haired women.

Hair reduction Different circumstances may cause hair reduction without disease of the scalp. One of these is trichorrhexis nodosa. Nodes appear along the hair shaft which apparently is weaker in these places where it tends to break off. Mechanical or chemical damage is most likely responsible for this disorder; however hair may be damaged, become fragile, split or break through use of chemicals without the presence of nodes.

The cause of breakage, reduction and shortening of scalp hair is monilethrix, also known as beaded hairs. It can be due to a scalp disorder or to an inherited disposition.

Pili torti or twisted hair shafts, a tendency that runs in some families, is usually observed in children.
Pili annulati indicates alternating light and dark colour stripes in head hair. The hairshaft itself appears normal. This deviation is usually a family trait and is seen mostly in children.

The process of greying is a loss of pigment in the hairshaft, the reason for which is not yet completely understood. The discolouration is accompanied by air bubbles in the shaft. The hair usually starts greying in a few portions on the scalp. There is no set age for the beginning of grey hair showing. Inheritance plays a decisive part.

Ingrown hair is a hair which is abnormally curved, thus tending to grow into the surrounding skin tissue instead of reaching the surface.

Loss of hair may occur in patches or totally. Its origin is sometimes hard to detect and might be a local inflammation or infection in the body. A circumscribed area with little or no hair growth may be due to inheritance, constant rubbing or pressure, pulling or twisting of the hair, or damaging hair preparations. Loss of hair can be, as well, the reaction of the scalp to an inflammation in the hair follicle (folliculitis decalvans) or can follow a skin infection.

The disorder known as alopecia areata develops without prior indications. One or more coin-sized bald patches evolve though no skin disease is present. Body hair and eyebrows may also be affected, and the condition may lead to complete baldness. The cause for this loss of hair is internal disease or a nervous condition; however, the hair has a good chance of growing back.

Idiopathic alopecia or premature loss of hair in youth or middle age, occurs more often in men than in women. The hair thins at the crown or at the hairline along the forehead. In women, the loss of hair is frequently disseminated, while in men it can lead to complete baldness. This can, in most cases, be genetically traced.

After skin diseases such as the seborrheic dermatitis or pityriasis, the hair grows in again in the majority of cases. Following the intake of certain medications or after internal disease, an increased shedding of hair may be noticed. Growth generally recovers after the disturbing factor is no longer active.

If, as a consequence of a skin disease, scars remain on the scalp, the hair does not grow back over these portions.

Alopecia cicatrisata results in a permanent loss of hair either in patches or in larger areas. There are no inflammations present in the course of this disease. The cause of alopecia cicatrisata is as yet unknown.

COMMON TERMS REFERRING TO SKIN LESIONS

A skin lesion is a defined injury of the cutaneous membrane. The initial state, a primary lesion, may develop into a subsequent manifestation or secondary lesion.

Primary lesions

Macule Flat discoloured marks or patches on the skin surface caused by bruising, pigment concentration or expansion of blood vessels.

Papule Small, solid skin elevation, like a hard blemish without fluid or pus.

Pustule A pyogenic small skin elevation, a pimple. The centre generally appears white or yellow, due to its pus content and is often surrounded by a reddish inflammation. More severe and with the involvement of hair follicle, it is called a boil or carbuncle.

Nodule A small rounded, deeper-seated node, solid to the touch.

Wheals or Hives A temporary flat skin swelling without fluid which may result from hypo-sensitivities like urticaria, usually itchy.

Vesicle A small, clear, fluid-containing skin pocket, like a blister. In a larger diameter, it is termed Bulla.

Erythema Abnormal redness produced by congestion of the capillaries giving an indication of allergic reaction or systemic disorder.

Secondary lesions

Scale A dry, flat keratinous cell disquamated from the epidermis. Retained on some primary lesions as in the case of psoriasis and other skin disorders.

Scab A crust formed by drying of secretion of blood, lymph or pus over a lesion.

Excoriation Scratching of the skin producing loss of tissue accompanied by bleeding.

Fissure A deep cleft or break reaching into the dermis occurring secondary in damaged or hardened skin.

Lichenification Leathery thickening of the skin, the result of long-term continuous rubbing and scratching.

Ulcer An open sore usually extending below the epidermis with loss of surface tissue and often pus.

Scar A mark left by healing of skin tissue with the formation of new connective tissue in the dermis. An elevated, excessive, fibrous scar is a keloid.

Hygiene

Contents

Hygiene serves to maintain health and includes those practices which counteract harmful agents and their consequent effects to bring about more favourable living conditions. Public hygiene deals with housing, food, water, air, sewage, rubbish disposal, and disease control. Prevention of infection and accidents belong to the category of professional hygiene, while personal hygiene comprises care for a healthy body and mind.

HYGIENE IN A COSMETIC INSTITUTE

When setting up a cosmetic institute, the principles of professional hygiene must be taken into consideration, and the regulations set out by health authorities followed. These are primary considerations, more important than location or decoration. It goes without saying that a cosmetic institute should be located in a building with appropriate heating, ventilation and reasonable soundproofing. Insulation from outside noises is significant insofar as the client comes for both treatment and relaxation. Every effort should be made to create a quiet, comforting atmosphere. Doors and windows must be adequate, and windows must be provided with insect-proof screens unless the building is air-conditioned.

If there is only a small space available and no partitions for booths have been planned, privacy for the client can still be created by setting up plastic walls or partitioning with curtains. It is important to note that the treatment room should be completely separate from the reception area, and from any boutique. Windows must be large enough to supply daylight, and electric light must be adequate and not distorting. The entire premises of the cosmetic institute has to be easily kept clean. The walls and floors of the treatment section must be washable, covered with paint or a material that does not stain from chemicals and cosmetics. Carpeting is unsuited for this portion; it may only be used in the reception area.

A large cosmetic institute should include a separate staff room, where the employees may retire if unoccupied. It makes a poor impression if an employee stands around idle. For hygienic purposes, the staff room is the place for smoking and coffee breaks, away from presence of clients.

The treatment lounge must be easy to clean with soap and water. It must give repose to the client and permit the aesthetician to work in a natural, comfortable posture. All appliances must be of a material that can be cleaned physically and/or chemically, i.e. by sanitizing. This applies to steamer, electrical applicances, tweezers, scissors, comedone extractors, brushes, spatulas, etc. Clean cotton, tissue and towels must be employed for each step of a treatment and never re-used. A clean, washable headband and scarf must be available for each customer. Tissue may be a replacement for both as it is disposable, but it absorbs moisture if not handled with great care, leaving the hairline damp after application of compresses. However, a plastic headband cannot be kept as clean as required, and therefore can never fully replace a washable one.

A supply of hot and cold water and containers for rubbish and used towels are part of the standard equipment of any cosmetic institute. Sinks must be kept clean and sanitary at all times.

Because of the obvious opportunity of spreading diseases all equipment in a cosmetic institute must be thoroughly cleansed and sanitized after each use. A complete sterilization can hardly be obtained, but sanitation serves the purpose unless the appliances have come into contact with pathogenic or pus-forming bacteria. In this case greater care must be taken, and disinfecting is indicated. A client with signs of a skin disorder must not be treated, but should be tactfully advised to see a doctor.

DISINFECTING, STERILIZING AND SANITIZING

The differences between disinfecting, sterilizing and sanitizing are as follows: in disinfecting and sterilizing, all bacteria, pathogenic as well as beneficial, are destroyed; whereas in sanitizing the growth of bacteria is retarded. Complete asepsis, which means a total elimination of bacteria, can only be achieved under strict conditions, as there are bacteria constantly present in the air surrounding us and in the superficial skin layers. There are two ways of disinfecting and sanitizing; the physical and the chemical, which produce various reactions depending on the method employed. A radical, complete method of destroying bacteria is the burning of the infected material. This, of course, can only be used on flammable, non-valuable items. For appliances and apparatus the physical means of sterilization by steam or water are indicated, using a temperature of 100 °C for approximately 30 minutes. Dry temperatures of 200 °C and ultra-violet rays have also proven very effective for this purpose. When commercial containers are used the manufacturer's instructions must be observed as to the point of sterilization.

Chemical agents

Liquids are for disinfecting and sanitizing the chemical way. They are very effective and convenient, and can be used to disinfect plastics which are damaged at high temperatures. The efficacy of the chemical and the length of time the appliance must remain in the solution depend upon the concentration of the liquid. The proportions for dilution are given in the manufacturer's instructions.

Chemical agents, when used according to directions, inactivate micro-organisms on objects, impeding their transfer from one person to another. The disinfectant has to have the following properties, to be reliable in its effect, even in low concentration and to destroy bacteria permanently. Its chemical components must be well tolerated by the skin and implements should not be damaged, even if the liquid has been used repeatedly over a length of time. It is desirable for the disinfectant to be combined with a cleansing action.

Commercial disinfectants have been tested and are under strict control of the relevant drug laws. The container should list the ingredients and their composition. A bactericide is an agent destroying bacteria, a fungicide, fungi. A microbicide is lethal to microbes and a sporidice to spores. A virucide neutralizes or destroys viruses.

Composition Chemical disinfectants are, in general, mixtures of defined compounds and their effect is based not only on one ingredient but due to the composition of different components, for example:

1 *Alcohols*, solutions of 70 per cent isopropanol (C_3H_8O), 70 per cent ethanol (C_2H_6O). Alcohol is a base of fast-acting disinfectants against fungi and bacteria. However, a number of spores are resistant to alcohol.

2 *Aldehyde* and derivatives, e.g., formaldehyde (HCHO), acetaldehyde (CH_2CHO), inactivate bacteria, fungi and viruses.

3 *Phenol* (C_6H_5O) and its derivatives, like chlorophene ($C_{13}H_{11}Cl\,O$), chlorocresol ($C_7H_7Cl\,O$), 2-phenylphenol ($C_{12}H_{10}O$) and hexachlorophene ($C_{13}H_6Cl_6O_2$). These substances destroy bacteria, fungi and their spores.

4 *Halogens* containing bromine (Br), chlorine (Cl), fluorine (F) and iodine (I) counteract bacteria, viruses, fungi and their spores.

5 *Oxidation* agents are unstable compounds which split off oxygen. When oxygen atoms are freed, they attack the micro-organisms, counteracting fungi and bacteria. H_2O_2 is the disinfectant suitable to be used on the skin after removal of impurities. Potassium permanganate ($KMnO_4$), dark purple crystals, can be used topically in an aqueous solution. Ozone (O_3) acts by reducing micro-organisms present on the skin (ultra-violet lamps and vapozone) and in the air.

6 *Tensides* (detergents) are cleansing media and recommended in a solution for disinfecting of laundry.

7 *Organic and Inorganic Acids* have the properties of preservatives counteracting inflammation, bacteria, fungi and viruses. Examples of organic acids are lactic acid, benzoic acid, citric acid and acetic acid. Inorganic acids used for this purpose are salicylic acid, boric acid and silicic acid.

Uses

To clean sinks, walls, floors, etc., Lysol or similar agents are feasible. Solutions based on formaldehyde, quaternary ammomium compounds or alcohol can be used to disinfect appliances and implements. Metal or other instruments can be disinfected after washing by rubbing with a cotton ball soaked in 70 per cent alcohol.

All equipment must be washed with soap and water after each use, then sanitized, dried and kept in a clean place. The chemical solution of the disinfectant in a container must be changed regularly.

Towels for compresses or other purposes during a treatment, as well as blankets to cover the customer, must be immaculate and tidy. Towels must never be reused.

Personal hygiene

Hands must be washed and the fingernails thoroughly cleaned with soap, water and a nail brush, before and after each treatment as well as between the different steps. A disinfectant is indicated if the hands have been in touch with pus-forming bacteria. No jewellery can be worn on hands or arms during a treatment because it hinders action and collects cosmetics.

The uniform of the aesthetician must be made of an easily-washed material, clean and neat at all times. A cotton uniform is preferred for someone with a tendency to perspire. Cotton allows an exchange of air between the body and the surrounding air, maintaining a normal temperature between skin and clothes. The cotton fibre absorbs moisture and lets it evaporate more readily than a synthetic. The shoes worn by the aesthetician must be well-fitted and ventilated, preventing heat congestion and discomfort.

Regular body and footcare is a vital necessity when it comes to dealing with the public. Body care is discussed in detail under the heading 'At Home Care'.

A regular check-up at the dentist coupled with daily oral hygiene is indispensable for beauty and health. This includes routine cleaning of the teeth as well as fresh breath. Bad breath may be the result of tooth decay, stomach trouble or other disorder, or the consumption of spicy food. The doctor should be consulted if it is a constant concern. A good mouthwash or chlorophyll taken in tablet or other form will help overcome the odour of spices.

First aid

Contents

The aesthetician has to be able to assist in case of accidents at the place of work. A first aid kit must be available, equipped with all material necessary to extend initial help. The injured and/or sick person must be sent to the doctor, or a doctor must be called if required.

Accidents caused by electric current may occur as a result of carelessness. They can be prevented by keeping all electrical appliances, switches and outlets in perfect condition. Safety rules must be observed to protect both aesthetician and client, since accidents from electric shocks are serious. It is imperative never to touch electrical appliances with damp hands, for wet skin has less resistance to the current and is a good conductor of electricity. Dry skin is a poor conductor, reducing the possibility of shock.

Advice and instructions are given by first aid training centres. Examples of first aid are listed below, extracted from the St. John Ambulance First Aid Handbook issued by Sun Life Assurance Company of Canada.

ARTIFICIAL RESPIRATION

May be required after drowning, poisoning by gases (household gas, automobile exhaust gas) or electrocution (electric shocks, lightning).

Remove victim from water or from gas-filled room, taking care not to fall victim yourself. If in contact with electricity, break the current or contact by switching off the current or by using a non-conductor such as a long, dry wooden pole.

Send for doctor.

Oral resuscitation mouth-to-mouth method

Press the casualty's head to the fully extended position and draw the chin well forward. The airway to the lungs will now be fully open unless it contains foreign matter of some sort. In some cases it may be necessary to insert the thumb into the mouth in order to hold the tongue forward.

The rescuer now takes a deep breath, and places his mouth over the mouth of the casualty. The rescuer's cheek may block the casualty's nose. If not, the rescuer should pinch closed the casualty's nostrils, using the hand not engaged in holding the chin up. This is generally the better procedure.

The rescuer then blows into the casualty's lungs, sufficiently strongly to cause the casualty's chest to rise. This movement may be seen by the rescuer looking out of the corner of his eye.

The rescuer then turns his head away, takes another breath and repeats the cycle. In the interval, air passively exhales from the casualty's lungs. There may be an audible sound and the chest will fall.

The cycle should be repeated about every three to five seconds for an adult, and a little more frequently for a child. The blowing will be less strong for a child or baby, but in any event should be strong enough to cause the casualty's chest to rise.

Note When it is not possible to make a satisfactory seal mouth-to-mouth, the operator's hand supporting the chin should be brought up over the casualty's mouth to close it off completely while the operator blows through the casualty's nose.

In the case of very small infants, it may be found better for the operator to cover with his mouth both the mouth and nose of the casualty, and blow through both at the same time.

The Holger–Nielsen method of artificial respiration

Lay the victim in the prone position and place his hands, one over the other, under his forehead.

To ensure that the air passages are straight tilt the head and chin upward by putting a book or folded clothing or a heap of earth or sand, under the victim's hands.

The nose and mouth must be unobstructed.

Position of the operator Place one knee with the inner side in line with the casualty's cheek, six to twelve inches from the top of his head.

Place the other foot with the heel in line with the casualty's elbow.

Place the hands on the casualty's back with the heel of the hands on the lower part of the shoulder blades, the thumbs alongside the spine, and the fingers pointing to the casualty's feet. Or, the fingers may be spread downward and outward, with the tips of the thumbs just touching.

Movement 1 Keeping the arms straight, rock gently forward until the arms are vertical or almost vertical, depending on the build of the casualty or that of the operator, using no special force, counting 'one, two'. This pressure causes expiration.

Movement 2 The operator now rocks back, counting 'three' and slides his hands past the casualty's shoulders until they can grip his upper arms near the elbows. He raises and pulls on the arms until tension is felt, counting, 'four, five'. He should take care not to raise the chest from the ground. This movement causes inspiration. The operator's arms should remain straight for the whole period.

Counting 'six' the operator gently lowers the casualty's arms to the ground and replaces his hands in the original position.

BLEEDING FROM THE NOSE

Loosen collar, sit patient upright, have him breathe through the mouth. If bleeding persists pinch the nostrils firmly together for at least five minutes by the clock. If bleeding still continues take patient to doctor or hospital.

BLISTERING FEET AND HANDS

Prevent by wearing properly-fitted footgear with heavy socks. Treat by washing in warm soapy water, by drying and rubbing with rubbing alcohol.

Do not break the blisters. Dust with powder and cover with sterile dressing.

BRUISES

The size of a bruise can partly be controlled by the application of cold dressings immediately following the injury.

BURNS AND SCALDS

Do not remove clothing. Do not break blister. Cover entire area with sterile dressings or freshly laundered handkerchief or sheets. Bandage firmly. Wrap patient in blankets. Give warm fluids, preferably weak tea sweetened with sugar.

BURNS BY STRONG ACIDS

Drench the area with water followed by an alkaline solution (two tablespoons of bicarbonate of soda to each pint of water). Treat as a burn.

BURNS BY STRONG ALKALIS

Drench the area with water. Cover with sterile gauze dressing and refer patient to a doctor or hospital as soon as possible for further treatment. If caused by quicklime, brush off any particles before washing.

CLOTHING ON FIRE

Smother flames by covering patient with rug or other material. If in the open, roll patient over and over. Treat as for burns.

FAINTING

The patient should lie flat with the feet raised on a pillow. Recovery will occur naturally but may be hastened by using smelling salts. Insist upon further rest after consciousness is regained.

FITS AND CONVULSIONS

These pass of their own accord and first aid is limited to efforts to prevent the patient injuring himself during fit.

If not a known epileptic the patient should visit a doctor.

FOREIGN BODY IN EAR

Do not attempt to remove – take the patient to a doctor.

FOREIGN BODY IN EYE

Prevent the patient rubbing the eye. If under lower lid, pull down gently and remove with corner of handkerchief. If under upper lid or if difficult to remove, do not persist in your efforts as serious damage to the eyeball may result. Cover eye with pad and take patient to doctor.

HEADACHES

Headaches should never be treated by first aid worker. They may be caused by serious disease. Patient should be referred to a doctor.

HICCUPS

Have the patient draw a deep breath and hold it to cover the time when the next hiccup should occur. Success may require this manoeuvre to be repeated several times.

UNCONSCIOUSNESS

Never jump to conclusions as regards to the cause of unconsciousness. It is often difficult even for a fully equipped hospital to make the correct diagnosis and therefore this is not a matter for a first aid worker's decision.

If breathing is not noisy, lay the casualty on his back with the head and shoulders slightly raised and supported, and turn the head to one side. Be prepared to modify the position if breathing becomes difficult or obstructed.

If breathing is noisy (bubbling through secretions), turn the casualty into the three-quarter prone position. Support him in this position with a pad in front of the chest or draw up the upper knee.

If the casualty is on a stretcher, raise the foot of the stretcher to help to drain secretions from the lungs.

Undo all tight clothing about the neck, chest and waist.

WOUNDS

Arrest bleeding by firm pressure with a sterile or clean pad. Do not use antiseptics. It is permissible to clean the wound gently with boiled water and soap. Keep injured part at rest, using a sling or splint if necessary. Remove patient to doctor or hospital.

What to know about aesthetic surgery

Contents
Aesthetic surgery   Facial surgery   Skin treatments   Mammaplasty   Lipectomy   Hair transplants

AESTHETIC SURGERY

Aesthetic or cosmetic surgery is a field of plastic, reconstructive surgery. The word 'plastic' comes from the Greek *plastikos*, meaning the art of creating or moulding a three-dimensional image. The progress and success of aesthetic surgery during the past few decades is remarkable.

Facial and bodily flaws, either congenital or acquired, may have a negative psychological effect, and aesthetic surgery can contribute in overcoming this problem. However, the problem must be genuine; correction of an insignificant imperfection cannot cure profound complexes and character shortcomings; this will be realized by the individual after surgery.

Aesthetic surgery is carefully planned to obtain the best outcome possible. The adjusted portion of the face or body must be in harmony with the features or figure. We do not need to resign when the years start to show; we can continue to try and be attractive and energetic with the twin assets of a mature mind and external youth. The investment in surgery is also worth while for those in professions where appearance denotes fitness and mental performance.

Rejuvenation

When it comes to rejuvenation, permanence depends on the variable factors: the person's age, skin texture, muscle tone, physiology, healing and care. Looking after oneself is a decisive factor in postponing the maturing process; nevertheless, the point will be reached when the best cosmetic treatment can no longer lessen the progressing signs of ongoing time.

There is no exact time for aging symptoms to become apparent. They are influenced by inheritance, health, life-style and environment. In general, indications become visible from the age of thirty-five, and it is advisable not to wait too long after the first signs appear before taking action. Greater success can be achieved if aesthetic surgery is done early, and a woman of forty-five who looks thirty-five following surgery profits more from the change than a woman ten years older. The clock moves on from the point to which the face has been rejuvenated. All features do not age necessarily simultaneously. The surgeon advises which parts should be rejuvenated and which surgery brings about the most satisfying result. In all, the longer a woman waits while feeling she needs improvement, the more difficult it is to obtain the best possible outcome. Rejuvenation procedures can be repeated, depending upon the individual case.

Bone structure

Adjustments involving the bone structure are done soon after the skeleton is fully developed. The advantage in carrying out these corrections on a young person is that the change is more easily accepted than it would be by an older individual.

The aesthetician whose task is to advise her client in beauty problems needs insight into aesthetic surgery. She should be aware of its possibilities and limitations as well as knowing how to direct skin care and make-up after the surgical procedures heal. She should be able to reply to common questions asked by someone contemplating surgery. For all other essential information the client must seek the authentic advice and judgment of the surgeon, who can inform her about hospital confinement, potential improvement, surgical method and anaesthesia.

The problems discussed in this chapter are those of direct, practical interest to the aesthetician. They are: retardation of aging; corrections of nose, chin and ears; breast improvements; reduction of excessive body fat; and the elimination of scars and disfiguring birthmarks.

FACIAL SURGERY

Possibilities of facial rejuvenation are various. One of the most gratifying is blepharoplasty, the eye-smoothing surgery.

Blepharoplasty

The eye area ages most rapidly, with laughing lines losing their attraction and turning into wrinkles, while the skin of the lids becomes crepey and sags to give a tired appearance. It is not uncommon also to find baggy lower lids as an inherited trait in young people. The harmony of the features is restored by tightening the afflicted tissues.

Superficial skin layers, including the herniated orbital fat which causes puffiness and discomfort, are removed during surgery. The incisions are delicate lines in the upper-eye crease and along the bottom lash base. Stitches remain for up to five days, but swelling and bruises will continue after this time. Dark glasses must be worn for one to two weeks, while the sutures are kept clean and protected from ultra-violet rays. Eye make-up can be applied after about ten days. In the subsequent three months the scars will lighten until they are almost invisible. Pulling of the skin must be avoided during this period, therefore no massages or other manipulations.

A blepharoplasty lasts ten years or more. As with most cosmetic surgery there is no pain, only a few days of discomfort.

Should the eyelids not need emendation, though the area is afflicted by a drooping brow and crow's feet, the eyebrows may be lifted. The incision is carried out along the upper brow brim, and after the skin is loosened from the underlaying tissue, a crescent-shaped section is removed. The skin is remodelled to the forehead, returning the brow into its natural position. If desired, the flow of the brow can be changed simultaneously. After three months the scar is barely visible. Skin care after this operation is the same as after blepharoplasty.

Rhytidectomy

In the event of face and neck sagging to proclaim the loss of youth, a facelift or rhytidectomy (rhytidoplasty) is indicated. Skin wrinkles when its elastic qualities decrease, causing features to descend. As a consequence jowls appear at cheeks and mouth corners, emphasizing the nasolabial fold. The neck shows lines and crepeyness. Correction of these symptoms requires raising the facial parts back into a position where they were previously, taking about ten years off the face.

The incision for a facelift starts in the hair at the temples, leads along the front of the small cartilage of the ear, encircles the earlobe, and disappears into the hairline at the neck. Bruising on cheeks and neck vanishes slowly while the scars whiten; healing takes at least three months, depending upon the state of health and skin type. The doctor advises when a normal skin care programme can be reassumed, but until then no massages or stimulating preparations can be employed. During recovery creams and moisturizers are applied tenderly as is the make-up to camouflage the scars.

Rhytidectomy does not damage the cutaneous membrane. On the contrary, the skin detached from the lower layers at temples, cheeks, chin and neck will age more slowly as the healing process encourages a better circulation and regeneration of the tissues.

A rhytidoplasty does not create a new identity nor unnatural facial expressions. It is a physical change that erases many of the imprints of time, bringing about a more positive attitude to life. A woman aware of her youthful appearance feels younger, acts younger and will demonstrate her new image in increased vigour.

If weight loss is planned, it should be undertaken before surgery to ensure a better outcome. The appropriate weight should be maintained thereafter.

In a young person, a double chin can be removed without touching the neck. In an older individual this submental lipectomy also requires a facelift to prevent larger jowls. The excision under the mandible heals in about ten days and the scar fades gradually. There should be no massaging or pulling of the area for several weeks.

Rhinoplasty

One of the most popular surgical procedures is a rhinoplasty, or change in the nasal framework. The nose creates an impression of personality by stamping the facial character, and therefore this operation brings about a decisive transformation of the physiognomy. The nose may be remodelled for different reasons, being disturbing to the individual or as a focal point of others. The conception of a perfectly sculptured nose differs in the beauty ideals of various cultures. On the whole, while a striking hooked nose may add personality to male features,

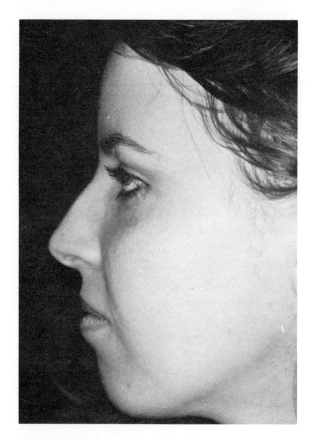

Rhinoplasty and mentoplasty (preoperative)

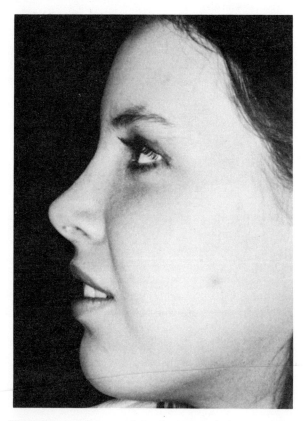

Rhinoplasty and mentoplasty (postoperative)

for a young or a mature female it can create an impression of masculinity and advanced age. A bulbous tip may make the dainty contours of female facial architecture appear vulgar. A sunken nose back or saddle nose may add an expression of brutality. Nasal malformations are frequently caused by injury and improper healing. It is not unusual for several disturbing characteristics to be present simultaneously.

Rhinoplasty requires great precision and artistic feeling by the surgeon. No single design suits everybody's features, and decisions of proportion should be left to the doctor.

A rhinoplastic operation is usually performed entirely within the nostrils. The skin is elevated from the nasal skeleton, the septum lowered, a hump removed if required or the nose tip brought into a new shape. If the bridge is broad and flat, rhinoplasty involves augmentation of the depression by means of an implant or graft. The sutures are invisible in the mucosa and the skin adapts to the new proportions. There is no pain encountered and after a week to ten days, the shield over the nose is removed. At this point possible bruises and swelling under the eyes will have become unnoticeable to other people. Apart from some slight swelling, the nose attains its revised appearance three to four weeks after surgery. The tissues require four to six months to complete the healing phase. Sports, vigorous exercise and pulling of the skin are not advisable during convalescence.

Mentoplasty

Sometimes the chin needs reshaping, together with the nose, to balance the profile. Mentoplasty can involve aesthetic and oral surgery for the correction of the bone structure and alignment of teeth. To reconstruct a retruding chin an implant is inserted between the mandible and covering muscle tissue. In the opposite case a segment of bone is removed to shape a protruding jaw line. Both procedures can be carried out in two ways: either in the submental crease, or intra-orally with an incision in front of the lower incisors. A week postoperative the suture is healed and only a fine line remains. For at least two months there should be no manipulation of the face or neck.

Otoplasty

Offstanding ears can be concealed by hair styles but still add nothing to a favourable appearance. By otoplasty they can be brought into normal position, with very large ears reduced and unsightly ones recontoured. Excision of cartilage and skin is performed at the posterior surface of the ears. A dressing is applied for three days and the area must be treated with care for about eight weeks.

SKIN TREATMENTS

Dermatoplasty

This serves to restore an unblemished complexion by eliminating scars, wrinkles and fine lines including pigmentation. There are two effective avenues to achieve this: dermabrasion and chemosurgery.

Dermabrasion

This physical approach to skin renewal involves sanding or planing the skin with a rotating brush. A single facial abrasion efficiently removes scars, but to eradicate deep, pitted lesions like those of acne, a local repetition may be required.

Chemosurgery

This is a chemical, more superficial exfoliation which corrodes the top layers of skin. After either of these procedures a scab forms 48 hours later which peels off within ten days and a fine, rosy, youthful skin emerges. Swelling and discomfort are common. The skin remains tender and sun exposure must be avoided for almost a year.

Spot peeling

Spot peeling around the mouth to erase fine lines is sometimes done in connection with a rhytidoplasty. In a Caucasian skin the remaining pinkness disappears in a couple of months, but a dark skin is left with a lighter area. For this reason and because dark skin has the tendency to be keloid, dermatoplasty is not recommended. Similarly, to avoid subsequent scarring, it is not advisable for the skin of the chest, back and other regions which have poorer healing qualities in everybody.

Cryotherapy

This is a local procedure destroying skin structures, scars, moles, pigmentation and warts by the application of extreme cold. A blister is formed scabbing in the process of healing.

Tretinoin

Tretinoin (vitamin A acid) is a very effective medication employed to treat acne. It acts as a peeling agent, impeding comedones, pustules and lumps. Tolerance of vitamin A acid varies greatly and the treatment can extend over months to be fully successful.

Collagen injections

To raise single scars and facial lines, collagen injections have proved efficacious. The treatment is a subcutaneous injection of soluble bovine collagen. This procedure requires a sequence of sessions to show an improvement. A primary test for possible allergic reaction to the proteins of the implant is needed.

Pigmentations and skin elevations removed with the great skill of a plastic surgeon leave no indication of their former presence.

MAMMAPLASTY

Mammaplasty can change the female silhouette, which is greatly determined by whether the size and contours of the breasts are in proportion to the rest of the body structure. The ideal is seldom the rule, and diversities like underdeveloped, sagging or hypertrophic breasts are often seen. By augmentation mammaplasty, reduction mammaplasty or a combination of both, all these shortcomings can be remedied.

Hypotrophy of the bust affects numerous women in all age groups. A silicic gel implant inserted between chest wall and breast tissue results in augmentation of breast size. The soft prosthesis is encapsulated by the surrounding fibres so that it looks and feels completely natural. Because of its location there is no interference with the breasts' normal functions. The small scar is inconspicuously hidden in the bust crease.

Heavy breast tissue droops, letting the straps of the brassiere cut painfully into the shoulders. This reflects on posture and results in backaches; it also creates a moist, uncomfortable environment underneath the bust. These inconveniences are distressing for a woman. Reduction mammaplasty is the reshaping of the breasts by resecting skin and body fat. The nipples are brought to a normal size and are relocated to a higher site. Sutures run vertically from an incision under the bust and encircle the areola.

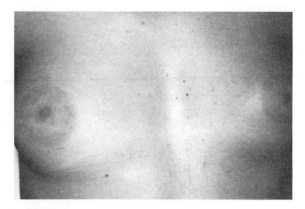

preoperative
Augmentation mammaplasty

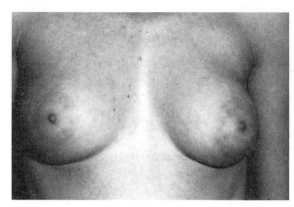

postoperative

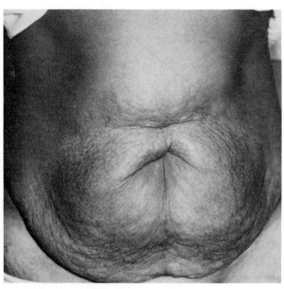

preoperative
Abdominal lipectomy

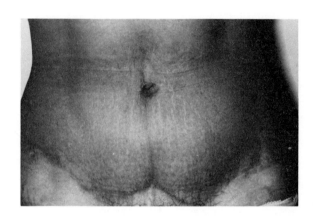

postoperative

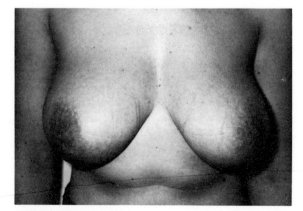

preoperative
Reduction mammaplasty

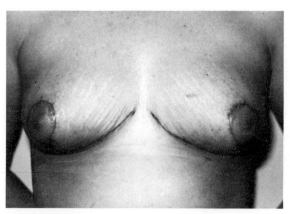

postoperative

66

Their colour lightens after a few months. In case of atrophy, the method is combined with a plastic implant. Assymetric breasts can also be adapted in this way.

After all operations involving the bust a brassiere must be worn constantly for eight weeks, with no vigorous exercising or heavy lifting for that time.

LIPECTOMY

Lipectomy refers to local surgical reduction of excess body fat such as that found on the abdomen in middle age. The dermal fibres have lost their resiliency by overstretching, and together with adipose tissue this can create a heavy, hanging fold. An abdominal lipectomy brings relief from this unpleasantness. Residual fat and skin are removed by means of a horizontal sickle incision in the bikini line. If necessary the navel is transferred back to its natural location.

A few months after surgery the scars fade. The doctor has to be consulted as to when physical exercise can be resumed.

Slack upper arms can be trimmed by surgery in which the sutures run inside longitudinally towards the axilla. To drape thighs, incisions are hidden in the inner inguinal fold. To minimize the so-called 'riding-breeches syndrome', an incision is made along the lower buttocks.

Reduction of fat deposits as found in thighs and buttocks by means of a curette is a method allowing the surgeon to shape body parts most favourably. The small incision runs along the fold of the buttocks. A solution is injected loosening up the fatty tissue so that it can be sucked out by curetage. There will be swelling at the start before the skin commences to shrink adjusting itself to the new shape. The doctor's advice should be followed as to resuming of physical exercise and massage.

HAIR TRANSPLANTS

Balding affects men who have a genetic predisposition for hair loss generally at the forehead. Surgical techniques are for hair transplantation from the dense growth at the back of the scalp to the bald area in front. Small plugs containing only a few hairs are punched out and inserted into the bare location. The hair starts to grow in, however the hairline does not appear in the original density. The Juri method is done by moving an entire strip graft of hair-bearing skin, inserting it into an incision in the bald area. The excised flap contains its own blood supply and is at first still nourished by the donor area after it was implanted into its new site. When the graft has taken it is detached and the remaining scar tissue removed.

Vitamins

Contents

The term 'vitamin' was coined by Kasimir Funk, a Polish chemist who discovered vitamin B_1 in 1911. The name is actually misleading as it means, literally translated, 'vital amine'. Amines, however, are substances marked by the presence of the amino group (NH_2) in their molecule. Vitamin B_1 happens to be an amine; later on it was proven that other so-called vitamins are not amines chemically, but have a completely different structure.

Vitamins belong to the biocatalysts, like the hormones, trace elements and enzymes. A biocatalyst is a substance that activates and speeds up a biological process without undergoing a change itself. Their presence is essential and irreplaceable in the preservation of health. We need vitamins for growth, metabolism and many other functions. Thirteen vitamins are of importance to human beings as well as other substances under the heading of vitamins, of which the actual properties have not been proven.

Vitamins derive from natural sources, but can also be produced synthetically. In food, vitamins may either exist in ready form or in a preliminary stage, the so-called pro-vitamins. The body requires vitamins only in small quantities, but if they are lacking, deficiency diseases occur. For example, lack of vitamin C causes scurvy, a disease of the gums experienced by sailors on long sea voyages. It is the first vitamin deficiency recorded. Shortage of vitamin B_1 brings about beri-beri, which spread in Eastern Asia when polished rice was introduced in place of brown rice. The need for vitamins differs according to age, sex and physical condition.

Vitamins have been named by the alphabet. The most essential are: A, B, C, D, E, F, H, K and P. We distinguish betwen two groups:

1 fat-soluble vitamins – A, D, E, and K,
2 water-soluble vitamins – B, C, F, H, and P.

Some vitamins are in reality a group of factors for which the name complex is chosen.

Fat-soluble vitamins cannot be consumed in any quantity as the body does not dispose of them and hypervitaminosis, which might have harmful effects, can result. Therefore, they should be only taken according to a doctor's prescription. Water-soluble vitamins, on the other hand, can be excreted if taken in too high doses.

Some vitamins are still measured in international units; as their chemical compositions become known, they are weighed in grams. Certain vitamins have a direct or indirect influence on the skin, and are of importance in cosmetology.

VITAMIN A (RETINOL)

Vitamin A and/or provitamin A is found in dairy products, eggs, animal liver, etc. It is present in the carotene contained in carrots, spinach, apricots, tomatoes and rose hips. Vitamin A is stable to heat in general cooking though unfavourably influenced by oxidation and drying. It affects mainly the eyes, bones, teeth, kidneys and skin. It is stored in the human body in the liver. Deficiency expresses itself in rough, dry skin, loss of hair and brittle nails. The teeth can become defective and the final stage may be night blindness.

Vitamin A is used in preparations for dry, rough and keratinous skin.

THE B VITAMINS

This vitamin is not a single unit, but a group or complex of compounds.

Vitamin B_1 (thiamine)

This is present in yeast, milk, soya beans, liver, wheat germ, pork, peanuts and brown rice. It is destroyed by heat and chemicals. Vitamin B_1 helps regulate the carbohydrate metabolism and influences the functioning of nerves. When lacking, loss of appetite and weight are the consequences, as well as fatigue, depression, and finally the disease beri-beri. Storage of this vitamin in the human body is limited.

Vitamin B_1 is added to cosmetic preparations in wheatgerm or peanut oil.

Vitamin B_2

Also called vitamin G, riboflavin or lactoflavin, this vitamin belongs to the vitamin B complex. Vitamin B_2 is found in eggs, yeast, animal livers, milk and green vegetables. It is decomposed by light and chemicals but is heat-resistant. It is stored in a small amount in the human body in the liver and kidneys. The importance of riboflavin lies in the process of vision. In case of a shortage the lips tend to crack (cheilosis), burning and inflammation of the eyes may occur, or there may be skin irritation with loss of hair.

Riboflavin is in cosmetic creams as an ingredient of plant extracts.

Vitamin B_3 or nicotinic acid (niacin)

Sources of this vitamin are dry yeast, wheatgerm, peanuts, green vegetables, fruit, potatoes, milk, kidneys, liver, lean meat and fish. The body holds only a small amount of nicotinic acid and therefore a daily supply is required. Vitamin B_3 resists heat and oxygen. A shortage of niacin may cause pellagra, reflecting in loss of skin elasticity, oedema formation and problems of the gastronomic system.

Nicotinic acid is often added to cosmetic preparations, in particular to hair lotions.

Vitamin B_5 (pantothenic acid)

Another vitamin of the vitamin B complex, this is contained in nuts, soya beans, barley, skimmed milk, potatoes, liver, kidneys, lean beef and tomatoes. Pantothenic acid is easily soluble in water. It is widespread in nature and plays an important part in the breakdown of fatty acids in food. It also influences growth and pigmentation of hair. Deficiency of pantothenic acid results in fatigue, loss of appetite and dermatitis.

Vitamin B_5 is mainly an additive to hair lotions.

Biotin

This member of the vitamin B complex was formerly called vitamin H. It is found in rice, egg yolk, liver, spinach, milk, mushrooms and yeast. Biotin is stable to heat but susceptible to oxygen and ultra-violet light. Lack of biotin shows in flaky skin on the hands, arms and legs. Nervousness, depression, loss of appetite and muscle pain are the consequence.

Biotin is employed against disturbances in skin and nails.

Vitamin B_c

Also called folic acid, this vitamin forms a part of dairy products, pork, carrots, liver, kidneys, grain, spinach and other leafy vegetables. It is destroyed by sunlight. Folic acid is necessary for blood regeneration and protein metabolism. Its deficiency leads to anaemia and disturbances in the skin and hair growth.

Folic acid is found in cosmetic preparations with plant additives.

Vitamin B_6 (pyridoxine)

The human body receives this vitamin through a normal diet. It is necessary for blood formation and for body metabolism. The intestinal bacteria of an adult are able to form vitamin B_6.

Yeast, liver, grain, vegetables, soya beans and fish contain this vitamin. It reacts to light but is stable to oxygen and acids. Its deficiency causes dermatitis and inflammation of the mucous membranes. Vitamin B_6 is in cosmetic products together with other compounds of the vitamin B complex.

Vitamin B_{12} (cobalamin)

This vitamin contains cobalt in its molecule. It is found in fish, lean meat, milk and eggs. A deficiency induces anaemia. It is stable to heat, acids and light but destroyed by alkali. Vitamin B_{12} is required for the formation of erythrocytes, for the nervous system, for body growth and for cell metabolism. Its value lies in its effect on our body's health.

VITAMIN C

Also called ascorbic acid, this is one of the most important of all vitamins. It is present in nearly all living tissue. Fresh fruit, especially citrus fruits, apples, tomatoes and rose hips, are rich in vitamin C, as are raw, leafy vegetables. Although it is found in all cells, very little is stored in the body. Vitamin C is easily destroyed by light and oxygen. It activates cell metabolism, and firms muscles, bones, gums and blood vessels. It creates resistance to infectious diseases, particularly colds. Lack of vitamin C expresses itself in fatigue.

A deficiency of this vitamin instigates scurvy, anaemia, tiredness, muscle or bone weakening and easy susceptibility to infection. Vitamin C is used in cosmetics for bleaching purposes, and in preparations for oily skin.

VITAMIN D (calciferol)

This is in fact a group of chemically different sterol compounds. Provitamin D (ergosterol) in the skin turns to calciferol under the influence of ultra-violet rays. Ergosterol is a vitamin D precursor in plants. Fish liver oil and dairy products supply this vitamin, which is not lost by boiling. The liver retains it in the human body. Vitamin D controls the calcium and phosphorus metabolism. If it is insufficient in childhood, rachitis i.e. bowed legs because of soft bones, results. Teeth, nails, hair and skin require vitamin D. In skin-care preparations it extends elasticity and resistance to atmospheric factors.

VITAMIN E (tocopherol)

This is available in nuts, soybeans, wheatgerm oil, fish liver oil, dairy products and green vegetables. Not changed by heat, it reacts to oxygen exposure. Vitamin E, the antisterility vitamin, plays a part in the endocrine, muscular and vascular systems. Degeneration of muscles and nerves, gland disturbances and reduced resistance to poisoning may result from a shortage of this vitamin. In cosmetics vitamin E is in wheatgerm oil.

VITAMIN F (lanicidin)

Nowadays this is often named an essential fatty acid instead of a vitamin. It is in almost all fats, oils and nutrients with esters from natural sources. Vitamin F furthers healing; its lack brings about dry skin, skin scaliness or even acne. It is recommended as a supplement to nourishing creams.

VITAMIN K (menadione, phytonadione)

Presents itself in nature in different forms, in green plants like spinach, nettle, horse chestnut, and alfalfa; in vegetables such as potatoes and cabbage; in fruits such as tomatoes, rose hips and strawberries; and in animal tissues like liver, meats, and blood. Vitamin K is the product of the metabolism of bacteria in the intestines. It is stable to light and alkali. The vitamin is essential for the formation of prothrombin in the liver for blood clotting. Where it is lacking, a greater tendency for haemorrhaging is a consequence. Horse chestnut extracts are an addition to preparations concocted to counteract expanded capillaries.

VITAMIN P (Bioflavonoid/Rutin)

Contained together with vitamin C it is found in all citrus fruit. It was discovered with vitamin C in the search for a cure for scurvy. Vitamin P affects the walls of the capillaries.

It is in cosmetics in combination with Vitamin C.

CONCLUSION

When adding vitamins to cosmetic preparations, it must be taken into consideration that many vitamins are susceptible to oxygen, acids and ultra-violet rays; to oxidation by contact with metal; or to changes through the presence of other ingredients. It is therefore advisable not to experiment but to ask for the advice of a chemist.

About herbs

Contents
Methods of obtaining plant components · Herbal extracts · Minerals and enzymes · A choice of herbs and their effects on the skin

Herbs have always been a natural aid to humanity. In the antique period they served the physician for healing. Although their chemical compositions were unknown, plant extracts were recognized for their effects on the human body. Herbs as such are still employed in the Far East. In the Middle Ages herbs were cultivated in monastery gardens for their medicinal properties and for their value as spices in cooking. Herbal extracts were added to skin care preparations, just as they are to sophisticated caring products today. They offer many benefits to varying skin types.

In most cases the isolated plant extract is more effective for skin tissue than the entire herb. The desired component may be present only in certain parts of the plant, for example:

Fruit or seed: fennel, linseed, almond, cocoa bean, caraway, lemon, rose hip, anise and coriander.

Flower: camomile, rosemary, limetree, arnica, lavender, rose and marigold.

Leaves: birch, sage, witch hazel (hamamelis), rosemary, dandelion, sage, mint, melissa, coltsfoot and eyebright.

Bark: willow, oak, cinnamon and witch hazel.

Wood: liquorice and sandalwood.

Root: calamus, burdock, soapwort, valerian and orris.

Entire plant: yarrow, thyme, spearmint, and valerian.

When adding herbs to cosmetics two requirements must be fulfilled: the plant matter must be of advantage to the skin type to which it is applied, and it must be well tolerated. Both these aspects must be tested before the herb is incorporated into the product. The plant's natural principles are powerful in a concentrated form and may need to be diluted. However, compared to synthetic compounds, plant extracts are in general friendlier to the skin.

In order to derive the most from a herb, it should be fresh, not wilted. The plant's leaves or blossoms have to be dried carefully to keep a supply for the winter months without diminishing the natural values. The herb is bundled, hung up by the stem and air dried at a moderate temperature. In storage the plant loses some of its ingredients, mainly essential oils. The herb is then stored in an airtight jar. Some fresh herbs can be kept in a deepfreeze, preserved the same way as vegetables. Herbal extracts are obtained by various methods and enclosed in lotions, creams, compresses, masks and packs. An essence may be added to a facial steamer.

METHODS OF OBTAINING PLANT COMPONENTS

Juice

The plant is cut into small pieces and run through a juicer. Large fruit needs to be divided into small sections. The liquid obtained is added to packs, compresses and steamer. The fresh juice is rich in vitamins and is susceptible to oxygen and bacteria, so it should be used shortly after preparation.

Cold water extracts

These are made from wooden plant parts. Pieces of the stem, branch or bark are put into water at room temperature and left for 10 to 12 hours to steep. Time is required to release the effective ingredients.

Alcoholic liquid tinctures

Difficult to make, these can be purchased from druggists or chemical firms. Only a few drops are needed in a preparation. Tinctures are liquid extracts diluted in alcohol; for example fennel tincture: pulverize the seed, cover well with ethyl alcohol, close container and set aside for 24 hours. This makes fennel extract, an effective addition to facial steamers or to preparations for dry and sensitive skins.

Teas or infusions

Boiling water is poured over blossoms or leaves, or they are placed in cold water and brought to a simmer. After sitting for approximately 15 minutes away from heat until luke warm, the tea is filtered through a fine sieve or cloth. Infusions can be used in packs and compresses. Those made from rosemary leaves are applied to emulgate skin creams and extend moisture to benefit dry or mature skin. Camomile tea is recommended for the treatment of sensitive skin. For oily skin a tea may be prepared from yarrow, camomile, sage and small doses of parsley. The lid of the pot must be kept closed during the process of extraction.

Decocting

This process is for wooden plant parts only. Essential oils and acids would be lost from leaves, blossoms and fruit if this method were used. Before decocting, the woody plant parts are soaked in cold water for 3 hours. They are then boiled for 5 minutes and allowed to sit for another 3 minutes removed from the heat. This eliminates the release of bitter principles that may be irritating to the skin.

HERBAL EXTRACTS

Components obtained by extraction for cosmetic preparations fall into the following categories.

Essential oils, balsams and resins

These are present in all plant parts, but are concentrated in fruit, blossoms and leaves. Some herbs especially rich in essential oils are peppermint, lavender, bergamot, rosemary and camomile. Flowers such as roses, lilies of the valley, lime tree blossoms and violets as well as all citrus fruits, also contain these substances. Essential oils differ from fatty oils in that they evaporate leaving no oily spots, but under the influence of ultra-violet light they can cause a lasting pigmentation of the skin. Essential oils are found in all plant parts that have an odour. When applied to the skin surface, they cause a warm feeling which, in a more condensed form, can lead to a burning sensation or irritation. Added to cosmetic preparations in small doses, essential oils have a slightly stimulating effect. They are used widely in perfumery. Balsams and resins are in concentration in secretions from pines, olives and myrtle shrubs. They have a place in perfumery and cosmetics similar to that of the essential oils.

Dyes

There are three main plant dyes of importance in cosmetology.

1 The blue azulene found in the essential oil of the camomile is healing and soothing. It is added to bath oils, creams, masks and cleansing lotions, or used in facial steamers and to make compresses. Azulene is an unsaturated compound and therefore should be kept in a closed container, away from light and oxygen.

2 Carotene is a complicated, unsaturated substance easily forming a chemical bond with other matter. It is susceptible to ultra-violet light and oxygen. Carotene is a precursor to vitamin A and has an orange-yellow colour. It is found in green plants and concentrated in carrots. Carotene is used in cosmetic preparations for tired, dry, oily, blemished skin. Carrot extract is high in both vitamin A and C.

3 Chlorophyll, the colour matter of green plants and fruit, is a supplement to cosmetics. It is fat and water soluble, and is added to creams, lotions and deodorants. Chlorophyll helps healing. It is applied in cosmetic treatments in combination with ultra-violet light on blemished skin. It filters the ray and distributes it to the areas where it is required. Green olives are rich in cholorophyll.

Saponin and glycosides

The word saponin is derived from *sapon*, meaning soap. Saponin mixed with water is a colloid solution which foams and has a low surface tension like soapy water. Saponin makes the skin more receptive to other substances. Saponin and glycosides from plants cleanse and emulsify. Saponin can cause irritation to sensitive, dry skin and mucous membranes. It reduces oiliness to some extent on seborrheic and thick skin and prepares it for treatment. Saponin is found in horse chestnuts, soap bark, soap wort, liquorice, primroses, asparagus, birch leaves, pansies, daisies, elder blossoms, lime tree blossoms and sloe tree blossoms. The leaves of ivy also hold large amounts of saponin and glycosides.

Salicylic acid

This is not derived from a herb in a pure form but combined with carbohydrates. In concentration, this organic acid is an anti-keratotic and disinfectant suited for thick, horny skins. Salicylic acid is in the bark of the willow, pansy and marigold.

Mucilage

Mucilage is a gelatinous substance similar to plant gums in that both mix easily with water and can therefore be distributed evenly over the skin to form a protective layer on the surface. Through the use of mucilage as a cosmetic base, the release of accompanying ingredients takes place slowly giving a better result. Temperature and irritating substances are moderated by mucilage. Mucilage is found in marigold, fennel, coltsfoot, linseed, marshmallow, iceland moss, mallow and mullein.

Tannin

An organic acid used for leather tanning. When it is applied undiluted to the skin it reacts chemically as it does on a hide, forming a compound with the protein in the tissue. The skin becomes leathery, a situation which cannot be remedied afterwards. However, if the skin is treated with diluted tannin, it causes only a temporary effect. The tissues are slightly tightened making them less permeable. A weak tannin solution is astringent and stimulating. It reduces gland excretion and is therefore useful in hair lotions to make the hair shiny and the scalp less greasy.

Plant sources of tannin are willow, chestnut, birch, oak, blueberries, leaves of witch hazel, vermouth, yarrow, green and black tea, heather, valerian and hops.

Silicic acid

Used in compresses and facial steamers it causes stimulation and a warm feeling on the skin. The herbal extract has been proven advantageous for blemished skin, as a component in hair cosmetics and in nail preparations. This organic acid is found in caraway seeds, yarrow and horsetail.

Plant or phyto hormones

Essential for plant growth, formation of roots, healing and development of blossoms. They are used as additives to caring products for a tired, not-so-young skin.

MINERALS AND ENZYMES

Aside from vitamins and other matter, herbs are a good and easily accessible source of minerals and enzymes essential for human metabolism and endocrine glands. They add to the favourable influence of plant extracts on the skin, in nutrition from inside and by application from outside.

Enzymes, like bromelin, found in pineapple and papain of the papaya fruit, are incorporated into peeling matter for a superficial exfoliation of the stratum corneum by splitting sebum and keratin.

Plants differ in their mineral content – not all elements are found simultaneously and some have to be provided from other sources in our diet, as can be seen from the following examples:
Calcium – beans, kelp, broccoli, cress and almonds.
Chlorine – celery, kelp, spinach, tomato.
Chromium – nuts, corn.
Cobalt – grain.
Copper – almonds, nuts, wheat, avocado, blueberries.
Fluorine – kelp
Iodine – kelp, cress, blackcurrants, cucumber.
Iron – apricots, beans, strawberries, parsley, oats, cucumber.
Magnesium – almonds, avocado, bananas, peanuts.
Manganese – apricots, parsley, nuts, wheatgerm, watercress and blueberries.
Phosphorus – wheatgerm, oats, blueberries, dandelion, parsley and strawberries.
Potassium – bananas, apricots, figs, potatoes, lemons and grapes.
Selenium – nuts, grain.
Sodium – kelp, wheat germ, raspberries, strawberries.
Sulphur – nuts, beans and dandelions.
Zinc – nuts, onions, oats, blackcurrants.

Each plant contains a mixture of compounds, and consequently can have a number of properties combined in its extracts. A mixture of herbs with similar ingredients can reinforce or complement each other's achievements.

A CHOICE OF HERBS AND THEIR EFFECTS ON THE SKIN

Algae – purifying, stimulating
Asparagus – cleansing
Angelica – stimulating
Almond (sweet) – soothing, lubricating
Anise – lubricating, stimulating
Apricot – soothing
Arnica – stimulating, astringent
Avocado – regenerating, lubricating
Blueberry – tonic, refreshing
Birch tree – astringent
Burdock – tonic, firming
Carrot – hydrating, normalizing
Castor bean – stimulating, lubricating
Camomile – cleansing, soothing
Cocoa bean – softening, protecting
Corn oil – lubricating
Cinnamon – stimulating, regenerating
Cucumber – moisturizing, cleansing, firming, clearing

Dandelion – clearing, astringent
Eucalyptus – antiseptic, purifying
Eyebright – refreshing, soothing
Fennel – soothing
Gentian – astringent, purifying
Hamamelis (witch hazel) – astringent, relaxing, anti-couperose
Hawthorn – soothing, anti-blotch
Iris – softening, soothing
Liquorice – soothing
Lily – anti-couperose, firming, tonic
Lemon – acid balancing, astringent, clearing
Lime tree leaves – very soothing
Mallow – calming, hydrating
Mint – refreshing
Marigold – soothing
Nettle – stimulating
Oats – cleansing, soothing

Olive – regenerating, lubricating
Orange – astringent, acid balancing
Peach – normalizing, soothing
Parsley – deodorizing, stimulating
Plantain – tonic, firming
Raspberry – hydrating
Rose – refreshing, relaxing
Rosemary – antiseptic, equalizing
Strawberry – slightly tonic
Soybean – hydrating, lubricating
Sage – antiseptic, astringent
Tea (black and green) – astringent, firming
Thyme – tonic, stimulating, astringent
Valerian – astringent, firming
Verbena – tonic
Walnut – astringent, firming
Wheatgerm – lubricating, stimulating
Willow (bark and leaves) – firming, tonic
Yarrow – soothing, healing

camomile (*Anthemis nobilis*)

angelica (*Archangelica officinalis*)

fennel (*Foeniculum vulgare*)

parsley (*Carum petroselinum*)

thyme (*Thymus vulgaris*)

yarrow (*Achillae millefolium*)

lavender (*Lavandula vera*)

anise (*Pinpinella anisum*)

Some common herbs

Cosmetic from the inside

Contents

THE DIET

Nutrition plays an important part in good health, mental and physical potential, and all-over appearance. It provides cosmetic care from inside and as such belongs to any effective aesthetic programme. Sleep and a sensible way of life come under the same heading. Skin care can never be successful without these basic health provisions.

In many cases improvement of the skin and of the general state of health results when the diet is changed. It must contain all the essential nutrients in a proper relationship. To avoid becoming overweight or having unnecessary fat deposits, a diet must be balanced to provide an adequate number of calories daily, depending upon individual metabolism and way of life. Requirements for food vary with age and output of energy. During growth and development we need more nutrients than in advancing age when we tend to be less active and the metabolic rate slows down.

We need nutrients both with and without calories. Water, bulk, minerals and vitamins are not sources of energy. Proteins, fats and carbohydrates provide the calories that produce heat and energy in the human body.

Oxygen is the catalyst essential to metabolize food in body cells. To maintain the balance of substances exchanged in this vital process, oxygen is continuously provided by respiration. Water is the second human need next to oxygen. The fluid constantly excreted over skin, lungs and digestive system has to be replaced in nutrition or by beverages, to prevent constipation and dehydration. Six to eight cups of liquid each day are recommended.

PROTEIN

Protein is one of the great aids in a beauty diet. Many body structures such as hair, skin, nails and connective tissue are formed by proteins and their derivatives. In particular the skin needs a constant supply of protein to maintain its normal sequence of renewal and shedding of cells.

Proteins are made up of different amino acids; the percentage not produced in the human body has to be supplied daily. These are the so-called essential amino acids. Proteins vary in their contents of amino acids according to whether they are of plant or animal origin. Those from animal sources are of higher value because they have all eight essential amino acids. Foods providing them are: meat, fish, eggs and dairy products. In vegetable protein one or another amino acid may be missing. Therefore a combination of grains, nuts and other vegetable products should be consumed; a vegetarian diet can be balanced with eggs and dairy products.

Protein furthers the metabolism and assists in maintaining a normal weight. The body does not store amino acids in the same way as it does fats and carbohydrates.

FATS

Fats or lipids are the most concentrated source of energy. They originate either from plants or animals and are organic compounds of carbon, hydrogen and oxygen, units of fatty acids and glycerol. Although not always visible, they are present in nearly all foods as so-called hidden fats. They are needed to some extent in every diet to transmit fat soluble vitamins. Not all fatty acids can be synthesized by the body and therefore must be supplied daily.

Fat is stored in the body around organs and muscles and under the skin. An excess of fat deposited under the skin leads to damage to the elastic fibres through expansion of adipose tissue. The intake of fatty food should be limited so as not to overburden the digestive system, especially by those who wish to lose weight. One gram of fat has about nine calories, the highest of all nutrients. Next comes alcohol with seven calories. Foods rich in lipids are cream, butter, whole milk, margarine, oils and meats.

CARBOHYDRATES

Carbohydrates represent the body's most available and economical sources of energy. Carbohydrates can be more completely and readily used by a healthy system than fats and proteins. They are either simple sugars or substances that can be reduced to simple sugars by a chemical process employing enzymes in the digestive system. Like fats, carbohydrates are made up of carbon, hydrogen and oxygen. Three main types may be distinguished: monosaccharides or simple sugars; disaccharides or double sugars and polysaccharides or complex sugars.

Monosaccharides and disaccharides are present in fruit, vegetables (fructose, glucose, sucrose) and milk (lactose). Honey is a rich source of fruit sugar. Polysaccharides are mainly the starches and cellulose plants employ to store carbohydrates. Grain, potatoes, roots and bananas contain starches. Glycogen is deposited in the liver where a small amount is converted into glucose for energy and heat. The remainder is converted into body fat.

VITAMINS

Biocatalysts such as vitamins are vital for body functions, but are needed only in exceedingly small quantities. If they are deficient or missing in our nourishment, the skin becomes grey, tired-looking or even blemished. Hair and nails are also affected as appendages of the skin, becoming brittle and dull. More hair than normal may be shed. This proves that biocatalysts are indispensable for the organism and must be supplied in appropriate, proportioned amounts (see chapter: Vitamins). Usually a good diet provides all the vitamins and minerals needed by a healthy, human body.

MINERALS

The minerals that occur in largest quantities in the body are calcium and phosphorus. Many others are more or less trace elements. Most nutrients with calcium also contain phosphorus; for example, dairy products. Lack of these two minerals reflects on skin, nails, hair and, more importantly, on bones and teeth. Fluorides are recommended for prevention of caries. They combine with calcium to give the tooth substance a greater resistance to acids. Fluorine is sometimes added to tap water.

Iron is found in meat, lettuce, green vegetables, grain, fruit and liver. A shortage of iron in the diet induces fatigue and a pale complexion, and may be an indication of anaemia. Iron is present in almost all body tissue and is required for the formation of haemoglobin within the red corpuscles. A lack of iron can be caused by loss of blood. Iron resources in the body are limited, and additional supplies from food are required. Iron is stored in the kidneys, liver, bone marrow and spleen.

Iodine is important for the functioning of the thyroid gland and for regulation of the energy metabolism. The main supplier is iodized cooking salt. Most dishes are seasoned with salt, and frequently we consume much more than is suitable. Mineral salts such as sodium chloride have the ability to attract and retain water. To avoid unnecessary collection of fluid in the tissues, fresh or dried herbs can replace or supplement salt and spices in many recipes.

Skin impurities and oiliness sometimes result from irregularities in the digestive system and can disappear through a proper diet. Cellulose, bulk which assists regular, normal elimination of wastes, is found in grains and plants (fruit, vegetables). Energy can only continue to accrue if waste products are eliminated and replaced with new nutrients.

FOOD INTAKE

All substances required for performance and appearance of the body are provided by the blood through the vascular system. The quantity and quality of these elements depend upon daily food intake, since only some of them are preserved in the body and to a limited extent. However, an excess is just as harmful as a deficiency.

When food is 'burnt' by our system energy is released for activity, growth and functions. Heat and energy from nutrients are measured in calories or joules. If intake is higher than output a weight gain results by building up reserves.

The ideal weight of an adult has been reached at the age of twenty-five to thirty. One should try to keep that weight from then on. The body also has a relative weight which seems to be its normal weight by nature. This can be maintained easily by keeping up the right supply of food. Even if the weight varies from time to time, going above or below this point, we have the tendency to return to this normal weight where we look and feel our best.

Many women have a problem acquiring or maintaining a slender, well-proportioned figure. By inheritance the standards in body build are: slim, muscular or heavy set. Any attempt to drastically alter the all-over silhouette harms health and therefore would be foolish. The same applies to changes in beauty conceptions: they can hardly be achieved. A good figure is a harmonius figure relevant to bone structure and height. Age also plays a part in appearance, since women tend to gain weight during adolescence and menopause. In both cases the weight regulates itself when the internal changes are completed.

Overweight

Sedentary professions can cause local weight gain on hips, abdomen and thighs. Diet and exercise can reduce fat deposits on trouble spots. These are also common locations for the development of orange skin or cellulite, a bumpy, unsightly unevenness caused by liquid retention in the subcutaneous tissue. Stimulants like coffee, tea and alcohol should be replaced by juices and water taken only between and not during meals. The diet should exclude strongly seasoned food and limit fats and carbohydrates. The problem areas can be massaged gently. Sauna and exercise are of advantage. There are also medical approaches to cellulite.

The most common cause of overweight is overeating. In this case there is only one cure and one way to lose weight: by dieting and counting calories. Overeating has different causes, ranging from lack of self-control to habit or mental state. Frustration and boredom can lead to an excessive consumption of unnecessary food, generally rich snacks.

Obesity is in many respects a physical handicap as well as a health hazard. Weight loss must be controlled, under supervision of a doctor. It is important to have determination and stick to a diet for completely satisfactory results.

Reducing weight

By dieting a person either intends to maintain or reduce weight. There are two different approaches: counting calories or burning more energy. Exercising, gymnastics or swimming firms the muscles and decreases measurements by increasing body density with little or no change in weight. Muscle-toning exercises are part of a proper weight-reduction diet. Massages increase body metabolism but cause little weight loss. A suitable combination of nutrients and meal distribution overcomes hungry feelings and makes a diet less bothersome. There are many ideas about dieting: a useful old rule is to watch food intake, have a good breakfast, eat less at noon and little at night. The evening meal is the one that contributes most to weight gain.

A reducing diet has to do justice to the entire system, inside and out. It must consider all the organs to function smoothly without fatigue and faintness caused by malnutrition. Daily healthy meals include milk, lean meat or fish, eggs, vegetables, fresh fruit, herbs and dark bread. One has to stay away from hard-to-digest fried food; broil or grill instead. Animal fats can be replaced by vegetable oils which are healthier and carry many vitamins (see Chemistry: Unsaturated Fatty Acids). To provide proteins choose substances low in fat; for example, skimmed milk and cottage cheese. Eat fruit raw; have only a few carbohydrates; avoid refined flour and sugar. Honey is a better sweetener if one is desired. Meals must be regular and the dieter self-disciplined. When it receives fewer calories than it needs, the body is forced to draw upon surplus deposits. Once the set goal has been reached, a vegetarian day once a week helps maintain the desired weight.

The skin Forced loss of adipose tissue is not in the interest of health nor beauty. It took months or even years to build it up, and one cannot expect to lose it miraculously over a short period of time. The skin must be considered when setting up a diet plan so that it stays in a satisfactory condition. The stretched elastic fibres above the diminishing fatty layer are deprived of the tonus, causing sagging and wrinkles in a mature person. However, in youth they have the ability to regain their strength. It follows that dieting has to be done slowly and to sensible limits.

Stretch marks (striae) are white lines or stripes appearing on overstretched skin on the abdomen, buttocks, thighs and breasts, usually during pregnancy but sometimes in adolescence or in obese women. These marks are caused by weakening of the elastic tissue. If they do not vanish by themselves they are there to stay.

Underweight

Being underweight can also cause problems. A rapid weight loss is a sure sign that a person belongs in a doctor's care. Although leanness seems sometimes to be in vogue, a healthy, skinny woman is just as far from the aesthetic concept of physical harmony as her obese counterpart. To gain weight, high-calorie snacks between meals are better than overeating, which burdens the stomach. Walking and exercising in fresh air combined with stimulating tonics increases appetite.

With the assistance of good nutritional habits a young, attractive complexion can be maintained. The body's aging process can be postponed by an early support of its functions with the essential regeneration materials, and by continuing the mental and physical activity. Internal and external cosmetic care must be combined to produce a truly lasting effect.

Table 1. Composition per 100 g (raw edible weight except where stated)

Food	Inedible waste	Energy		Protein	Fat	Carbohydrate (as monosaccharide)	Water	Calcium	Iron	Vitamin A (retinol equivalent)	Thiamin	Riboflavin	Nicotinic acid equivalent	Vitamin C	Vitamin D
	%	kcal	kJ	g	g	g	g	mg	mg	µg	mg	mg	mg	mg	µg
Milk															
Cream, double	0	447	1 841	1.5	48.2	2.0	49	50	0.2	500	0.02	0.08	0.4	1	0.28
Cream, single	0	195	806	2.4	19.3	3.2	72	79	0.3	155	0.03	0.12	0.8	1	0.12
Milk, liquid, whole	0	65	272	3.3	3.8	4.7	87	120	0.1	46[1] 32[2]	0.04	0.19	0.9	2	0.03[1]
Milk, condensed, whole sweetened	0	322	1 362	8.3	9.0	55.5	26	280	0.2	124	0.08	0.48	2.2	2	0.09
Milk, whole, evaporated	0	158	660	8.6	9.0	11.3	69	280	0.2	108	0.06	0.51	2.3	1	2.91[3]
Milk, UHT	0	65	274	3.3	3.8	4.7	88	120	0.1	40	0.04	0.19	0.9	0	0.02
Milk, dried, skimmed	0	355	1 512	36.4	1.3	52.8	4	1 190	0.4	0	0.42	1.60	9.7	6	0
Yogurt, low fat, natural	0	52	216	5.0	1.0	6.2	86	180	0.1	10	0.05	0.26	1.2	0	0.01
Yogurt, low fat, fruit	0	95	405	4.8	1.0	17.9	75	160	0.2	22	0.05	0.23	1.1	2	0.01
Cheese															
Cheese, Cheddar	0	406	1 682	26.0	33.5	0	37	800	0.4	412	0.04	0.50	6.2	0	0.26
Cheese, cottage	0	96	402	13.6	4.0	1.4	79	60	0.1	41	0.02	0.19	3.3	0	0.02
Meat															
Bacon, rashers, raw	11	422	1 744	14.4	40.5	0	41	7	1.0	0	0.36	0.14	5.8	0	0
Bacon, rashers, cooked	0	447	1 851	24.5	38.8	0	32	12	1.4	0	0.40	0.18	9.2	0	0
Beef, average, raw	17	266	1 107	17.1	22.0	0	64	8	1.8	0	0.05	0.17	7.3	0	0
Beef, corned	0	217	905	26.9	12.1	0	58	14	2.9	0	0.01	0.23	9.0	0	0
Beef, stewing steak, raw	3	176	736	20.2	10.6	0	69	8	2.1	0	0.06	0.23	8.5	0	0
Beef, stewing steak, cooked	0	223	932	30.9	11.0	0	57	15	3.0	0	0.03	0.33	10.2	0	0
Black pudding	0	305	1 270	12.9	21.9	15.0	44	35	20.0	0	0.09	0.07	3.8	0	0
Chicken, raw	33	230	954	17.6	17.7	0	65	10	0.7	0	0.08	0.14	9.3	0	0
Chicken, roast, light meat	0	142	599	26.5	4.0	0	69	9	0.5	0	0.08	0.14	15.3	0	0
Ham, cooked	0	269	1 119	24.7	18.9	0	54	9	1.3	0	0.44	0.15	8.0	0	0
Kidney, average	12	89	375	16.2	2.7	0	79	9	6.0	120	0.39	1.90	10.7	10	0
Lamb, average, raw	17	335	1 388	15.9	30.2	0	53	7	1.3	0	0.09	0.19	7.4	0	0
Lamb, roast	25	291	1 209	23.0	22.1	0	54	9	2.1	0	0.10	0.25	9.2	0	0
Liver, average, raw	0	162	680	20.7	8.1	2.0	69	6	11.4	14 670	0.26	3.10	18.1	16	0.75

[1] Summer value   [2] Winter value   [3] fortified

Food															
Liver, fried	0	243	1 016	24.9	13.6	5.6	56	14	8.8	19 010	0.26	4.30	20.4	12	0.38
Luncheon meat	0	313	1 298	12.6	26.9	5.5	52	15	1.1	0	0.07	0.12	4.5	0	0
Pork, average, raw	26	325	1 343	16.0	29.0	0	54	8	0.8	0	0.59	0.16	7.0	0	0
Pork chop, grilled	22	332	1 380	28.5	24.2	0	46	11	1.2	0	0.66	0.20	11.0	0	0
Sausage, pork	0	367	1 520	10.6	32.1	9.5	45	41	1.1	0	0.04	0.12	5.7	0	0
Sausage, beef	0	299	1 242	9.6	24.1	11.7	50	48	1.4	0	0.03	0.13	7.1	0	0
Steak and kidney pie, cooked	0	286	1 195	15.2	18.3	14.6	49	37	2.8	126	0.14	0.52	6.8	2	0.55
Tripe, dressed	0	60	252	9.4	2.5	0	88	75	0.5	0	0	0.01	2.1	0	0
Fish															
White fish, filleted	5	76	322	17.4	0.7	0	82	16	0.3	0	0.08	0.07	4.9	0	0
Cod, fried in batter	0	199	834	19.6	10.3	7.5	61	80	0.5	0	0.04	0.10	6.7	0	0
Fish fingers	0	178	749	12.6	7.5	16.1	64	43	0.7	0	0.09	0.06	3.1	0	0
Herring	37	234	970	16.8	18.5⁵	0	64	33	0.8	45	0	0.18	7.1	0	22.50
Kipper fillets	2	184	770	19.8	11.7⁵	0	68	60	1.2	45	0.02	0.30	7.0	0	22.25
Salmon, canned	6	155	649	20.3	8.2	0	70	93	1.4	90	0.04	0.18	10.8	0	12.50
Sardines, canned in oil, fish only	7	217	906	23.7	13.6	0	58	550	2.9	0	0.04	0.36	12.6	0	7.50
Eggs															
Eggs, fresh	12	147	612	12.3	10.9	0	75	52	2.0	140	0.09	0.47	3.7	0	1.75
Fats															
Butter	0	740	3 041	0.4	82.0	0	15	15	0.2	985	0	0	0.1	0	0.76
Lard; cooking fat; dripping	0	892	3 667	0	99.1	0	1	1	0.1	0	0	0	0	0	0
Low-fat spread	0	366	1 506	0	40.7	0	57	0	0	900³	0	0	0	0	7.94³
Margarine, average	0	730	3 000	0.1	81.0	0	16	4	0.3	900³	0	0	0.1	0	7.94³
Oils, cooking and salad	0	899	3 696	0	99.9	0	0	0	0	0	0	0	0	0	0
Preserves, etc.															
Chocolate, milk	0	529	2 214	8.4	30.3	59.4	2	220	1.6	6.6	0.10	0.23	1.6	0	0
Honey	0	288	1 229	0.4	0	76.4	23	5	0.4	0	0	0.05	0.2	0	0
Jam	0	262	1 116	0.5	0	69.2	30	18	1.2	2	0	0	0	10	0
Marmalade	0	261	1 114	0.1	0	69.5	28	35	0.6	8	0	0	0	10	0
Sugar, white	0	394	1 680	0	0	105.0	0	2	0	0	0	0	0	0	0
Syrup	0	298	1 269	0.3	0	79.0	20	26	1.5	0	0	0	0	0	0
Vegetables															
Beans, canned in tomato sauce	0	64	270	5.1	0.5	10.3	74	45	1.4	50	0.07	0.05	1.3	0	0
Beans, broad	75	69	293	7.2	0.5	9.5	77	30	1.1	22	0.28	0.05	5.0	30	0

³fortified   ⁵Fat content varies throughout the year between 10 and 25 per cent.

Composition per 100 g

Food	Inedible waste %	Energy kcal	Energy kJ	Protein g	Fat g	Carbohydrate (as monosaccharide) g	Water g	Calcium mg	Iron mg	Vitamin A (retinol equivalent) µg	Thiamin mg	Riboflavin mg	Nicotinic acid equivalent mg	Vitamin C mg	Vitamin D µg
Beans, haricot, dry	0	271	1 151	21.4	1.6	45.5	11	180	6.7	0	0.45	0.13	5.9	0	0
Beans, runner	14	24	102	2.3	0	3.9	89	27	0.8	50	0.05	0.10	1.3	20	0
Beetroot, boiled	20	44	189	1.8	0	9.9	83	30	0.7	0	0.02	0.04	0.4	5	0
Brussels sprouts, raw	25	26	111	4.0	0	2.7	88	32	0.7	67	0.10	0.15	0.9	87	
Brussels sprouts, boiled	0	18	75	2.8	0	1.7	92	25	0.5	67	0.06	0.10	0.9	41	0
Cabbage, green, raw	30	22	92	2.8	0	2.8	88	57	0.6	50	0.06	0.05	0.8	53	0
Cabbage, green, boiled	0	15	66	1.7	0	2.3	93	38	0.4	50	0.03	0.03	0.5	23	0
Carrots, old	4	23	98	0.7	0	5.4	90	48	0.6	2 000	0.06	0.05	0.7	6	0
Cauliflower	30	13	56	1.9	0	1.5	93	21	0.5	5	0.10	0.10	1.1	64	0
Celery	27	8	36	0.9	0	1.3	93	21	0.6	0	0.03	0.03	0.5	7	0
Crisps, potato	0	533	2 224	6.3	35.9	49.3	3	37	2.1	0	0.19	0.07	6.1	17	0
Cucumber	23	9	39	0.6	0	1.8	96	23	0.3	0	0.04	0.04	0.3	8	0
Lentils, dry	0	304	1 293	23.8	1.0	53.2	12	39	7.6	10	0.50	0.20	5.8	0	0
Lettuce	20	9	36	1.0	0	1.2	96	23	0.9	167	0.07	0.08	0.4	15	0
Mushrooms	25	7	31	1.8	0	0	92	3	1.0	0	0.10	0.40	4.6	3	0
Onions	3	23	99	0.9	0	5.2	93	31	0.3	0	0.03	0.05	0.4	10	0
Parsnips	26	49	210	1.7	0	11.3	83	55	0.6	0	0.10	0.08	1.3	15	0
Peas, frozen, raw	0	50	212	5.7	0	7.2	79	33	1.5	50	0.32	0.10	3.0	17	0
Peas, frozen, boiled	0	38	161	5.4	7.7	4.3	81	31	1.4	50	0.24	0.07	2.4	13	0
Peas, canned, processed	35	76	325	6.2	0	13.7	94	9	0.4	33	0.08	0.03	0.9	100	0
Peppers, green	14	12	51	0.9	0	2.2	94	9	0.4	33	0.08	0.03	0.9	100	0
Potatoes, raw	27[6], 14[7]	86	369	2.1	0	20.8	76	8	0.5	0	0.11	0.04	1.7	8–30[8]	0
Potatoes, boiled	0	79	339	1.4	0	19.7	81	4	0.3	0	0.08	0.03	1.1	5–18[8]	0
Potato chips, fried	0	253	1 065	3.8	10.9	37.3	47	14	0.9	0	0.10	0.04	2.1	6–21[8]	
Potatoes, roast	0	157	662	2.8	4.8	27.3	64	10	0.7	0	0.10	0.04	1.9	6–21[8]	0
Spinach	25	21	91	2.7	0	2.8	91	70	3.2	1 000	0.12	0.20	1.3	60	0
Sweet corn, canned	0	76	325	2.9	0.5	16.1	73	3	0.6	35	0.05	0.08	0.3	4	0
Tomatoes, fresh	0	14	60	0.9	0	2.8	93	13	0.4	100	0.06	0.04	0.8	20[9]	0
Turnips	16	17	74	0.8	0	3.8	93	59	0.4	0	0.04	0.05	0.8	25	0
Watercress	23	14	61	2.9	0	0.7	91	220	1.6	500	0.10	0.10	1.1	60	0

[6]old potatoes [7]new potatoes [8]vitamin C falls during storage [9]Feb, 27; May, 14; Aug, 20; Nov, 21 mg per 100 g

Fruit

Food														
Apples	20	46	196	0.3	0	11.9	84	4	0.3	5	0.04	0.02	0.1	5	0
Apricots, canned (including syrup)	0	106	452	0.5	0	27.7	68	12	0.7	166	0.02	0.01	0.4	2	0
Apricots, dried	0	182	772	4.8	0	43.4	15	92	4.1	600	0	0.20	3.8	0	0
Bananas	40	76	326	1.1	0	19.2	71	7	0.4	33	0.04	0.07	0.8	10	0
Blackcurrants	2	28	121	0.9	0	6.6	77	60	1.3	33	0.03	0.06	0.4	200	0
Cherries	13	47	201	0.6	0	11.9	82	16	0.4	20	0.05	0.07	0.4	5	0
Cherries	13	47	201	0.6	0	11.9	82	16	0.4	20	0.05	0.07	0.4	5	0
Dates, dried	14	248	1 056	2.0	0	63.9	15	68	1.6	10	0.07	0.04	2.9	0	0
Figs, dried	0	213	908	3.6	0	52.9	17	280	4.2	8	0.10	0.08	2.2	0	0
Gooseberries, green	1	17	73	1.1	0	3.4	90	28	0.3	30	0.04	0.03	0.5	40	0
Grapefruit	50	22	95	0.6	0	5.3	91	17	0.3	0	0.05	0.02	0.3	40	0
Lemon juice	64	7	31	0.3	0	1.6	91	8	0.1	0	0.02	0.01	0.1	50	0
Melon	40	23	97	0.8	0	5.2	94	16	0.4	175	0.05	0.03	0.5	25	0
Oranges	25	35	150	0.8	0	8.5	86	41	0.3	8	0.10	0.03	0.3	50	0
Orange juice, canned, unsweetened	0	33	143	0.4	0	8.5	89	9	0.5	8	0.07	0.02	0.3	35	0
Peaches, fresh	13	37	156	0.6	0	9.1	86	5	0.4	83	0.02	0.05	1.1	8	0
Peaches, canned (including syrup)	0	87	373	0.4	0	22.9	74	4	0.4	41	0.01	0.02	0.6	4	0
Pears, fresh	28	41	175	0.3	0	10.6	83	8	0.2	2	0.03	0.03	0.3	3	0
Pineapple, canned (including syrup)	0	77	328	0.3	0	20.2	77	13	0.4	7	0.05	0.02	0.2	12	0
Plums	8	32	137	0.6	0	7.9	85	12	0.3	37	0.05	0.03	0.6	3	0
Prunes, dried	17	161	686	2.4	0	40.3	23	38	2.9	160	0.10	0.20	1.9	0	0
Raspberries	0	25	105	0.9	0	5.6	83	41	1.2	13	0.02	0.03	0.5	25	0
Rhubarb	33	6	26	0.6	0	1.0	94	100	0.4	10	0.01	0.03	0.4	0	0
Strawberries	3	26	109	0.6	0	6.2	89	22	0.7	5	0.02	0.03	0.5	60	0
Sultanas	0	250	1 066	1.8	0	64.7	18	52	1.8	5	0.10	0.08	0.6	0	0

Nuts

Food														
Almonds	63	565	2 336	16.9	53.5	4.3	5	250	4.2	0	0.24	0.92	4.7	0	0
Coconut, desiccated	0	604	2 492	5.6	62.0	6.4	2	22	3.6	0	0.06	0.04	1.8	0	0
Peanuts, roasted	0	570	2 364	24.3	49.0	8.6	5	61	2.0	0	0.23	0.10	21.3	0	0

Cereals

Food														
Barley, pearl, dry	0	360	1 535	7.9	1.7	83.6	11	10	0.7	0	0.12	0.05	2.3	0	0
Biscuits, chocolate	0	524	2 197	5.7	27.6	67.4	2	110	1.7	0	0.03	0.13	1.4	0	0
Biscuits, cream crackers	0	440	1 857	9.5	16.3	68.3	4	110	1.7	0	0.13	0.08	2.5	0	0
Biscuits, plain, semi-sweet	0	457	1 925	6.7	16.6	74.8	3	120	2.1	0	0.13	0.08	2.0	0	0
Biscuits, rich, sweet	0	469	1 966	6.2	23.4	62.2	3	87	1.8	0	0.16	0.04	1.7	0	0
Bread, brown	0	223	948	8.9	2.2	44.7	40	100	2.5	0	0.24	0.06	2.4	0	0

Composition per 100 g

Food	Inedible waste	Energy		Protein	Fat	Carbohydrate (as monosaccharide)	Water	Calcium	Iron	Vitamin A (retinol equivalent)	Thiamin	Riboflavin	Nicotinic acid equivalent	Vitamin C	Vitamin D
	%	kcal	kJ	g	g	g	g	mg	mg	μ	mg	mg	mg	mg	μ
Bread, starch reduced	0	234	996	10.5	1.5	47.6	36	100	1.3	0	0.18	0.03	2.7	0	0
Bread, white	0	233	991	7.8	1.7	49.7	39	100	1.7	0	0.18	0.03	2.2	0	0
Bread, wholemeal	0	216	918	8.8	2.7	41.8	40	23	2.5	0	0.26	0.06	1.7	0	0
Cornflakes	0	368	1 567	8.6	1.6	85.1	3	3	0.6	0	1.80[3] 0[4]	1.60[3] 0.03[4]	21.3[3] 0.9[4]	0	0
Custard powder; instant pudding; cornflour	0	354	1 508	0.6	0.7	92.0	12	15	1.4	0	0	0	0.1	0	0
Crispbread, rye	0	321	1 367	9.4	2.1	70.6	6	50	3.7	0	0.28	0.14	1.8	0	0
Flour, white	0	350	1 493	9.8	1.2	80.1	13	150[3]	2.4[3]	0	0.33[3]	0.02	2.8[3]	0	0
Oatmeal	0	401	1 698	12.4	8.7	72.8	9	55	4.1	0	0.50	0.10	2.8	0	0
Rice	0	361	1 536	6.5	1.0	86.8	12	4	0.5	0	0.08	0.03	1.5	0	0
Spaghetti	0	378	1 612	13.6	1.0	84.0	11	23	1.2	0	0.14	0.06	2.8	0	0
Beverages															
Chocolate, drinking	0	366	1 554	5.5	6.0	77.4	2	33	2.4	2	0.06	0.04	2.1	0	0
Cocoa powder	0	312	1 301	18.5	21.7	11.5	3	130	10.5	7	0.16	0.06	7.3	0	0
Coffee, ground, infusion	0	3	12	0.3	0	0.4	—	3	0	0	0	0	10.0	0	0
Coffee, instant powder	0	100	424	14.6	0	11.0	3	160	4.4	0	0	0.11	25.1	0	0
Coca cola	0	39	168	0	0	10.5	90	4	0	0	0	0	0	0	0
Tea, dry	0	0	0	0	0	0	—	0	0	0	0	0.90[10]	6.0[10]	0	0
Squash, fruit, undiluted	0	122	521	0.1	0.1	32.2	63	16	0.2	0	0	0.01	0	1	0
Alcoholic beverages per 100ml															
Beer, keg, bitter	0	31	129	0.3	0	2.3	—	8	0	0	0	0.03	0.5	0	0
Spirits, 70° proof	0	222	919	0	0	0	—	0	0	0	0	0	0	0	0
Wine, red	0	68	284	0.2	0	0.3	—	7	0.9	0	0.01	0.02	0.1	0	0
Puddings and cakes etc.															
Apple pie	0	281	1 179	3.2	14.4	40.4	42	42	0.8	2	0.08	0.02	0.9	2	0
Bread and butter pudding	0	154	649	5.3	7.1	18.5	67	112	0.7	79	0.06	0.22	1.5	1.5	0.30

[3]fortified [4]unfortified [10]90 to 100 per cent is extracted into an infusion

Food															
Buns, currant	0	328	1 385	7.8	8.5	58.6	25	88	1.6	24	0.15	0.10	2.0	0	0.27
Custard	0	118	496	3.8	4.4	16.8	75	140	0.1	43	0.05	0.21	1.0	0	0.03
Fruit cake, rich	0	332	1 403	3.7	11.0	58.3	21	75	1.8	121	0.08	0.08	1.2	0	1.14
Jam tarts	0	384	1 616	3.5	14.9	62.8	19	62	1.6	0	0.08	0.01	1.1	4	0
Plain cake, Madeira	0	393	1 652	5.4	16.9	58.4	20	42	1.1	82	0.06	0.11	1.4	0	1.20
Rice pudding	0	131	552	4.1	4.2	20.2	72	130	0.1	33	0.04	0.14	1.1	1	0.02
Soup, tomato, canned	0	55	230	0.8	3.3	5.9	84	17	0.4	35	0.03	0.02	0.2	0	0
Trifle	0	160	674	3.5	6.1	24.3	65	82	0.7	60	0.05	0.14	1.0	1	0.17
Marmite	0	172	730	39.7	0.7	1.8	25	95	3.7	0	3.10	11.00	67.0	0	0
Ice-cream, vanilla	0	166	698	3.5	7.4	22.8	65	130	0.3	7	0.04	0.17	1.0	1	0

Exercising & relaxation

Contents
Relaxation   Exercise

Physical and mental aging depend primarily on health and the state of mind. Physical aging may be postponed if fitness is maintained through good muscle tone. Exercise benefits circulation and posture, as well as promoting pliability of tendons and ligaments and flexibility of the spine and the joints. The result is a good figure and a vigourous, youthful appearance. A feeling of fitness and health also creates confidence and a relaxed attitude to life.

RELAXATION

The first step toward this goal is to achieve mental relaxation and to ease physical strain. Mind and body are inter-related, and require a harmonious unity to produce energy. Emotional disturbances and stress cause tension, one of the greatest enemies of beauty. They frequently generate unpleasant facial lines and expressions, apathetic, dull eyes; and fatigue which reflects on the complexion. Prolonged sitting in one position, standing on a hard floor or moving in a limited area acts on the body by creating tight muscles and general stiffness. The portions particularly affected are the neck, shoulders and back, with physical symptoms of constant, gnawing pain and bad carriage.

Yoga teaches two ways to overcome tensions. Raja Yoga calms and controls the mind. It would exceed the purposes of this book to explain all its interacting influences. Hatha Yoga improves muscle tone through breathing and exercise, creating poise and better functioning of all the body organs.

It begins with proper, conscious breathing, carried out in a resting position. Tranquil, deep inhalation strengthens the lungs and diaphragm, helping to overcome fatigue and increase vitality. Sleep is improved with subsequent relief from nervousness. The complexion benefits from the regular supply of oxygen to the cells.

EXERCISE

Physical exercise in which muscle contraction follows muscle expansion makes one appreciate the movement and function of each muscle, simultaneously gaining strength and flexibility and releasing strain. Tightening muscles results in decreased measurements and normalization of weight as exercise gradually replaces a lack of physical activity. Yoga assists in maintaining and renewing the elasticity of a youthful body. Neglected muscles are firmed, skin tonus is improved and circulation stimulated, resulting in a healthy skin.

In this chapter some exercises are given, each one designed to tone certain body regions. Thorough study is necessary to make the best use of muscle contraction and relaxation with exploration of all their possibilities. Yoga can be adjusted to all age groups for proper, beneficial relaxation and graceful movement and as such, is part of the programme for the care of feminine beauty.

To guarantee success, these exercises must be done daily at about the same hour, for a period of fifteen minutes. Too much enthusiasm is not desirable. By over-exercising, strong muscles are built-up, giving a masculine effect rather than a soft, limber, feminine look.

For daily exercising choose a quiet atmosphere, a place with adequate fresh air and space to move. The floor must be neither hard nor too soft, and clothes should be comfortable and not restrictive. All motions are carried out slowly; the change-over from one position into another is never rushed. Stretching motions are done only as far as they are comfortable, so as not to pull muscles. All postures are held for a couple of seconds without moving, and a period of repose follows each exercise.

An exercise can be repeated about three times in a session, and the time of holding the position increased gradually by thirty seconds over a period of weeks. Inhale and exhale through the nose unless instructed otherwise.

1 The backward bend

Exercise to stretch back and chest, to make ankles, feet and toes flexible.

Sit erect with buttocks on the heels, keeping knees and feet together. The fingertips touch the floor at both sides.

Walk slowly back on the palms behind the feet. Shoulder, arm and hand are in one line; hands point backward.

Slowly let head drop back, with neck loose and relaxed. Stay in position and push abdomen forward, so that the spine forms an arch. Remain in this position a few seconds keeping eyes closed, breathing in a regular and relaxed manner.

Release the spine, raise head slowly and walk slowly back with hands into former sitting position.

Bend forward, resting the body weight on the forearms. Relax with forehead touching the floor.

2 The spread leg stretch

Exercise to flex back and spine, to firm thigh and calf.

Sit erect with both legs together stretched out in front. Slowly spread legs apart as far as possible without bending knees. Palms rest flat on thighs close to body. Glide hands slowly down over legs until arms are straight. Continue to slide down legs, bending body forward from hips, as far as possible without discomfort.

Grip legs at part reached, bend elbows, drop head, close eyes and stay in this position without motion for a few seconds. Breathe quietly.

Stretch elbows, glide back with palms over legs until again in upright position. Relax.

3 The half locust

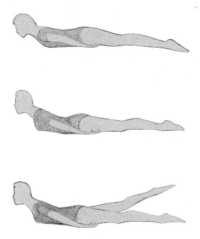

Exercise to firm thighs, buttocks and hips and to strengthen abdominal muscles.

Lie relaxed on the abdomen with hands resting at sides.

Bring legs and feet together stretched flat on the floor. Make a fist and press with thumb of the fist against floor, holding arms straight and close to the body. Turn head forward and rest front part of chin on floor.

Slowly lift right leg from hip, without bending the knee. Assist movement by pressing fists against floor.

Hold the position for a few seconds, breathing normally.

Lower leg in slow motion back to floor and relax. Repeat with left leg.

4 The Cobra

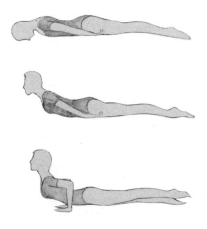

Exercise to stretch the spinal column, to release tension and to strengthen chest and bust muscles.

Lie relaxed on abdomen on floor, arms resting at the side. Forehead rests on the floor. Slowly raise eyes, then head, neck, back and chest as far as you can, without support.

Bringing arms slowly forward, place hands in front on floor in line with the body, fingertips in line with shoulders.

Continue bending spine and raising trunk supported by the arms, but do not raise hipbones from the floor. Keep legs and feet together all the time. Hold position a few seconds motionless when reaching the utmost flexibility. Then bend arms and slowly bring body back to the floor, first abdomen, then chest and head. Repeat four times.

Bring arms back to the sides as soon as the body can be lowered without support. Lie stretched out, head to the side and relax.

5 The shoulder stand

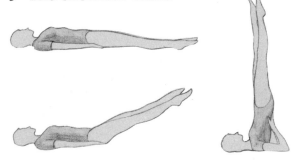

Exercise to stimulate circulation in the upper portion of the body, benefiting the complexion.

Lie on back, hands at sides, palms facing the floor.

Tighten leg and abdominal muscles. Slowly lift legs from the floor, keeping knees straight. Assist movement by pressing palms firmly down. When legs are straight up in the air, slowly start lifting buttocks and lower part of back from floor. Support yourself by placing fingers on the back, both thumbs under the hipbone in front.

Hold position for a few seconds, then complete shoulder stand by stretching legs straight up into the air. Again stay motionless.

Bend knees so that they almost touch the face.

Return one hand after the other slowly to the floor.

Keep head and shoulders on the floor and slowly roll back and buttocks back onto the floor.

Straighten legs and return them to initial position without bending the knees. Relax.

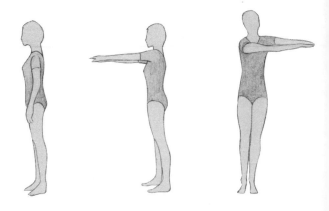

Exercise to flex the spine to remove neck tension, to assist posture, to reduce the waist, and to tone leg muscles.

Stand straight, heels together and abdomen pulled in.

Raise arms stiff and straight with thumbs touching each other until right in front. While raising the arms slowly, go up on toes and inhale deeply. Exhale through mouth and start to breathe normally again.

Slowly move arms, thumbs still touching, to the right as far as comfortable. The eyes are fixed on the hands, feet stay in position. Hold the posture for a short while without moving. Then return arms back to the front of the body, lower them to the sides and come down from the toes onto the feet and relax.

The same is repeated with the arms to the left side.

7 The arm and leg stretch

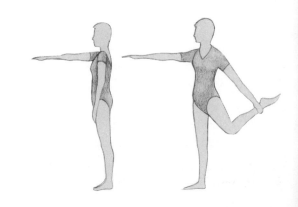

Exercise to improve poise and to relieve tension.

Stand straight, feet together and chest high. Slowly raise right arm in front towards the head, keeping it in sight all the while.

Place the body weight on the right leg, bend the left leg and raise the foot so that you can grasp it with the left hand. Hold the left foot and bend backward at the waist, keeping balanced by moving the right arm back over the head.

Drop head back and remain without motion in this position.

Slowly bring right arm forward, release the left leg, raise head, go into a straight position, lower right arm and relax.

The same exercise is repeated by lifting the left arm.

For information

Isometric exercises – opposing muscles are contracted with little shortening of the muscle but great increase of muscle tone.

Isotonic exercises – equal tension of muscle fibres strengthens the muscle.

Physics

Contents
Light   Electricity   Apparatus

LIGHT

The sun's spectrum comprises different electro-magnetic rays. Their properties change with the variations of the wave lengths. The spectrum ranges from short wave cosmic rays, via X-rays and ultra-violet rays (imperceptible to the human eye), to the small scale of visible light. The visible rays perceived as white light are followed by infra-red rays. These are also invisible to the human eye but the body registers them as a heat source. Beyond infra-red rays are radio waves and others.

Ultra-violet, visible and infra-red rays are in the shorter wave area of the spectrum. Their wavelengths are measured in Ångström units (Å) or nanometres (nm). Ångströms are generally used to measure ultra-violet rays, nanometres for all other rays. Light travels at a rate of 300 000 km per second.

Ultra-violet rays have the shortest wave lengths of the aforenamed. Wavelength increases gradually from violet to red visible rays and is longest in the subsequent infra-red rays.

Visible light is composed of coloured rays. This can be observed if white light is refracted by a prism breaking it down into a sequence of colours: violet, indigo, blue, green, yellow, orange and red. The same phenomenon is displayed in a rainbow, when rain-drops or mist serve as a prism to disperse light rays. Visible rays make up only 12 per cent of sunshine. The remainder is invisible heat or infra-red rays (80 per cent) and ultra-violet rays (8 per cent).

Ultra-violet light

Because of its biological effect ultra-violet light is of interest in cosmetology. Detailed, they can be classified as U.V.A, U.V.B and U.V.C rays. Most of the U.V.C rays do not reach the surface of the earth, since they are almost completely absorbed by the atmosphere. U.V.C rays have a wave length of 2800 to 1800 Å and are the shortest rays of ultra-violet light. Even a brief exposure to U.V.C rays causes a light erythema of the skin. U.V.B rays have a wave length of 3150 to 2800 Å. They also induce erythema followed by indirect pigmentation, that is, formation of pigmentation in the skin as a defence reaction. Prior skin exposure to U.V.B radiation spontaneously increases generation of melanin when influenced by U.V.A rays. This so-called direct pigmentation is a protecting action of the skin and the cause of tanning. Ultra-violet A rays have the longest wave length of ultra-violet light, 5000 to 3150 Å. They are the only part of ultra-violet sun irradiation not leading to an erythema. Sun screen preparations are intended to filter out U.V.C and U.V.B rays, only letting U.V.A rays reach the skin.

Ultra-violet radiation assists in the formation of vitamin D from ergosterol in the upper layers of the skin. Vitamin D is required for the calcium and phosphorus metabolism of bones. Ultra-violet light stimulates the circulation and builds up winter resistance of the skin. It has a favourable effect on acne or seborrheic skin through its healing and disinfecting qualities. The body regions react differently to U.V. radiation. Shoulders, back, chest and inner extremities are more sensitive than the face, hands or scalp, and thus respond readily with an erythema even if exposed to the sun for a short time.

Almost all electric bulbs radiate a minor amount of ultra-violet rays as well as visible light. Ordinary glass lets visible rays pass, but largely absorbs U.V. light. This is why skin does not tan behind closed windows. Because of its transparency to ultra-violet rays, quartz glass is used for bulbs in U.V. lamps. The

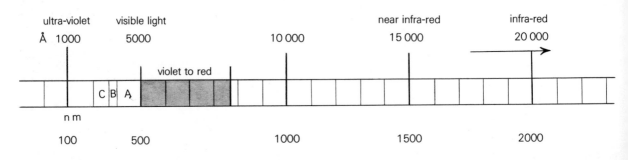

dosage of ultra-violet radiation from an artificial source should be carefully controlled to prevent an erythema. Shortening the distance between the light and the tissue can result in a stronger reaction. The bluish colour of U.V. lamps is due to the blue rays of the visible spectrum present in the bulb. A U.V. lamp should be employed 75 cm from the skin. Eyes must be protected. Start with 30 seconds, gradually increasing time of exposure to about 5 minutes.

If used with prudence a solarium can be profitable to the body's looks and health. The innate protection against damages of the skin must be built up gradually to avoid adverse results. The face has to be cleansed thoroughly; remainders of make-up may result in spotty areas later on. Strongly perfumed body lotions should be avoided. They, as well as medications and consumption of citrus fruit, including some vegetables like celery and components in tanning products, may result in skin reaction. The eyes have to be protected. Strict timing, not to overdose, and proper spreading of sessions, is recommended. The skin needs a good moisture lotion afterwards.

Other wavelengths

Blue light has a minor depth effect. It soothes nerves and develops a warm, mild sensation on the skin. It is applied when intensive heat is not required.

Red light contains red and infra-red rays. Its penetration into the skin tissue is relatively deep, causing a high surface temperature accompanied by a tonic, stimulating action.

Infra-red radiation invades the body, dilating blood vessels and furthering the circulation by heat irritation, as it relaxes and soothes muscles and nerves, relieving tension and pain. Sebum and sudor excretion are increased.

The skin may be exposed to infra-red light for up to 20 minutes; the longer the exposure, the greater the impact. However, the lamp must be kept at a suitable distance to prevent burning. If it is used on the face the eyes should be covered. It enhances the benefit of a mask or pack by opening the pores.

In diathermy infra-red rays achieve medical purposes. They are also employed to destroy the hair papilla in permanent hair removal.

ELECTRICITY

Various electrical devices successfully assist the aesthetician to care for the client's skin. She should have a general understanding of their function, know the effects of their use and be able to follow operating instructions. She must also be familiar with the necessary vocabulary.

Electricity is a current, a course of electrons by which natural energy is created. The electrons flow from a positive to a negative pole or vice versa. The entire path of the electric current from its source along wires and appliances back to its origin forms an electric circuit. Wire serves as a conductor or carrier of electricity. Copper and aluminium are good conductors with the ability to transmit electricity easily. There are also a number of substances including acids, salts and alkalis which, diluted in water, become good conductors. Such a solution is called an electrolyte.

Terminology

An *electrode* is a conductor establishing an electrical contact to include a non-metallic part (e.g. a liquid) in a circuit.

An *insulator* is a poor conductor, a material that does not readily pass an electric current. It prevents damage to the surroundings from undesired electricity.

The rate of flow of electricity is the current. This is measured in *amperes*.

Electrical 'pressure' is measured in *volts*.

Ohm is the unit which measures the resistance to the electric current. (According to Ohm's law: the amperage equals the voltage divided by the resistance in Ohms.)

Watt is a unit to measure electrical power. One thousand watts are a *kilowatt*.

Hertz is a unit for measurement of frequency, i.e. the number of cycles per second of a vibrating body. One *hertz* = one cycle per second.

A *fuse* is a device used for protecting electrical appliances against the effect of excess current. A *circuit breaker* acts similarly to a fuse, but is an automatic switch.

A *battery* is a device in which chemical reactions at the electrodes produce electricity, i.e. chemical energy is transformed into electrical energy.

A *dry battery* consists of voltaic dry cells which are treated to prevent spilling.

A *transformer* is an apparatus which lowers or increases the voltage of an electrical current.

A *generator* converts mechanical energy into electrical energy.

Alternating current (A.C.) is an electric current reversing its direction of flow at fixed intervals. It is used for muscle exercising and strengthening.

Direct current (D.C.) is a current in which the movement of the electrons is in one direction only.

Galvanic current is a direct current of low voltage generated by direct current or a battery. It stimulates muscles and nerves, increases circulation and improves muscle tonus (electrophoresis).

Faradic current is an assymetric, alternating current. It is used for muscle and nerve stimulation and a general invigorating effect on the body. Faradic current is meant for therapeutic application.

High frequency is electrical energy with 10 000 Hertz or more per second. It is used in epilation, U.V. lamps, and appliances for body, face and scalp treatments.

Static electricity is produced by friction.

APPARATUS

The *steamer* is a beauty appliance which has a heating device for water vaporization. The steam is carried to the skin in the form of fine mist. A plant extract can be added to the water or a herbal infusion used instead. Vapour relaxes, refreshes, stimulates and softens the tissue.

Vapozone is a steamer with valuable cosmetic effects. This apparatus atomizes steam by decomposing water molecules. The water vapour passes an ozone-producing U.V. lamp. Ozone is distributed among the water particles and brought into contact with the skin. The tissue is disinfected, strengthened and softened. The pores are opened and the circulation is activated.

Ozone results from the reaction of U.V. rays on oxygen in the air i.e. by electric discharge. $(O_3 \longrightarrow O_2 + O)$

An ionozone bath is a small cabin covering the body only. The client is in a sitting position. Ozone vapour or herbal steam flows through the cabin for the improvement of body skin.

The value of a cosmetic treatment lies in its prophylactic or improving properties; that is, prevention of skin damage or betterment of damage that is already present. In both cases a favourable counteraction of the tissue is sought by cosmetic methods or substances. Almost always the circulation in the capillaries is stimulated to accelerate the blood supply and aid the constant regeneration of skin cells. This may be achieved by physical, mechanical stimulation (massage and apparatus of different kinds), thermic methods (heat, e.g. infra-red light) or chemicals. Frequently, electrical apparatus assist and complement more conventional methods for an improved result.

A vacuum massage is done by alternating suction and compressed air. Carried out simultaneously with two cups on the action of air cushions, pulling or stretching of tissues does not occur. The size of the glass ventouses is adjusted for various manipulations and areas: smaller for the face, larger for body parts. In turn vacuum and air pressure can be regulated. The technique comes closest to gentle, manual movements. Through its use tonus is improved, the skin's metabolism is revived, scales are loosened and removal of comedones is made easier. The procedure is suitable for face, back and décolleté treatments, as well as for lymph drainage. Specialized cosmetics can be used simultaneously. Similar apparatus is also available in combination with a sprayer.

Electrophoresis

This is also known as iontophoresis or simply phoresis, and unites a physical with a chemical technique. It solves the great problem of cosmetic effectiveness. By means of galvanic current matter is infiltrated into the unbroken skin. Ionization overcomes the barrier that normally prevents substances from penetrating the skin from outside the body.

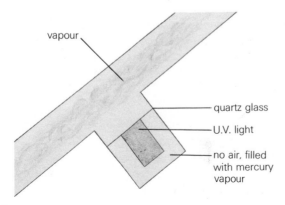

vapour

quartz glass

U.V. light

no air, filled with mercury vapour

The expression 'to nourish', commonly used to describe distribution of substances on the skin surface to improve its texture, is not to be taken literally. Cells can only be nourished in the true sense of the word from inside the body, and all matter required for regeneration is conveyed to the cell by the circulatory system. On the other hand, electrophoresis allows ions to be brought to the skin cell from outside, transported efficiently by galvanic current.

Note The human body acts as an electrolyte; absorption may take place by way of osmosis. Ionized products or a saline solution (NA^+Cl^-) serve as a vehicle for a non-ionized matter. Thus a better absorption takes place than would be possible if the substance was applied manually.

Method The skin must first be cleansed thoroughly and freed of all oil. The electrodes must also be clean with no greasy surfaces. Fat acts as an insulator and impedes the course of the ions. For this reason the best suited preparations for electrophoresis consist of a watery liquid. An oily consistency renders a less worthy carrier.

The ampoules (vials) for electrophoresis should be of tested preparations, and their composition known, to avoid undesired side effects. The ampoules are prepared from chemicals or plant extracts. They serve to close pores, moisturize, disincrust, lighten, stimulate and regenerate. Each manufacturer indicates how long phoresis should be carried out with a specific preparation, and also explains if positive and/or negative, and when to reverse to give all ions the chance to move with the fluid, depending on their polarity. The usual time is 10 minutes for the face and about 30 minutes for other areas. A good result is achieved when enzyme peeling precedes electrophoresis. Applied with distilled water before a mask or pack, phoresis enhances the outcome by loosening cell spaces.

An electric current has polarity, an active and an inactive pole. In case of infiltration, the active electrode infiltrates and the inactive conducts the current. From the positive pole or anode, the ions move towards the negative cathode. These ions have a positive charge and are called cations. The procedure is called cataphoresis. The reaction on the tissue is acid as ions are brought into the skin. Nerves are soothed, blood supply decreases and the membrane is firmed.

By reversing the current, negatively-charged particles called anions move from the cathode to the anode. This is the process of anaphoresis. It causes an alkali reaction, stimulates nerves and skin glands, increases blood supply to the capillaries, opens pores and relaxes tissues.

An electrophoresis is equipped with a number of electrodes which may be shaped as tweezers, balls, rolls, or be flat. The contact point with the body must be kept moist at all times for good conduction.

The client During treatment the client keeps close touch with one electrode while the aesthetician directs the other. The circuit path flows through the client; therefore, before breaking it, the current must be discontinued to avoid discomfort. During ionization the current is set low, so that the client perceives nothing but a minor prickle. There are some appliances equipped for the client to regulate this herself.

Pustules and lesions must not be touched.

The galvanic or ionto mask is principally the same idea as electrophoresis. Before covering the face with the mask, wet cotton or cloth is spread over it to serve as contact between electrode and skin.

Alternating current

This tones muscles. The nerve points of the muscle are stimulated by touching them with an electrode, causing them to contract and relax. Muscles are strengthened and the circulation is improved. For the apparatus different size electrodes are available. This way muscles which are hard to influence can be exercised. Electrodes are removed after the current has been discontinued. During treatment a slight sensation in the muscles is felt.

A vibrator is reserved for the heavier muscle tissue on shoulders, back, etc. It exerts a deep pressure, relaxes, and stimulates lymph and blood circulation. A vibrator must not be used on persons with heart trouble, on those running a temperature, on inflamed areas or on the delicate facial tissue.

The high-frequency apparatus has glass attachments radiating infra-red or U.V. rays. It accomplishes the same results as the lamps: stimulating, disinfecting and healing. In direct H.F. the electrode glides over the client's face. Another way to make use of the apparatus is indirect H.F., when the client holds the electrodes (bar) while the aesthetician taps lightly with her fingertips over the face. Sparking or fulguration is a method to dry and sterilize spots and pimples by rapidly lifting and re-pressing the U.V. glass electrode to the skin, letting the current jump across the gap. Skin feeling moist receives a fine layer of talcum powder.

A brush massage apparatus equipped with different sized brushes is one of the oldest appliances in physical care. It is employed dry on the body and moist for deep cleansing of the face. Lymph and blood circulation are thus activated, tonus and turgor are improved and a general relaxation takes place. Attachments include extremely fine-ground pumice and a synthetic sponge for removal of skin scales or superficial planing of rough elbows, upper arms or thighs.

Apparatus like electrophoresis, vacuum suction and muscle toners play an important part in dealing with trouble spots on the body. They should not, of course, be applied over varicose veins, during pregnancy, on indisposed persons, somebody with a metal implant or those with high blood pressure.

The soft laser (Ne-He-laser) has been successfully employed for the improvement of certain skin conditions by the medical profession.

Electrosprayers atomize watery or oily solutions to reach the skin in a microscopic form. A well-equipped cosmetic institute also employs electric heaters for oil, lotions and wax; diagnostic lamps; skin testers; sterilizers; apparatus for permanent hair removal; pedicure implements; and those for general physical care (see relevant chapters).

Precautions must be observed when handling electric appliances: keep the hands dry, stand on a dry floor, do not overload connections, and keep cords, plugs and all equipment in perfect condition.

Chemistry

Contents

In order to understand the compositions of cosmetic preparations, the cosmetologist requires a basic knowledge of chemistry. In this chapter, the most important laws of general and organic chemistry are discussed, as well as the significance of chemical compounds used in the practice of cosmetology.

Chemistry is the scientific study of matter and its chemical changes. All matter is made up of atoms. The term is derived from a Greek word meaning indivisible. An atom is the smallest unit of an element maintaining its characteristic features. It is composed of neutrons, protons and electrons. Several atoms together form a molecule. A molecule can be constructed of atoms of the same type, i.e. atoms of one and the same element, or of atoms of unlike elements arranged in a definite way. Molecules of atoms of different types form matter like water, salt, etc.

The universe is made up of 105 different elements. Each element has a symbol, often taken from the letters of its Latin name. Elements may be classified according to their natural state: gaseous, liquid or solid. In all, there are 11 gaseous elements, e.g. oxygen (O), nitrogen (N), hydrogen (H) and inert gases that do not normally react chemically with other elements, e.g. helium (He), and neon (Ne). The liquid elements are bromine (Br) and mercury (Hg). The remaining elements are solids.

Elements may also be classified as metals or non-metals. Metals differ from other elements in that they are good conductors of heat and electricity. Two or more metals can be fused together by melting. They dissolve in each other to form an alloy. Each metal has its particular melting point. Metals can be classified as heavy metals such as copper (Cu), iron (Fe), lead (Pb), silver (Ag) and light metals such as: aluminium (Al), calcium (Ca), magnesium (Mg), sodium (Na), and potassium (K). Mercury (Hg) is a heavy semi-noble metal. Platinum (Pt), gold (Au) and silver (Ag) are also designated noble metals.

THE AIR

The air surrounding the earth is a mixture of odourless invisible gases. It is comprised of approximately 21 per cent oxygen (O_2) and 78 per cent nitrogen (N_2), carbon dioxide (CO_2) and several other gases as well as dust and water vapour.

Nitrogen (N_2) is an essential component of human nourishment. It is present in protein, a constituent of plant and animal tissue. Protein is required for healthy skin, hair and nails.

Oxygen (O_2) is the most abundant element on earth, comprising about 50 per cent of the earth's crust. Life cannot exist without oxygen. It is required in all vital processes to produce energy and heat. Oxygen is added to such cosmetic preparations as reviving and refreshing masks and sprays. Its invigorating effect on the skin makes it suitable for use in bubbling bath additives.

Ozone (O_3), a light blue gas, is usually prepared by passing an electric discharge through oxygen. Ozone decomposes exothermically to yield oxygen. Because of its disinfectant and stimulating effect, ozone is used in cosmetic treatments. In a vapozone, ozone is produced under the influence of an electric discharge and carried to the skin by vapour.

Hydrogen peroxide ($H—O—O—H$) is unstable and decomposes readily. Diluted aqueous solutions of H_2O_2 have a strong bleaching effect and are disinfectant. Solutions of H_2O_2 are added to cosmetics for bleaching purposes.

THE EARTH'S SURFACE

The main elements of the earth's surface besides oxygen are: Iron (Fe) 4.7 per cent, silicon (Si) 27.6 per cent, magnesium (Mg) 2.1 per cent, calcium (Ca) 3.6 per cent, aluminium (Al) 8.1 per cent, sodium (Na) 2.8 per cent and potassium (K) 2.4 per cent.

Silicon (Si)

This is the second most abundant element on earth. It is a non-metal, widely known in nature as silicon dioxide (SiO_2) or quartz; and in numerous plants in the form of silicic acid. Quartz in its pure state is a crystal. It is transparent to ultra-violet rays and is used in ultra-violet lamps.

Silicates are salts of silicic acid. Glass is a transparent amorphous mixture of silicates. Silicic acid ($SiO(OH)_2$) is contained in plant juices, which are added to facial steamers and compresses for stimulation of the skin. It is also an additive to hair and nail cosmetics. Silicones are organic silicon compounds of many-sided applications.

Aluminium (Al)

This is a light, highly heat resistant metal always in combination with other matter. Alum, potassium aluminium sulphate ($KAl(SO_4)_2$), is used in cosmetic preparations for astringent purposes. Aluminium acetate ($Al(OCOCH_3)_3$) counteracts inflammations and is found in specialized cosmetic products. Aluminium sulphate ($Al_2(SO_4)_3$) and aluminium chloride ($AlCl_3$) are antiperspirant and deodorizing, and are used in antiperspirant creams, sticks and liquids.

Iron (Fe)

Iron is a heavy metal, and has been the most common and most useful metal over centuries. It is vital for the maintenance of the biological processes in the human body. Iron atoms are present in haemoglobin, the pigment matter of the blood. An iron deficiency leads to anaemia, a condition characterized by a pale complexion.

Calcium (Ca)

This is a white metal and occurs in nature in combination with other matter as chalk, marble and limestone. Calcium is the most abundant mineral in the human body. It is present in teeth and bones in the form of calcium carbonate ($CaCO_3$) and calcium phosphate ($Ca_3(PO_4)_2$). For the proper utilization of calcium, vitamin D and phosphorus (P) must be present. Calcium plays an important part in blood coagulation and in normal response to nerve stimuli. Calcium sulphide (CaS) is a constituent of chemical depilatories.

Sodium (Na)

This is a silver-white, soft alkali metal widespread in nature, for example as sodium chloride (NaCl) in the sea water. Sodium is found in blood plasma and fluids surrounding tissue and is present in sweat excreted over the skin. Sodium is responsible for the retention of liquid in body cells. Sodium chloride (NaCl) is common cooking salt. Sodium bicarbonate ($NaHCO_3$) is used in baking soda. Sodium hydroxide (NaOH) is used in soap manufacture and for bleaching purposes. Sodium carbonate (Na_2CO_3) is utilized in water softeners, soap production and bleaching chemicals.

Potassium (K)

This is a white metal generally found in mineral deposits and in the soil. Vegetables and fruits are nutritional sources of potassium. In the human body potassium partly maintains the fluid balance. Potassium carbonate (K_2CO_3), or potash, is used in the manufacture of soap. An aqueous solution of potassium permanganate ($KMnO_4$) serves as a disinfectant.

Magnesium (Mg)

This is a white, light metal, and occurs in nature in minerals, rocks and sea water. Magnesium is present in chlorophyll and thus found in vegetables and fruits. Magnesium is required by the nervous system and muscles of the human body. Magnesium silicate ($Mg_3Si_4O_{10}(OH)_2$) or talcum is added to powder and creams. Magnesium oxide (MgO), a fine white powder, is used in toothpastes.

THE HUMAN BODY

Four major elements make up more than 90 per cent of the body's weight. They are oxygen, carbon, hydrogen and nitrogen. Calcium, phosphorous, potassium, sulphur, sodium, chlorine, magnesium, iron, manganese, fluorine, silicon, iodine, aluminium and copper form the remaining percentage, including the so-called trace elements of which only a very minor amount is present. Some of these are: cobalt, zinc, bromine, arsenic and boron. In all, 29 of the natural elements exist in the human body. Each is required in a certain proportion to maintain body health and each has its specific function.

The chemistry and function of oxygen and nitrogen in the human body have been discussed previously.

Carbon (C)

This is a non-metallic element. It is a component in some inorganic compounds and in all organic compounds. It is found in nature as coal, graphite, and in a crystallized form as diamonds. Coal represents an important raw material for many chemical products. Graphite is black and of soft consistency, and used in lubricants, lead pencils and electrodes. The diamond, hardest of all minerals, is a nearly-colourless, valued precious stone and, because of its hardness, is used industrially for drilling, cutting, etc. Carbon monoxide (CO) is a poisonous gas, resulting from burning carbon with a scanty supply of oxygen. Carbon dioxide (CO_2), a colourless, odourless gas, is important in the control of both respiration and circulation in the human body and is exhaled by the lungs. Carbon dioxide is found in reviving bath additives like bubble baths, and is an excellent skin freshener when combined with watery liquids or spray. Carbonated drinks contain carbon dioxide and water (carbonic acid H_2CO_3).

Hydrogen (H_2)

This is the lightest in weight of all elements. H_2O is the formula of the water molecule. Without water there would be no life on earth. It covers the greater half of the globe and makes up about 70 per cent of the human body's volume, as all cells require water to carry out their vital tasks. Water serves as a solvent for chemicals and minerals. Sea water is rich in various minerals. Because of its stimulating and invigorating effect, sea water is used in compresses and packs in cosmetic treatments. It is also added to cosmetics for skin types requiring stimulation.

Water is able to dissolve chemicals until a state of saturation is reached. Such a liquid is called a saturated solution. Water is a good conductor of electricity. This property is utilized during electrophoresis, when compounds are absorbed into the unbroken skin as ions.

Phosphorus (P)

This is a non-metallic element and occurs in combination with calcium as calcium phosphate ($Ca_3(PO_4)_2$) and in the form of phosphorous acid (H_3PO_3) in the human body. The greater percentage is combined with calcium in the bone structure and the rest is found in the soft body tissues and body fluid.

Sulphur (S)

This is a solid, yellow, non-metallic element, contained in body cells as a constituent of protein and in the melanin of skin and hair. It is added to cosmetic preparations to treat an oily skin and acne vulgaris and serves as an ingredient in lotions and shampoos to treat an oily scalp.

Chlorine (Cl_2)

This is widely spread in the form of salts called chlorides of which cooking salt is the most common. Chlorine is found in body fluid and is present in the digestive juices in the stomach as hydrochloric acid (HCl). Chlorine is a bleaching agent and is used as a disinfectant during water purification.

Manganese (Mn)

This is a hard, brittle metallic element, being present only in a minor amount in the body. In combination with potassium as potassium permanganate ($KMnO_4$) it is a disinfectant and deodorant.

Fluorine (F)

This is found in nature mainly as fluorides and is important primarily in bones and teeth in the body. Fluoride reduces tooth decay.

Iodine (I_2)

This is generally found in nature in the form of salts called iodides. Iodine is of great physiological importance and is required by the body for the normal functioning of the thyroid gland which regulates the metabolism. Iodine tincture is known to be an effective disinfectant.

Copper (Cu)

This is a metal combined in many alloys. Its characteristic of being a good conductor makes it a suitable material for wiring and electrical appliances. Copper is essential for the formation of haemoglobin, the iron-containing red colour matter found in the blood. Some lower animals have copper in their blood (haemocyanin) instead of iron. Haemoglobin carries oxygen to the body cells.

Zinc (Zn)

This is a white metallic element. Zinc oxide (ZnO), a fine white powder, is added to cosmetic products because of its astringent effect and for sun protection.

Silicon, aluminium, iron, calcium, sodium, potassium, magnesium, oxygen and nitrogen have been dealt with previously. The elements discussed are those relevant to the practice of cosmetology.

THE STRUCTURE OF THE ATOM

The atom is the smallest unit of an element still maintaining its characteristic features. An atom consists of smaller particles: a nucleus surrounded by electrons. The central portion, the nucleus, holds two kinds of elementary particles: protons and neutrons. Electrons, the third kind of elementary particles, circle around the nucleus.

1 A proton is a particle with positive charge.
2 An electron is a particle with negative charge.
3 A neutron is a particle with no electrical charge.

The nucleus

The nucleus (protons and neutrons) comprises practically all of the atom's weight or mass. The nucleus of the hydrogen atom is an exception as it contains only one proton. Hydrogen is thus the lightest of all the elements. The electrons are almost weightless and have little influence on the atom's weight. The atomic weight is a relative figure; by definition 1/12 of a carbon atom is one gram-atom. Thus, a carbon atom weighs 12 gram-atoms. The gram atomic weight of all atoms is based on the carbon scale.

The electrons

The number of electrons in an atom equals the number of protons in the nucleus while the number of neutrons varies. By changing the number of neutrons in the nucleus of an atom, it is possible to obtain a heavier or lighter atom of the same element. These atoms are the isotopes of the element.

The electrons are distributed over one to seven energy levels (shells) around the nucleus. According to a law of nature, each of them can hold only a limited number of electrons. The first energy level contains two electrons, the second eight, the third eighteen, etc. The formula to calculate the number of electrons that an energy level can hold is:

$$x^{th} \text{ energy level } = 2x^2.$$

x is replaced by the number of the energy level in the calculation. Thus the formula to obtain the figure of

electrons that the 5th orbital can take must be:

$$5^{th} \text{ energy level } = 2(5)^2 = 50 \text{ electrons.}$$

The ordinal number of an element in the periodic table is determined by the number of electrons in the energy levels: number one is hydrogen (H) with one electron and the last number 105 is hahnium (Ha) with 105 electrons. The outer energy level of noble elements is filled to its capacity, making them inert or inactive; e.g., helium (He) has one energy level and two electrons, neon (Ne) has two energy levels and ten electrons. The chemical properties of an atom are determined by the distribution of the electrons. This refers in particular to the number of electrons in the outer, highest-energy level. The position of an electron relative to the nucleus at any given time is indeterminable.

The teachings of chemistry are based on the conservation of matter: i.e., no matter can be lost nor newly obtained. It can only undergo a chemical change by chemical reaction with its environment. The atoms of one element always bond with a certain number of atoms of other elements or of the same element to form a molecule.

Valency

Valency is the degree to which an atom is able to bond with other atoms. Simply explained, the atom has arms that reach out for other atoms to attach. The number of ways an atom can bond depends upon how many electrons there are in its highest energy level or outer shell. The hydrogen atom has one free space available for bonding in its outer energy level; consequently, hydrogen has a valency of one (it is univalent). The oxygen atom has two spaces and has a valency of two (it is bivalent); the nitrogen atom has three spaces and has a valency of three (it is tervalent) and the carbon atom has four spaces and has a valency of four (it is quadrivalent). However, there are the odd exceptions when atoms of the same element have varying valencies; e.g. phosphorus. Inert elements have completed outer shells and are unable to form bonds; thus they have a valency of zero.

Definitions

Oxide – a compound of oxygen with another element.

Solution – a homogeneous mixture of solids, liquids, or solid and liquid.

pH Value – the measurement of the concentration of free hydrogen ions in a solution expressing the acidity or alkalinity of the solution.

Acid – a substance which yields hydrogen ions to a base in a chemical reaction. In a solution, the acid; i.e. the hydrogen ion, causes litmus paper to turn red. A non-metallic oxide plus water often forms an acid.

Fractional distillation – a process used to separate a mixture of liquids by making use of varying boiling points. Each pure liquid is freed from the mixture by vaporization at its individual boiling point.

Radical – a group of atoms reacting as a unit.

Halogens – a group of chemically similar elements. Each halogen atom has seven electrons in its highest energy level. Halogens react with metals to form salts called halides.

Derivative – a chemical substance related to another substance as indicated by the relationship to the basic structure.

Dot notation – each dot represents an electron in the outer shell of the atom, e.g.

$$H\cdot \qquad :\overset{\cdot}{\underset{\cdot}{O}}: \qquad \cdot\overset{\cdot}{C}\cdot \qquad :\overset{\cdot}{\underset{\cdot}{F}}\cdot$$

hydrogen oxygen carbon fluorine

Base – a solution of an alkaline compound. It colours litmus paper blue and forms salts when mixed with acids. Bases are often formed by dissolving metal oxides in water. Metal oxide plus water = a base.

Salt – a compound of a base with an acid or replacement of the hydrogen of an acid by a metal.

Buffer – a substance capable of maintaining the original pH of a solution by neutralizing any acid or base which is added to it.

CHEMICAL BONDS

The group of atoms making up a molecule is held together by a chemical bond. When a bond is formed, energy is released, whereas energy is required to break a bond.

A chemical bond may form in two ways: by transferring one or more electrons from the outer energy level of one atom to the outer level of another atom; or by sharing electrons, i.e., an electron on the outer energy level of one atom and an electron on the outer energy level of another atom are shared together.

When an electron is transferred, the atom that gives the electron away becomes positively charged and the atom that receives the electron becomes negatively charged. The two atoms become ions with a negative or positive charge. This chemical bond is called electrovalent or ionic and occurs mainly in inorganic compounds.

In a covalent bond the electrons in the highest energy level of atoms are shared. This type of bond is normal in organic compounds. The bonds in organic compounds are covalent bonds of one or more carbon atoms, frequently bonded with hydrogen. Thus, organic chemistry is the chemistry of the carbon compounds.

Organic and inorganic chemistry

The definitions organic and inorganic chemistry originate from the time when it was believed that carbon compounds were only obtainable from living sources, i.e. from vegetable and animal sources. Inorganic compounds were thought to be solely in minerals. In the past century, it was discovered that carbon compounds i.e. organic compounds could also be made in laboratories. The two terms organic and inorganic were conveniently continued. Some organic compounds are still isolated from plant and animal sources and are added to various products such as cosmetics, but most of them are produced synthetically. There are two important natural sources of organic matter: coal and oil (petroleum). Both are derived from decayed animals and plants.

Carbon has the valence four or is tetravalent. Its atomic weight is 12. The structure of the carbon atom is tetrahedral.

Carbon atoms have the ability to combine with atoms of other elements and with themselves. This outstanding characteristic of carbon enables it to form chains, which may have branches and/or rings. Thus it is possible for carbon to create an unlimited number of molecules. Approximately one million of these varied molecular structures are known at the present time and new ones are continually being discovered. Many substances used in daily life such as clothes, plastics, rubber, drugs, cosmetics and food products have an organic composition.

The molecular formula indicates the kind and number of atoms in the molecule. The structural formula shows the arrangement of the atoms in space. The positions of the atoms may vary although the molecular formula of the organic molecule is the same. The structure of the molecule determines its chemical properties. Molecules of the same molecular formula but with a different arrangement of their atoms are isomers. An example is given with butane, molecular formula C_4H_{10}.

Structural formula of butane and isobutane.

Atoms with more than one valence can be joined by double and triple bonds.

Single bond, double bond, triple bond

Compounds containing double and triple bonds are unsaturated and easily react to form other compounds.

The benzene ring (C_6H_6) is the most common of the aromatic compounds. A benzene ring can be bonded with other atoms.

benzene   simplified structure

In the simplified structure it is understood that each corner indicates the presence of a carbon atom and, if not otherwise shown, is bonded with a hydrogen atom.

Organic chemistry can therefore be grouped into compounds containing a carbon chain and compounds with a carbon atom ring formation. Steroid is the group name of numerous compounds containing carbon rings.

Hydrocarbons are compounds composed of only carbon and hydrogen atoms. They can be divided into several classes: aliphates, alkanes or paraffins, alkenes or olefins, alkynes or acetylenes, cyclic hydrocarbons, e.g. cyclohexane, aromatic hydrocarbons, e.g. benzene.

Alkanes or paraffins are carbon compounds saturated by hydrogen atoms. These compounds are unreactive. (The word paraffin is derived from the Latin *parum affinis* meaning little reactive). Paraffins are isolated from petroleum by fractional distillation. They are of an oily, pasty to solid consistency, depending upon the length of the carbon chain.

Following is a list of the chain alkanes. Note the gradual increase each time by CH_2 in the paraffin. The first four compounds are gases, 5C to 10C liquids, 11C to 15C oils, 16C to 18C sticky pastes, and above 18C they are solid.

Methane CH_4	Hexane C_6H_{14}
Ethane C_2H_6	Heptane C_7H_{16}
Propane C_3H_8	Octane C_8H_{18}
Butane C_4H_{10}	Nonane C_9H_{20}
Pentane C_5H_{12}	Decane $C_{10}H_{22}$

Paraffins do not become rancid. They are added for their gliding property to massage creams, sun screen lotions and protecting creams.

Methane, CH_4, molecular formula

is the first on the list of alkanes or paraffins. It is an odourless, colourless and flammable gas which rises from marshes and mines, originating from decomposed substances in the ground. It is a major constituent of natural gas. If one hydrogen atom is separated from the methane molecule a methyl group, CH_3, is the result, with a free valence able to bond with other atoms. Methane is part of the gas in aerosol containers for hairsprays, perfumes and other purposes.

Ethane, C_2H

$$H - \overset{\displaystyle H}{\underset{\displaystyle H}{\overset{|}{\underset{|}{C}}}} - \overset{\displaystyle H}{\underset{\displaystyle H}{\overset{|}{\underset{|}{C}}}} - H$$

is a colourless gas found in natural gas. It is also added to aerosols. The ethyl group arises from ethane minus one hydrogen atom.

Propane and butane are contained in natural gas and petroleum. They are highly flammable gases which can easily be liquified and are used as fuel.

Alkanes with a carbon chain of 5 to 15C are liquids and fats. The longer the carbon chain, the higher the boiling point.

Gasoline or petroleum, also called crude oil is a mixture of liquid hydrocarbons.

Liquid paraffin or paraffin oil is used after purification and bleaching to a clear, odourless and tasteless form as a raw material in cosmetics, like rouge, cream make-up, lipsticks, suntan preparations, baby oil, creams, cleansers and moisturizers.

Of the paraffins with more than 15C, vaseline, paraffin, and ozokerite are the best known raw materials for cosmetics. Vaseline and white petroleum jelly are the common names for petrolatum which, though originally of a yellowish colour, becomes a colourless, smooth substance after purification, with no taste nor odour. Vaseline has no biological effect and is added to cosmetics as a lubricant and to improve the consistency. It is a component of cosmetic O/W and W/O emulsions, rouge and ointments.

Paraffin is a firm, white, transparent, odourless, waxy substance. It is sparingly soluble in alcohol or other solvents. Paraffin adds firmness to deodorant and insect-repellent sticks.

Ozokerite is waxy, white and odourless when purified. It is an ingredient in lipsticks in combination with carnauba wax and beeswax. They improve the consistency and provide a firm, smooth gliding effect. Ceresin is purified ozokerite.

Alkenes and olefins are unsaturated hydrocarbon compounds.

As opposed to alkanes, in which the carbon atoms are saturated completely by hydrogen atoms, alkenes are characterized by the presence of carbon–carbon double bonds in the molecule.

Saturated compound Ethane, C_2H_6
(single bonds)

$$H - \overset{\displaystyle H}{\underset{\displaystyle H}{\overset{|}{\underset{|}{C}}}} - \overset{\displaystyle H}{\underset{\displaystyle H}{\overset{|}{\underset{|}{C}}}} - H$$

Unsaturated compound Ethylene, C_2H_4
(double bond)

$$\underset{H \diagdown \quad \diagup H}{\overset{H \diagup \quad \diagdown H}{\overset{C}{\underset{C}{\|}}}}$$

The names of the paraffins are recognized by the ending -ane, whereas the names of the olefin molecules end with -ene, e.g. ethylene C_2H_4; propylene C_3H_6; butene C_4H_8. Alkenes react easily with other elements.

Alkynes or acetylenes have a triple bond in their molecule. The simplest of these compounds is acetylene C_2H_2, $H - C \equiv C - H$. This is the base of many organic compounds.

Molecules with double or triple bonds can combine to form long-chain compounds, called polymers.

Hydrocarbon derivatives are alcohols, aldehydes and ketones.

Alcohols are hydrocarbon derivatives in which a hydrogen atom in the molecule has been replaced by an oxygen and hydrogen atom, called a hydroxyl group, and symbolized by —O—H. The hydroxyl group is a functional group and the reactive part in an alcohol molecule, giving to it characteristic properties. The ending -ol in a name indicates that the compound is an alcohol.

Alcohols are classified according to the type of carbon atom to which the hydroxyl group is bonded i.e. primary, secondary and tertiary alcohols:

$$\begin{array}{ccc}
H & C & C \\
| & | & | \\
C-C-OH & C-C-OH & C-C-OH \\
| & | & | \\
H & H & C
\end{array}$$

primary   secondary   tertiary

The term used to denote the number of OH groups present is:

2—OH, diol; 3—OH, triol etc.

methane, CH_4 methanol or methyl alcohol, CH_3OH

$$H-\overset{\displaystyle H}{\underset{\displaystyle H}{C}}-\boxed{H} \longrightarrow H-\overset{\displaystyle H}{\underset{\displaystyle H}{C}}-OH$$

replaced by an OH

Methanol or methyl alcohol (CH_3OH) is extremely toxic and is of no interest in cosmetic preparations. Its common name is wood alcohol. The consumption of methanol may lead to blindness or even death.

Ethanol or ethyl alcohol (C_2H_5OH) is known as wine spirit and is contained in all liquor. Ethyl alcohol is obtained by fermentation from sugar cane, sugar beets, fruit, grain or potatoes. It is important in the manufacture of cosmetics and as a disinfectant.

Ethanol acts as solvent for various ingredients in perfumes, toilet waters, astringents, deodorants, skin fresheners, eye-liners, mascara, rouge, insect repellent sticks, mouthwash, bath additives, hair lacquers and hair lotions.

Propanol or propyl alcohol ($CH_3CH_2CH_2OH$) is obtained from fusel oil in alcohol fermentation. There are two isomers. The normal propyl alcohol has an intensive characteristic odour. Isopropyl alcohol has an odour similar to acetone. Both propyl alcohols are better solvents than ethyl alcohol and are used to dissolve fats and resins in cosmetic preparations. They are superior to ethanol as disinfectants but toxic if consumed. Therefore they can only be added to products for external application.

Isopropyl alcohol ($CH_3-\underset{\underset{\displaystyle OH}{|}}{CH}-CH_3$)

Butanol or butyl alcohol (C_4H_9OH) occurs in four different isomers. It is used in organic synthetics and as a solvent in nail polishes and nail polish removers. Butyl alcohol is less soluble in water than the alcohols with a shorter carbon chain.

Pentanol or pentyl alcohol ($C_5H_{11}OH$) occurs in eight isomers. It is used mainly as a solvent similar to butanol. Pentyl alcohol may react with acids to form volatile esters with a pleasant aroma.

The alcohols from C_6 to C_{12} are smooth solids and soluble in liquid alcohols and fats. They are used in cosmetics to dilute fats and as emulsifiers. Some of these alcohols have pleasant odours, e.g. decanol or decyl alcohol ($C_{10}H_{21}OH$) smells of fresh oranges, and lauryl alcohol ($C_{12}H_{25}OH$) of lilac.

Myristyl alcohol ($CH_3(CH_2)_{12}CH_2OH$) is a reduction product of myristic acid occuring in various waxes. It is added to non-fatty creams.

Cetyl alcohol ($CH_3(CH_2)_{14}CH_2OH$) is a waxy solid. It is part of spermaceti, a wax originating from the sperm whale. Cetyl alcohol is well tolerated by the skin and can be blended with acid and alkali substances in cosmetics. It is a frequently used raw material for emulsions and lipsticks, improving the smoothness and stability of a product.

Stearyl alcohol ($C_{18}H_{37}OH$), a fatty matter with a slight odour, is a reduction product of stearic acid. It serves as an emulsifier for O/W emulsions and is a component in lipsticks, deodorants, blushers and other cosmetics made in stick form. It is used for its gliding effect.

Myricyl alcohol ($C_{30}H_{61}OH$) in combination with palmitic acid is an ingredient of beeswax which is added to lipsticks and other cosmetic preparations.

The alcohols with more than one hydroxyl group in their molecule are sweet, oily, runny liquids. The longer the carbon chain, the sweeter and firmer they become. They are water-soluble.

glycol

C_2H_4 (OH)$_2$

$$\begin{array}{c}
H \quad H \\
| \quad | \\
H-C-C-H \\
| \quad | \\
OH \quad OH
\end{array}$$

Ethylene glycol is a diol. Glycol itself is not used in cosmetics but some of its related substances, such as polyglycol, play a part in the manufacture of creams with low fat content and in moisture creams.

glycerol
or
glycerin

$$H-\underset{\underset{OH}{|}}{\overset{\overset{H}{|}}{C}}-\underset{\underset{OH}{|}}{\overset{\overset{H}{|}}{C}}-\underset{\underset{OH}{|}}{\overset{\overset{H}{|}}{C}}-H$$

Glycerin ($C_3H_5(OH)_3$) is a triol and the most important of this group. It is a colourless, odourless substance, thicker and sweeter in taste than glycol. It is hygroscopic which means that it readily attracts and retains water and, for this reason, is added to cosmetic moisture preparations and tooth pastes. It is present from 5 per cent to 10 per cent in some creams. Glycerin applied to the skin in pure form causes skin irritation and it is thus frequently replaced by sorbitol. Glycerin is a component of animal fats and plant oils.

Glucose ($C_6H_6(OH)_6$) occurs in nature in honey, grapes and other sweet-tasing fruit as fruit sugar.

glucose

CHO
|
CHOH
|
CHOH
|
CHOH
|
CHOH
|
CH$_2$OH

sorbitol

CH$_2$OH
|
(CHOH)$_4$
|
CH$_2$OH

Sorbitol ($C_6H_8(OH)_6$), is an alcohol with six hydroxyl groups in its molecule. Sorbitol is not as sticky as glycerin and does not take in water as readily but retains it better than glycerin. It is added to cosmetic preparations instead of glycerin or in combination with same.

Ethers are alcohol derivatives originating from two alcohol molecules bonded together by releasing water – H_2O. The two molecules can either be of the same alcohol or of two different alcohols. An example is dimethylether:

two methanol molecules $(CH_3OH)_2$ dimethylether (C_2H_6O)

$$H-\underset{\underset{H}{|}}{\overset{\overset{H}{|}}{C}}-\boxed{OH}-\boxed{H}O-\underset{\underset{H}{|}}{\overset{\overset{H}{|}}{C}}-H\longrightarrow$$

$$H-\underset{\underset{H}{|}}{\overset{\overset{H}{|}}{C}}-O-\underset{\underset{H}{|}}{\overset{\overset{H}{|}}{C}}-H + H_2O$$

Ethers are colourless, easily flammable liquids with a characteristic odour. Their fumes are explosive. The ethers made by combining two molecules of the same lower alcohol are mainly applied as solvents for resins, oils and fats. Ethyl ether is a familiar anaesthetic. Some of the higher ethers are used in perfumery as fragrances, e.g.

p-cresyl methyl ether $C_8H_{10}O$

anisole, C_7H_8O

safrole, $C_{10}H_{10}O_2$

Constituent of essential oils, used in perfumery.

Aldehydes are organic compounds of the general formula RCHO. The characteristic functional group of aldehydes, the carbonyl group, is symbolized by

$$-C\overset{\displaystyle O}{\underset{\displaystyle H}{}}$$

and always found at the end of the carbon chain, e.g.

methyl alcohol   formaldehyde HCHO

$$CH_3OH \quad H-\underset{\underset{H}{|}}{\overset{\overset{H}{|}}{C}}-\boxed{OH}\longrightarrow H-C\overset{\displaystyle O}{\underset{\displaystyle H}{}}$$

Formaldehyde is used as a disinfectant. It is a component in footcare cosmetics because of its deodorizing and disinfectant properties.

Aldehydes with a carbon chain of C_6 to C_{17} are oily, have a pleasant odour and serve as raw material for perfumery. They are applied to perfumes as topnotes, core odours, fonds and fixatives. Some of these aldehydes are mentioned here.

Caprylaldehyde $\quad C_7H_{15}-C{\overset{\displaystyle O}{\underset{\displaystyle H}{}}}$

$$(CH_3(CH_2)_6-C{\overset{\displaystyle O}{\underset{\displaystyle H}{}}})$$

has a dry, fruity odour. It is added to rose and jasmine fragrances.

Pelargonaldehyde $\quad C_8H_{17}-C{\overset{\displaystyle O}{\underset{\displaystyle H}{}}}$

$$(CH_3(CH_2)_7-C{\overset{\displaystyle O}{\underset{\displaystyle H}{}}})$$

has a fragrance reminiscent of roses and is an addition to fantasy compositions and perfumes with a rose or orange note.

Caprinaldehyde $\quad C_9H_{19}-C{\overset{\displaystyle O}{\underset{\displaystyle H}{}}}$

has the odour of an orange, and is contained in fantasy and flowery perfumes.

Laurinaldehyde $\quad C_{11}H_{23}-C{\overset{\displaystyle O}{\underset{\displaystyle H}{}}}$

has a strong heavy odour and is combined in perfumes with violet, tuberose, cassia and fantasy fragrances.

Ketones are characterized by the carbonyl group $>C=O$ bonded to carbon. Contrary to the carbonyl group of the aldehydes, this group is never at the end of a carbon chain, but bonded to a carbon atom within the chain and not necessarily in the centre. This way there may be two equal or different groups each side of the carbonyl group.

$$\overset{\displaystyle O}{\overset{\displaystyle \|}{}}$$
Acetone, $C_3H_6O \quad CH_3-C-CH_3$

is the simplest example of a ketone.

It is a volatile, flammable liquid with a pungent odour. It mixes with water, alcohol, ether, fatty and essential oils. Acetone is a common, effective organic solvent for many substances and an ingredient of nail varnish and nail varnish remover.

Ketones with long carbon chains are found in fragrant plant oils. A great number of complicated ketone compounds have odours and are used in perfumery.

The carboxylic acids constitute an important class of organic compounds. The characteristic functional group of carboxylic acids, termed the carboxyl group, is symbolized

as COOH or $-C{\overset{\displaystyle O}{\underset{\displaystyle O-H}{}}}$ The hydrogen of the

carboxyl group can be replaced by a metal

$$-C{\overset{\displaystyle O}{\underset{\displaystyle O^--Na^+}{}}}$$

The carboxyl group gives the carboxylic acids their acidic properties. The most significant compounds of this kind are the so-called fatty acids, e.g. C_{16} palmitic acid and C_{18} stearic acid $(CH_3(CH_2)_{16}COOH)$, the major parts of animal fats. C_4 to C_{18} (carboxylic acids) are also found in plant oils and animal fat. Fatty acids contain a carboxyl group bonded to a paraffin group, e.g.

methane, $CH_4 \qquad$ formic acid, HCOOH

ethane, $C_2H_6 \qquad$ acetic acid, CH_3COOH

hexadecane, $C_{16}H_{34} \longrightarrow$

palmitic acid, $CH_3(CH_2)_{14}COOH$

or $C_{15}H_{31}-C{\overset{\displaystyle O}{\underset{\displaystyle OH}{}}}$

The carboxylic acids with a short carbon chain are water-soluble liquids while the carboxylic acids with a long carbon chain are waxy substances, which are not soluble in water. Carboxylic acids play an important part in daily life owing to their presence in human food, in medicines and in cosmetics, as well as their many-sided uses in industrial products. Organic acids can be classified as weak acids compared to the much stronger inorganic acids.

$$O=\overset{O}{\underset{OH}{C}}-\overset{O}{\underset{OH}{C}}=O$$

found in plants. It is used in dyes and as a bleaching agent. Citric acid, $C_6H_8O_7$

$$
\begin{array}{l}
H_2C-COOH\\
\quad\;|\\
HO-C-COOH\\
\quad\;|\\
H_2C-COOH
\end{array}
$$

Acetic acid, $C_2H_4O_2$ ($CH_3C\overset{O}{\underset{OH}{\diagup}}$)

results from fermentation of ethyl alcohol. Wine and cider exposed to air over a length of time turn into vinegar. Common cooking vinegar is dilute acetic acid. Vinegar is added to cosmetic preparations such as shaving lotions and toilet waters. Acetic acid serves as solvent for many organic substances. The salts of acetic acid are termed acetates.

Propionic acid, C_2H_5COOH, butyric acid, C_3H_7COOH, caproic acid, $C_5H_{11}COOH$, caprylic acid, $C_7H_{15}COOH$ and capric acid $C_9H_{19}COOH$ are highly emulsifiable fatty acids found in milk. They are easily digested and well tolerated. Butter takes its name from the same root as butyric acid.

Pelargonic acid, $C_8H_{17}COOH$ is contained in the essential oils of lavender, pelargonium and other plants. It is a yellowish, light liquid.

Lauric acid, myristic acid, palmitic acid and stearic acid are fatty acids of waxy consistency, melting to an oil when heated.

Lauric acid, $C_{11}H_{23}COOH$ is found in coconuts. Myristic acid, $C_{13}H_{27}COOH$ is in most fats in the form of glycerides. Palmitic acid, $C_{15}H_{31}COOH$ is present in animal fats and fatty plant oils as glycerides, in essential oils and beeswax. Stearic acid, $C_{17}H_{35}COOH$ is part of the sperm whale oil, animal fats and beeswax. The higher the stearin content, the firmer the consistency of the fat. Cerotic acid, $C_{25}H_{51}COOH$ occurs in beeswax and carnauba wax.

Oleic acid, linoleic acid and linolenic acid are unsaturated fatty acids. Oleic acid $CH_3(CH_2)_7CH=CH(CH_2)_7COOH$, has one double bond in its molecule and is contained abundantly in food fats. Linoleic acid has two double bonds and linolenic acid has three double bonds in the molecule. These three unsaturated fatty acids occur in drying oils such as soybean, linseed, cotton-seed and corn oil as glycerides.

The carboxylic acids with two functional groups are termed dicarboxylic acids. An example with a simple structure is oxalic acid $(COOH)_2$ which is a poisonous acid

has three carboxyl groups in its molecule. It is of interest in cosmetic treatments as it is added to preparations for bleaching purposes and for an oily and blemished skin. Citric acid is found in nature in all citrus fruit, raspberries, strawberries and other fruit. This organic acid can also be synthesized.

Esters are compounds obtained by chemical reaction between an alcohol and an acid. During this process water is released

$$\text{alcohol} + \text{acid} \longrightarrow \text{ester} + \text{water}$$

$$\text{pentanol} \quad + \quad \text{acetic acid} \quad \longrightarrow$$

$$CH_3CH_2CH_2CH_2CH_2OH \quad CH_3-\overset{O}{\overset{\|}{C}}-OH \longrightarrow$$

$$\text{pentyl acetate} \quad + \quad \text{water}$$

$$CH_3CH_2CH_2CH_2CH_2O-\overset{O}{\overset{\|}{C}}-CH_3 + H_2O$$

Fats and oils from natural sources are esters. They are a compound of one glycerin molecule and three molecules of fatty acids. If fats are split in the presence of an alkali, soap is the result.

Natural fats are oils and fats deposited by animal or plant cells in a living organism. Most natural fats contain palmitic acid, stearic acid and oleic acid. If the oleic acid content of a fat is high, it is an oil; but if the stearic acid content is high, it is a solid. Beef tallow contains more stearic acid than the other two fatty acids. Unlike paraffins, natural fats become rancid. They are well tolerated by the skin and represent a raw material for W/O and O/W emulsions used as skin care products.

Olive oil is the oil of the fruit of the olive tree. This plant oil is not irritating to the skin. It is added to soaps and it is a base in protecting creams, moisturizers, night creams, nourishing creams and massage creams.

The main constituents are glycerides of:
oleic acid 83%
palmitic acid 9%
linoleic acid 4%
stearic acid 2%

Avocado oil is pressed from the avocado fruit. It is naturally yellow, thick-running, and becomes lighter in colour through purification. Avocado oil is rich in fat-soluble vitamins. It is an ingredient of light-protecting creams, nourishing creams and baby oils.

Peanut oil is found in the seed of the peanut. It is a colourless, thin-running oil and is added to fatty cosmetic creams.

The main constituents are glycerides of:
palmitic acid 8%
stearic acid 3%
arachidic acid 2%
behenic acid 3%
oleic acid 56%
linoleic acid 26%

Cacao oil is obtained from the cacao bean. It easily becomes rancid. This vegetable oil is non-irritating, hygroscopic and readily emulsified. It is used in lipsticks, nourishing creams and creams for a dry skin.

Linseed oil is pressed from linseed. It dries quickly and is added to dyes and soap. Linseed oil is rich in glycerides of oleic, linolenic, linoleic, stearic, palmitic and myristic acids. The ground seeds, mixed with water, can be used as a facial mask.

Almond oil, the oil of sweet almonds, is clear, mild, light yellow and almost odourless. It is a fine, delicate plant oil contained only in special cosmetic preparations. Almond oil contains chiefly glycerides of oleic acid with small amounts of linoleic acids, and no stearic acid.

Castor oil is the oil obtained from the castor bean. It is soluble in cold liquids such as alcohol but does not mix with minerals oils. It is added to soaps to enhance foaming, to hair lotions, to eyelash preparations and lipsticks.

Castor oil contains diglycerides of:
ricinoleic acid 86%
oleic acid 9%
linoleic acid 3%

Wheatgerm oil is pressed from fresh wheatgerm. The thick, golden-yellow substance has a smell of grain and holds lecithin, vitamin E and glycerides of:
linoleic acid 44%
oleic acid 30%
saturated acids 15%
linolenic acid 10%

If kept in a closed, non-metallic container, it is stable over a long period. Wheatgerm oil is of great nutritive value in food and is a raw material for creams.

Jojoba oil from the Mexican jojoba plant is similar to spermaceti.

Neatsfoot oil – (fixed oil from feet of bovine (neat) cattle) – is a pale yellow, clear, cold-resisting oil with a characteristic odour. It is obtained from cattle bones and contains linoleic, linolenic and arachidonic acids. It is a component in creams for a dry, sensitive skin and in cuticle oils.

Lard becomes rancid easily, and has a characteristic odour. In combination with lanolin or cetyl alcohol lard makes a hygroscopic cream base. Lard is also a raw material for soaps.

Waxes are fat-related substances, esters composed of primary higher alcohols and higher fatty acids. These compounds are the main components of the natural waxes, whether of plant or animal origin.

Carnauba wax is obtained from the leaves of the Brazilian carnauba palm and is a yellowish or grey, brittle, hard, high-melting substance. It is added to cosmetics for firmness and to improve consistency, especially in stick form make-up, e.g. lipsticks.

Candelilla wax, a plant wax from Mexico, is not quite as firm as carnauba wax but imparts smoothness and shine to cosmetics and is a component in lipsticks and rouge.

Sugarcane wax and *ouricuri wax* are plant waxes with characteristics similar to carnauba wax. Both are used in cosmetics, often in combination with carnauba wax.

Beeswax is the yellow excretion from a gland of the bee from which it builds the honeycomb. Beeswax purified and freed from honey is added to lipsticks, cream rouge, nail polish remover (cream), creams, eyebrow pencils and other cosmetics.

Lanolin, adeps lanae, is the wax of the sheep's sebaceous glands obtained by washing the sheared wool. After processing, the wax is odourless and almost colourless. Lanolin contains palmitic acid, stearic acid, caproic acid, butyric acid, etc., and is highly hygroscopic. As it is exceptionally well tolerated by the skin, it is the base for a number of cosmetic creams.

Spermaceti is a colourless, odourless oil found in the skull of the sperm whale. It is composed mainly of palmitic ester and cetyl ester. Spermaceti is hygroscopic and a valuable additive to creams.

Soap is a mixture of the following basic ingredients:

> ester (fat or oil of animal or plant origin)
> alkali and water (alkali: potassium or sodium)

Soaps vary in their preparation and composition according to their use. Transparent soaps contain glycerin, coconut-oil or alcohol. Potash, clay, tar, germicides, perfumes or dyes can be added. Soaps can be classified as cleansing soaps, soaps for different skintypes and as luxury soaps. Soap cleanses by emulsifying grease. When washing with soap and water, the soap emulsifies the oil of the skin and removes it together with dust and other matter. Hard water contains calcium and magnesium salts. They react with soap to form insoluble calcium and magnesium compounds which cause irritation to dry and sensitive skin. Owing to the absence of these chemicals in soft water, there is a greater development of foam. Water used in cosmetics is distilled water, free of inorganic salts.

Esters made of isopropyl alcohol and palmitic or myristic acid are similar in their properties to plant oils except that they do not become rancid. They are accessories to cosmetic preparations. Esters of fatty acids with an odour, e.g. butyric acid, pelargonic acid, propionic acid and benzoic acid are used in perfumery.

Amines contain the functional group $-N\begin{smallmatrix}H\\\\H\end{smallmatrix}$ (NH$_2$),

in their molecules. In an amine this functional group is bonded to carbon groups. Amines are strongly basic, turning red litmus paper blue.

Amino acids have in their structure two functional groups, the carboxyl group COOH and amino group NH$_2$. Amino acids make up proteins, which are present in all living cells. More than twenty of these are known and a single protein molecule contains numerous amino acid units. The presence of nitrogen distinguishes a protein from a fat or carbohydrate.

Aromatic compounds are organic compounds in which carbon atoms are arranged in a ring formation. The aromatic hydrocarbons include benzene and related compounds. All of them have a benzene ring or a similar structure in their molecule.

Benzene is a highly flammable, volatile liquid with a specific odour. It is distilled from coal tar. It is a solvent for fats, resins and essential oils and is used as fuel.

The hydrogen atoms in the benzene ring can be substituted by other atoms, atom groups and further benzene rings. The result is various aromatic molecules. Benzene derivatives have an essential influence on the development of plants, animals and human beings. Thyroxine, $C_{15}H_{11}I_4NO_4$ the hormone of the thyroid gland, is an example.

$$HO-\langle I \rangle-O-\langle I \rangle-CH_2-CH-\underset{COOH}{\overset{NH_2}{|}}$$

At present it is not required to discuss the details of these complicated and often complex structures.

A few examples of *aromatic compounds* are given below.

phenol C_6H_5OH toluene C_7H_8

naphthalene $C_{10}H_8$

Aromatic compounds are found in essential plant oils and in various synthetic perfume compositions.

PREPARATION OF COSMETICS

The cosmetologist must have a general knowledge of the composition of cosmetic products and must be aware of the major components of the most popular preparations. It is part of her professional knowledge to understand how the products she uses are prepared. Cosmetic creams and lotions are O/W and W/O emulsions which comprise most of the preparations used for skin care. For this important reason, they are further discussed for better understanding at the end of this chapter. Following this is a short list of basic formulae of different cosmetics. The examples are included to give an insight into the formula of a product, showing main ingredients and possible additives.

The question may arise whether or not an aesthetician should make her own cosmetics. In this regard, it should be mentioned that such an enterprise requires study, experience and capital. Products are brought onto the market by cosmetic manufacturers as a result of extended research and tests in laboratories and clinics. The chemical inter-reactions of the ingredients and their effects on the skin have both been thoroughly investigated. The quality and percentage of perfume, preservative, emulsifier or other additives have been carefully chosen. The properties of these various components have been adjusted to avoid later changes in the consistency of the product. The container is of a material which does not react chemically with any of the ingredients and eliminates the possibility of harmful interference by light and oxygen. Tasteful and appealing containers and wrapping are two important media for the success of the products.

After evaluation of all these points, it seems advisable to start out with an easily-prepared product, i.e. one with a simple formula which does not require the expense of additional equipment. The introduction of one good preparation is better than several products of mediocre quality which do not bring the anticipated success. It is recommended that a chemist experienced in the cosmetic field or in one of the chemical companies producing raw materials for cosmetics be consulted.

Self-made preparations

Self-made preparations from extracts of fresh herbs or fruit have the advantage of containing no chemicals, or only the essential ones such as an emulsifier. Perfume is missing. Since some chemicals may irritate the skin, these self-made preparations have a good chance of being well tolerated. On the other hand they are not stable, spoil easily and must be kept in a refrigerator and used soon after preparation. They are excellent if applied fresh as compresses, packs or masks during a cosmetic treatment for which they had been specifically prepared.

The manufacturer cannot bring any product on to the market without additional preservatives and stabilizers, as he cannot foresee how long it will sit on the shelf before finding its buyer. He also has to cater to a great number of different buyers who frequently buy a product because of its appealing pleasant odour.

EMULSIONS

If two substances which under normal circumstances are not soluble in each other are mixed to a stable consistency, an emulsion is formed. For example, if oil and water are poured together into a container, the oil stays completely separate from the water. By shaking, the oil (inner phase) disperses throughout the water (outer phase) in minute particles. The result is a milky-looking liquid called an emulsion. As soon as shaking is discontinued, the oil again separates from the water. In order to prevent separation of the two substances and to stabliize the mixture the addition of an emulsifier is required. The emulsifier lowers the water cohesion and encloses the oil droplets, preventing them from rising to the surface. The mixture is homogenized and the emulsion has become stable.

There are two types of emulsion.

1 Oil in water (abbreviated O/W) emulsion. The outer phase of the emulsion is water and the inner phase oil. (Vanishing cream)

2 Water in oil (abbreviated W/O) emulsion. The outer phase of the emulsion is oil and the inner water. (Cold cream)

The emulsifier added to a cream or lotion determines the consistency of the finished product. There is an emulsifier suitable for each individual cosmetic preparation.

The following is an excerpt from *Guide to the Use of Atlas Surfactants and Sorbitol in Cosmetic and Pharmaceutical Products* published and copyrighted by Atlas Chemicals Industries, Inc.

EMULSION PREPARATION

In Atlas Laboratories, the usual first step in preparing either O/W or W/O emulsions is to mix all emulsifiers into the *oil phase* of the product, i.e. the oils, fats, waxes and oil-soluble materials; then this oil phase with emulsifiers is heated to about 10 °C above the melting point of the highest-melting wax, taking care to avoid local overheating. Some formulators prefer to mix the oil-soluble emulsifier into the oil phase, and the water-soluble emulsifier into the water phase, before mixing the two phases. In large-scale production, one method may be found to give superior results for one type of product, while the other method will prove best for another product.

The water phase should be added slowly to the oil phase while the latter is being agitated, except in certain cases as noted in the next paragraph. It is advisable to have the water phase about 2 °C hotter than the oil phase, to allow for cooling during addition. For smoothness and stability, the mixture is sometimes homogenized at this point. The emulsion should be cooled slowly, with mild agitation. Creams are often poured into warm jars while fairly hot, just above the set point.

An exception to the usual principle of adding the water phase to the oil is made in the case of viscous, high oil-content (80–90 per cent of total) O/W emulsions. In preparing such emulsions, it is best to make a 'pre-mix' containing the total water and emulsifier with approximately an equal amount of oil, and then homogenize this while slowly adding the remaining oil.

When adding the water phase slowly to the oil phase, as noted above, an extremely heavy W/O emulsion sometimes forms at first. Suddenly the emulsion appears to 'break' or thin out, having 'inverted' to the desired O/W type of emulsion. After this point, the water can be added more rapidly.

If perfume or essential oils are included in the formula, add when the preparation is at about 45–50 °C to avoid reaction or volatilization of the oils. If salts or pigments are included, add them as finely ground powders or solutions after the emulsion is formed and cooled.

EFFECT OF THE RATIO OF PHASES OF AN EMULSION UPON CONSISTENCY

Adding increasing amounts of water to oil-emulsifier mixture

The photographs on the right show the addition of 400 cm³ of water to 100 cm³ of a mixture of oil and emulsifier (Fig. 1) to form a water-in-oil (W/O) emulsion. Figs 2–5 show the marked increase in viscosity as 25%, 50%, 75% and 100% of the water is added.

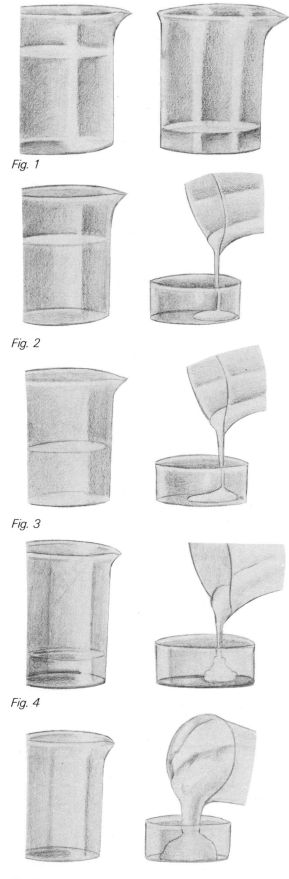

Fig. 1

Fig. 2

Fig. 3

Fig. 4

Fig. 5

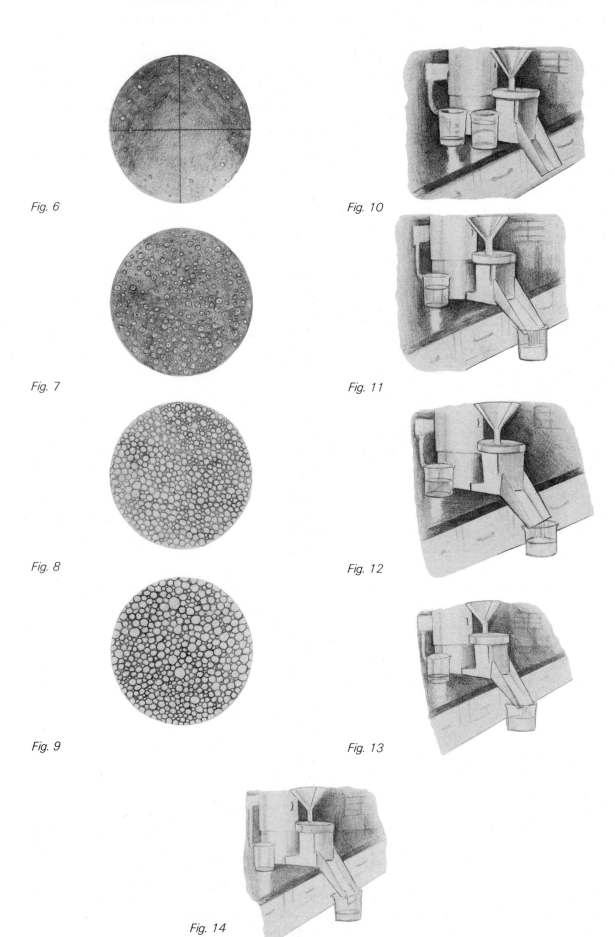

Fig. 6

Fig. 7

Fig. 8

Fig. 9

Fig. 10

Fig. 11

Fig. 12

Fig. 13

Fig. 14

The reason for this viscosity change is shown in the photomicrographs (Figs 6–9). A structural increase in viscosity occurs as the amount of water in the emulsion is increased, due to the mechanical crowding of the growing number of water particles. (While Figs 6–9 actually show increased crowding of *oil* particles in *water*, the addition of water to oil appears quite similar under the microscope.)

Adding increasing amounts of oil to water-emulsifier mixture

The photographs on the left show the increase in viscosity when 3000 cm³ of oil are added to 300 cm³ of water-emulsifier mixture (Fig. 10) to make an oil-in-water (O/W) emulsion. Figs 11–14 show the result of the successive addition of 25%, 50%, 75% and 100% of the oil.

Note that the same phenomenon occurs as in the making of a W/O emulsion. Again, the effect is due to a mechanical crowding of increasing numbers of particles of the dispersed phase, in this case, oil. Figs 6–9 are actual photomicrographs showing this crowding effect in an O/W emulsion and correspond in general to the stages shown in Figs 11–14.

EXAMPLES OF COSMETIC FORMULAE

The cosmetic raw materials with registered trade marks of the companies are listed with a short explanation at the end of the section.

If the percentage of colour or perfume is not mentioned in the formula or the abbreviation P.q.s. (perfume quantum satis) is given instead, it indicates that these substances are left to choice.

Ointment and cream bases (formulae BASF)

Formulation No. 1a
Cremophor A solid 6.0
Cremophor AP solid 1.0
Olive oil. 60.0
Water 33.0

No. 1b
Cremophor A solid 5.0
Almond oil. 45.0
Water 50.0

No. 1c
Cremophor A solid 6.0
Cremophor O 0.1
Cetyl alcohol 0.4
Vaseline 12.5
Paraffin 11.0
Water 70.0

No. 1d
Cremophor O 1.5
Cetyl alcohol 8.5
Water 90.0

Semi-fat creams (formulae BASF)

Formulation No. 7A
Cremophor A solid 3.00
Cetyl alcohol 0.35
Stearyl alcohol 0.15
Stearic acid. 5.00
Paraffin. 15.00
Triethanolamine 0.30
Water 76.20

No. 7b
Cremophor A solid 5.0
Lanolin, anhydrous. 5.0
Cetyl alcohol 3.0
Olive oil. 10.00
Paraffin 5.00
Water 72.00

All purpose creams (formulae Henkel)

Sports Cream (formula No. 11/127)
Amphocerin K 40.0
Preservative C 0.2
Water 59.8
P.q.s.

Sports Cream (formula No. 11/128)
Dehymuls K. 35.0
Preservative C 0.2
Water 64.8
P.q.s.

Sports Cream 'slightly oily' (formula No. 11/129)
Dehymuls K. 20.00
Cetiol V 5.0
Vegetable oil 5.0
White petroleum jelly 5.0
Preservative C 0.2
Water 64.8
P.q.s.

Day Cream (moisturizing) (formula Dragoco)
A) 300 g PCL-solid, self-emulsifying, oil-in-water
    10 g Extrapon VC or Dragovit F
B) 660 g Water
    10 g Dragocid Forte
    15 g Hydroviton
C)   5 g Perfume oil Crematest Dragoco
Total 1000 g

Day Cream (formula Dragoco)
A) 120 g Dragil or emulsifier 8475
    10 g Isopropyl myristate
    20 g PCL-solid
    10 g Paraffin oil
B) 12 g Bactericide MB
    10 g Hydroviton
    30 g Glycerol or sorbitol solution
   781 g Water
C)   7 g Perfume oil Crematest Dragoco
Total 1000 g

Day Cream, semi-fatty (formula Dragoco)
A) 50 g Dragil
    40 g PCL-solid
    70 g PCL-liquid
    60 g Stearic acid LA (L2SM)
    40 g Cetyl alcohol
B) 40 g Glycerol
    10 g Dragocid Forte
   680 g Water
     4 g Amino-methyl propanol (AMP)
C)   6 g Perfume oil Crematest Dragoco
Total 1000 g

Day Cream (formula No. 11/001) (formula Henkel)
Cutina MA 17.0
Cetinol V or Eutanol G 2.0
Eumulgin C 700 . . . . .3.0
Glycerine Henkel 28 °Be 3.0
Preservative C 0.2
Water 74.8
P.q.s.

Day Cream 'slightly oily' (formula No. 11/002)
(formula Henkel)
Cutina MD 6.0
Siegert Stearine L2SM 10.0
Eumulgin C 700 . . . . .3.0
Eutanol G 5.0
Vegetable oil 3.0
Liquid paraffin 3.0
Triethanolamine 0.5
1,2-Propyleneglycol 5.0
Preservative C 0.2
Water 64.3
P.q.s.

Day Cream (formula No. 11/003) (formula Henkel)
Dehydag wax N or SX 15.0
Cetiol V or Eutanol G 10.0
Vegetable oil 10.0
Glycerine Henkel 28 °Be 5.0
Preservative C 0.2
Water 59.8
P.q.s.

Day Cream formulation No. 20a (formula BASF)
Cremophor O 0.75
Butyl stearate H 3.00
Cetyl alcohol 4.25
Beeswax, white 4.50
Palmitic acid 8.00
Olive oil 5.00
Triethanolamine 0.40
Borax 0.50
Water 73.60

Glycerine Cream (formula No. 11/280) (formula
Henkel)
Cutina KD 16 . . . . .17.0
Eutanol G 12.0
Glycerine Henkel 28 °Be 40.0
Preservative C 0.2
Water 30.8
P.q.s.

Glycerine Cream, Transparent 'glycerine gel' (formula
No. 11/286) (formula Henkel)
Glycerine Henkel 28 °Be 35.0
Eumulgin C 700 . . . . .2.0
Carbopol 940*) 0.8
Triethanolamine 1.5
Preservative C 0.2
Water 60.5
P.q.s.
For transparent glycerine creams, water-soluble per-
fume oils should be used.

Glycerine Cream formulation No. 6a (formula BASF)
Cremophor A solid 8.0
Butyl stearate H 5.0
Paraffin wax, white, m.p. 50–55 °C 12.0
Stearyl alcohol 3.0
Silicone oil 1.000 . . . . .3.0
®Lanette E, Henkel & Cie., Düsseldorf 2.0
Glycerine 20.0
Water 47.0

Lanoline cream (formula Dragoco)
A) 250 g PCL-solid, self-emulsifying,
             Water-in-oil
     50 g Anhydrous lanoline
      5 g Dragocid
B) 690 g Water
C)   5 g Perfume oil Crematest Dragoco
Total 1000 g

Lanolin cream formulation No. 16a (formula BASF)
Cremophor A solid 8.0
Lanolin, anhydrous 15.0
Beeswax, white .2.6
Cetyl alcohol 0.4
Olive oil. 7.0
Almond oil. 5.0
Borax 1.0
Water 61.0

Massage Cream formulation No. 17 (formula BASF)
Cremophor A solid 3.0
Cremophor O 2.0
Cetyl alcohol 7.0
Vaseline 5.0
Olive oil. 13.0
Paraffin 25.0
Water 45.0

Massage Cream (formula No. 11/217) (formula Henkel)
Dehydag wax N or SX 7.0
White mineral oil. 38.0
White petroleum jelly 10.0
Preservative C 0.2
Water 44.8
P.q.s.

Massage Cream (formula No. 11/218) (formula Henkel)
Dehymuls K. 25.0
Vegetable oil 15.0
White mineral oil 15.0
Preservative C 0.2
Water 44.8
P.q.s.

Moisture Cream (formula No. 11/179) (formula Henkel)
Cutina MD 16.0
Eumulgin C 700 . . . . .4.0
Cetiol V 5.0
Vegetable oil 5.0
Liquid paraffin. .2.0
Hygroplex HHG*) 5.0
1.2-Propyleneglycol 5.0
Preservative C 0.2
Water 57.8
P.q.s.

Moisturizing Cream formulation No. 4 (formula BASF)
Cremophor A solid 3.00
Stearic acid. 3.00
Cetyl alcohol 0.35
Stearyl alcohol 0.15
Paraffin. 15.00
Triethanolamine .0.30
®Karion F, liquid, E. Merck AG, Darmstadt 7.00
Water 71.20

Moisturizing Cream (oil-in-water) (formula Dragoco)
A) 300 g PCL-solid, self-emulsifying, oil-in-water
     10 g Extrapone VC or Dragovit F
B) 655 g Water
     10 g Dragovit Forte
     20 g Hydroviton
C)   5 g Perfume oil Crematest Dragoco
Total 1000 g

Preparation: Heat A to 70 °C; heat B to 72 °C (without Hydroviton). Add Hydroviton to water phase (=B) shortly before emulsification. Add B at 70 °C, starting slowly by adding small portions and stirring; then add balance rapidly. Stir until mixture has cooled, and add perfume oil at 35 °C. The cream should be stirred until it has reached room temperature. Propeller-type agitators apt to incorporate air should be avoided.

Moisturizing Cream (water-in-oil) (formula Dragoco)
A) 120.0 g Isopropyl palmitate
    40.0 g Petrolatum, white
    50.0 g Sorbitan sesquioleate
    12.4 g Triethanolamine oleate
    12.0 g Crestalan A
B)   5.0 g Dragocid Forte
     3.6 g Magnesium sulphate (crystallized)
 730.0 g Water
   25.0 g Hydroviton
C)   2.0 g Perfume oil Crematest Dragoco
Total 1000.0 g

Preparation: Heat A to 65 °C; heat B (without Hydroviton) to 68 °C. Hydroviton is added to the water phase (=B) at that temperature, shortly before emulsification, and B is slowly stirred into A at a temperature of 65 °C. Stirring is continued until the mixture has cooled, and then the perfume oil is added at 35 °C. Slit homogenizing machines are recommended for use in homogenizing.

Nourishing cream formulation No. 18a (formula BASF)

Cremophor A solid 3.0
Cremophor O 2.0
Cetyl alcohol 6.0
Butyl stearate H 3.0
Beeswax, white 4.0
Lanolin, anhydrous 4.0
Almond oil 10.0
Vitamin F with 250 000 Sh.L. units/g* 1.0
Hamamelis extract dist. 5.0
Borax 0.5
Water 61.5
*Dr K. Richter, Berlin.

'Witch Hazel' Nutritive Cream 'very oily' (formula No. 11/074) (formula Henkel)

Dehydag wax N 10.0
Cetiol V 6.0
Vegetable oil 12.0
Lanolin, anhydrous 2.0
Witch hazel extract, dist. 10.0
Glycerine Henkel 28 °Be 8.0
Preservative C 0.2
Water 51.8
P.q.s.

Nutritive Cream 'moderately oily' (formula No. 11/076) (formula Henkel)

Cutina MD 16.0
Eumulgin C 700 . . . . 4.0
Cetiol V 10.0
Vegetable oil 10.0
Glycerine Henkel 28 °Be 5.0
Preservative C 0.2
Water 54.8
P.q.s.

Nutritive Cream 'moderately oily with azulene and allantoin (formula No. 11/078) (formula Henkel)

Cutina KD 16 . . . . 16.00
Eumulgin C 700 . . . . 1.00
Eutanol G 12.00
Vegetable oil 4.00
White mineral oil 6.00
25% Solution of azulene 0.05
Allantoin 0.20
1,2-Propyleneglycol 3.00
Preservative C 0.20
Water 57.55
P.q.s.

Nutritive and Night Cream (formula No. 11/081) (formula Henkel)

Dehymuls K 25.0
Cetiol V 10.0
Vegetable oil 10.0
Preservative C 0.2
Water 54.8
P.q.s.

Vanishing Cream (formula No. 11/004) (formula Henkel)

Dehydag wax N or SX 8.0
Cetiol V or Eutanol G 2.5
Siegert stearine L2SM 6.5
Triethanolamine 0.4
Glycerine Henkel 28 °Be 5.0
Preservative C 0.2
Water 77.4
P.q.s.

Vanishing Cream (formula No. 11/006) (formula Henkel)

Dehydag wax N or SX 5.0
Cetiol V or Eutanol G 1.0
Siegert stearine L2SM 15.0
Triethanolamine 1.0
Glycerine Henkel 28 °Be 7.0
Borax 0.1
Preservative C 0.2
Water 70.7
P.q.s.

Skin-food (stable to temperature) (formula Dragoco)

A) 300 g Apicerol 14081
      5 g Aluminium stearate
     20 g Beeswax
     30 g Lanoline
     50 g Isopropyl myristate
     20 g PCL-liquid
     10 g Extrapone VC
     20 g Ointment wax 2364 (Schliemann)

B)   10 g Dragocid Forte
     30 g Sorbitol solution
      3 g Borax
      3 g Magnesium sulphate, cryst.
    494 g Water

C)   5 g Perfume oil Crematest Dragoco

Total 1000 g

Creams and emulsions with special additions

Alcoholic Cream (formula No. 11/051) (formula Henkel)

Cutina MD	4.0
Eumulgin C 700	1.0
Cetiol V	5.0
Ethyl alcohol 96%	45.0
Carbopol 934	1.0
Triethanolamine	1.5
Preservative C	0.2
Water	42.3

P.q.s.

Processing instructions: Carbopol 934 is allowed to swell whilst stirring in 40 parts of ethyl alcohol and about half the amount of water.

Boric Acid Glycerine Cream (formula No. 11/276) (formula Henkel)

Dehydag wax N or SX	12.0
Cetiol V or Eutanol G	8.0
Vegetable oil	8.0
Boric acid	2.0
Glycerine Henkel 28 °Be	40.0
Preservative C	0.2
Water	29.8

P.q.s.

Cucumber Juice-Cream (formula No. 11/001) (formula Henkel)

Cutina MD	16.0
Eumulgin C 700	3.0
Eutanol G	15.0
Vegetable oil	10.0
1,2-Propyleneglycol	5.0
Cucumber juice	3.0
Preservative C	0.2
Water	47.8

P.q.s.

Hormone Cream (formula No. 11/178) (formula Henkel)

Cutina MD	16.0
Eumulgin C 700	3.0
Eutanol G	6.0
Vegetable oil	6.0
White mineral oil	4.0
Placenta liquid, oil-soluble	2.5
Preservative C	0.2
Water	62.3

P.q.s.

Vitamin Cream with Placenta (formula No. 11/177) (formula Henkel)

Cutina MD	15.0
Eumulgin C 700	3.0
Eutanol G	10.0
Wheat seed oil, Spec., hydrophilic	2.0
Placenta liquid, oil-soluble	3.0
White mineral oil	3.0
Preservative C	0.2
Water	63.8

P.q.s.

Hand cream (for rough, chapped hands) (oil-in-water) (formula Dragoco)

A)
120 g	Dragil
20 g	PCL-liquid
30 g	PCL-solid
10 g	Dragoco-extrapone VC or Dragovit F

B)
100 g	Glycerol
10 g	Bactericide MB
2 g	Triethanol amine, pure
15 g	Hydroviton
690 g	Water

C)   3 g Perfume oil Crematest Dragoco

Total 1000 g

Cucumber Juice-Emulsion (formula No. 111/011) (formula Henkel)

Cutina MD	8.0
Eumulgin C 700	3.0
Eutanol G	3.0
Vegetable oil	5.0
Cucumber juice	3.0
Preservative C	0.2
Water	77.8

P.q.s.

Vitamin Moisture Emulsion (formula No. 11/187) (formula Henkel)

Cutina MD	8.0
Eumulgin C 700	3.0
Eutanol G	10.0
PCL-liquid	10.0
Extrapon VC	2.0
Carrot oil	3.0
Hygroplex HHG	5.0
Preservative C	0.2
Water	58.8

P.q.s.

Emulsions

Cleansing Milk formulation No. 19 (formula BASF)

Cremophor A solid 4.0
Beeswax, white 1.0
Vaseline 3.0
Paraffin 30.0
Water 62.0
P.q.s.

Cleansing Emulsion (formula No. 11/117) (formula Henkel)

Cutina MD 4.0
Eumulgin C 700 . . . . .4.0
Cetiol V 8.0
White mineral oil .16.0
Preservative C 0.2
Water 67.8
P.q.s.

Moisture Emulsion (formula No. 11/186) (formula Henkel)

Cutina MD 8.0
Eumulgin C700 . . . . .4.0
Eutanol G 10.0
Vegetable oil 4.0
Liquid paraffin 4.0
Hygroplex HHG 5.0
1,2-Propyleneglycol .7.0
Preservative C 0.2
Water 57.8
P.q.s.

Moisture Emulsion formulation No. 5 (formula BASF)

Cremophor AP solid 4.0
Lutrol 9 . . . . .12.0
Cetyl alcohol 1.0
Spermaceti 1.0
Stearic acid 1.0
Glycerine monostearate 2.0
®Pur-cellin-oil, Dragoco, Holzminden 4.0
Isopropyl myristate .2.0
Paraffin 6.0
Karion F, liquid, E. Merck AG, Darmstadt . . .5.0
Triethanolamine 0.5
Water 61.5

Skin Emulsions formulation No. 11a (formula BASF)

Cremophor EL 5.0
Cremophor O 1.0
Cetyl alcohol 3.0
Olive oil 5.0
Glycerine 3.0
Water 83.0

Skin Emulsion (formula No. 11/021) (formula Henkel)

Cutina MD 3.0
Eumulgin C 1000 . . . . .3.0
Cetiol V 6.0
Vegetable oil 2.0
Glycerine Henkel 28 °Be 8.0
Preservative C 0.2
Water 75.8
P.q.s.

Toilet milk (formula Dragoco)

A) 100 g Hyrdo-myristenol 14082
     20 g PCL-liquid
      5 g Extrapone VC
B)   10 g Dragocid Forte
     20 g Sorbitol solution, 70%
   840 g Water
C)   5 g Perfume oil Crematest Dragoco
Total 1000 g

Lotions

Toilet lotion with moisturizing effect (formula Dragoco)

A)   90 g PCL-solid, self-emulsifying, oil-in-water
     25 g Eumulgin 05 (dehydag)
     10 g Eumulgin B-1 (dehydag)
     30 g Butyl stearate
     40 g Isopropyl myristate
     10 g Dragocid Forte
B) 700 g Water
     70 g 1,2-Propylene glycol
     20 g Hydroviton
C)   5 g Perfume oil Crematest Dragoco
Total 1000 g

Face tonic (formula Dragoco)

  250 g Alcohol (ethyl alcohol, 96%)
   40 g Polychol
   20 g Emulsifier 14156
    1 g Allantoin
    4 g Perfume oil, conc.
   40 g Hydroviton
  645 g Water
Total 1000 g

Face packs

Vitamin Face Pack (formula No. IV/106) (formula Henkel)

Cutina LE 12.0
Cetiol V or Eutanol G 4.0
Vitamin oil 5.0

Kaolin 2.0
Rice starch 3.0
Preservative C 0.2
Water 73.8
P.q.s.

Vitamin Face Pack (formula No. IV/107) (formula Henkel)
Emulgade F 5.0
Carrot oil 3.0
Zinc oxide 10.0
Kaolin 10.0
Almond bran 5.0
Camphor 0.1
Ethyl alcohol 96% 1.0
Vitamin F, water-soluble 0.2
Witch hazel extract, dist. 8.0
Viscontran M22 .2.1
Preservative C 0.2
Water 55.4
P.q.s.

Face mask (mask cream) (formula Dragoco)
A) 200 g PCL-solid, self-emulsifying, oil-in-water
    100 g Isopropyl myristate
     15 g Dragoco extrapone VC or Dragovit F
B)   5 g Extrapone hamamelis, dist., colourless, 'special'
     10 g Dragocid Forte
     20 g Hydroviton
    645 g Water
C)   5 g Perfume oil Crematest Dragoco
Total 1000 g

Homogenize 50 parts of this emulsion with: 40 parts kaolin; 10 parts aerosil (colloidal silicic acid).

Acne preparations

Acne Cream (formula No. 11/301) (formula Henkel)
Dehydag wax N .15.0
Rice starch 5.0
Powder pigment .1.0
Titanium dioxide 2.0
Resorcinol 1.0
Salicylic acid 0.4
Menthol 0.3
Hexachlorophene 1.0
Sulphur, precipitated 2.0
Preservative C 0.2
Water 72.1

Acne Emulsion (formula No. 11/311) (formula Henkel)
Dehydag wax N .3.0
Menthol 0.3
Hexachlorophene 1.0
Salicylic acid 0.4
Titanium dioxide 2.0
Pigment 1.0
Resorcinol 1.0
Bio-sulphur-fluid 2.0
Preservative C 0.2
Water 89.1

Sun and protection preparations

Sun-Tan Cream formulation No.2 (formula BASF)
Cremophor A solid 7.0
Stearyl alcohol 5.0
Stearic acid 4.0
®Miglyol 812, Chem. Werke, Witten 10.0
Olive oil 5.0
Glycerine 5.0
Dihydroxyacetone 5.0
Triethanolamine .1.0
Water 58.0

Sunscreen cream (formula Dragoco)
A) 290 g PCL-solid, self-emulsifying, oil-in-water
     60 g Prosolal S8
B)   35 g Sorbitol solution, commercial quality (Karion F, Sionit K, Sorbex)
     10 g Dragocid Forte
    600 g Water
C)   5 g Perfume oil Crematest Dragoco
Total 1000 g

Sun-Ray Filter Cream (formula No. 11/104) (formula Henkel)
Dehymuls E 10.0
White petroleum jelly 15.0
Lanolin, anhydrous 5.0
Cetiol V 10.0
Vegetable oil 5.0
Parsol ultra 5.0
Nut extract, oil-soluble 5.0
Nut extract, water-soluble 10.0
Preservative C 0.2
Water 34.8
P.q.s.

Skin-Protection Cream formulation No. 10a (formula BASF)
Cremophor A solid 5.0
Cremophor O 3.0
Cetyl alcohol 10.0

Olive oil 8.0
Paraffin 5.0
Silicone oil 1.000 . . . . .2.0
Hamamelis extract dist. 10.0
Water 57.0

Insect-Repellent Cream formulation No. 14 (formula BASF)
Palatinol M 35.0
Cremophor EL 4.0
Cremophor A solid 3.0
Cremophor O 1.0
Beeswax, white 2.0
Palmitic acid 8.0
Triethanolamine 1.0
Water 46.0

Deodorants

Deodorant Cream formulation No. 3 (formula BASF)
Cremophor O 4.0
Butyl Stearate H 15.0
Cetyl alcohol 18.0
Hexachlorophene L, Givaudan & Cie, Geneva 2.0
Water 61.0

Aerosol-Type Deodorant Spray (formula No. 111/181) (formula Henkel)
Eutanol G 10.0
Hexachlorophene 1.0
Perfume 1.0
Ethyl or isopropyl alcohol 88.0

Filling: 50% of the above mixture, 50% Propellant 12/114(40:60)

Depilatory Cream (Formula No. 111/201) (formula Henkel)
Dehydag wax N 10.0
Cetiol V 4.0
Thioglycolic acid 80% 10.0
Calcium hydroxide 12.0
1,2-Propyleneglycol 10.0
Perfume 1.0
Preservative C 0.2
Water 52.8

Method of manufacture

A cream is formed in the normal manner with Dehydag wax N, Cetiol V and water, 20 parts of which are retained, thioglycolic acid is diluted in the 20 parts of water and neutralised with calcium hy-

droxide. When completely cold, this solution is stirred into the cooled down cream and the perfume added. The finished cream is rolled.

Nail Polish Remover (Cream) (formula No. IV/051) (formula Henkel)
Dehymuls E 20.0
Dehydag wax O 4.0
Beeswax, white 6.0
Polyglycol 5/6000 . . . . .12.0
Ethyl glycol 15.0
Methyl glycol 10.0
Butyl acetate 33.0

Processing Instructions: The fatty substances and the glycols are melted on the water bath and then stirred until cold, whereupon the solvents are incorporated whilst stirring. Finally the cream is passed through a roller mill once.

Make-up

Make-up Emulsion (formula No. IV/121) (formula Henkel)
Dehydag wax O 1.0
Eumulgin C 700 . . . . .0.5
Cetiol V 10.0
White mineral oil 3.0
Lanolin, anhydrous 1.0
1,2-Propyleneglycol 5.0
Powdered pigments 12.0
3% solution of dehydazol 809 . . . . .34.0
Preservative C 0.2
Water 33.3
P.q.s.

Make-up Cream (formula No. IV/125) (formula Henkel)
Dehymuls K 30.0
White petroleum jelly .5.0
White mineral oil 5.0
Titanium dioxide 5.0
Powdered pigments 4.0
Preservative C 0.2
Water 50.8

Lipstick (formula No. IV/156) (formula Henkel)
HD oleyl cetyl alcohol K 20.0
Castor oil 24.6
Beeswax 5.0
Carnauba wax 8.0
Ozokerite 70–72 °C (158–161.6 °F) 11.0
Candelilla wax 3.0
Lanoline, anhydrous 8.0

White mineral oil 13.0
Ariabel brown 11.00 . . . . 0.4
Titanium dioxide C 47.051 . . . . 5.0
Rubicon red C 19.007 . . . . 0.5
Persian orange C 74.003 . . . . 1.5
Preservative, perfume and flavouring as required

Eye Shadow Pencil (formula No. IV/181) (formula Henkel)
Cetiol A 35.0
Beeswax, white 6.0
Carnauba wax 5.0
Candelilla wax 10.0
Castor oil 10.0
Fish silver 30.0
Cosmetic green oxide C61.6735 . . . . 4.0

Processing Instructions: All substances are melted together and poured into moulds at about 65 °C (149 °F).

Rouge Cream (formula No. IV/168) (formula Henkel)
Eutanol G 25.0
Castor oil 45.0
White mineral oil 4.0
Beeswax, white 2.0
Ozokerite 70–72 °C (158–161.6 °F) 5.0
Carnauba wax 6.0
Candelilla wax 5.0
Titanium dioxide C 47.051 . . . . 6.0
Light rubin lake C 19.022 . . . . 1.0
Toning orange C 15.007 . . . . 1.0

Processing Instructions: The fatty substances are melted on the water bath which is followed by adding the pigments. The resultant mixture is rolled two to three times and then poured into jars at approx. 70 °C (158 °F).

Rouge Compact Powder (formula No. IV/169) (formula Henkel)
Magnesium stearate 2.50
Colloidal kaolin 17.00
Rice starch 5.00
Magnesium carbonate 2.00
Titanium dioxide 5.00
Powderbrown 72.999 N 5.00
Datebrown KO 6.50
Talcum 57.00
Dehydag wax O 6.75
Eutanol G 3.75
Ethyl alcohol 96% 4.50
P.q.s.
Total 115.00

Bath additives

Bubble Bath (formula No. IV/355) (formula Henkel)
Texapon MLS 60.0
Dehyton AB 30 . . . . 5.0
Comperlan KD 3.0
Perfume, water-soluble 3.0
Preservative C 0.2
Water 28.8

Cream Bath, foaming (formula No. IV/452) (formula Henkel)
Texapon Q 86.0
Comperlan KD 3.0
Isopropyl myristate or Cetiol A 3.0
Cutina AGS 6.0
Perfume 2.0

Method of preparation: The substances are mixed with each other and warmed on a water bath until a homogeneous melt results, which is allowed to cool down to 30 °C (86 °F), when the perfume is added.

Mouth Wash 'emulsifying' (formula No. IV/292) (formula Henkel)
Mouth wash flavour 10.0
Glycerine Henkel 28 °Be 18.0
Ethyl alcohol 96% 56.0
Eumulgin C 1000 . . . . 3.0
Water 13.0

Toothpaste 'Foaming' (formula No. IV/257) (formula Henkel)
Texapon K 12 . . . . 2.00
Dehydazol FL 42 . . . . 1.20
Toothpaste flavour 1.00
White mineral oil 2.00
1% solution of saccharin 2.50
Glycerine Henkel 28 °Be 20.00
Chalk 16.00
Dicalcium phosphate 24.00
Aerosil 2.00
Preservative C 0.20
Water 29.10
P.q.s.

LIST OF RAW MATERIALS

BASF, Badische Anilin & Soda-Fabrik AG, Ludwigschafen, Federal Republic of Germany

®**Cremophor A solid**   Emulsifying agent derived from a low-hydroxyethylated, saturated fatty alcohol. Particularly suitable for emulsification of hydrocarbons and fats.

Cremophor AP solid   Ester of a polyethylene glycol with average molecular weight of approximately 400 with 1 mol stearic acid. Corresponds to polyethylene glycol-400-stearate of DAB 7.

Cremophor EL   Reaction product from castor oil with approximately 40 mols ethylene oxide. Hydrophilic, liquid emulsifying agent and solubilizing agent. Involves no physiological hazard.

Cremophor O   Highly-hydroxyethylated, saturated fatty alcohol. Particularly suitable for emulsification of fatty alcohols and fatty acids. Combinations of Cremophor O and cetyl and/or stearyl alcohol yield very stable and favourably priced ointment and cream bases. The advantage of the product is that it is supplied in the form of pourable, non-dusting, white microbeads.

®**Lutrol 9**   Polyethylene glycol 400, corresponds to DAB 7, has exceptionally high purity.

Emulsion type   The Cremophor grades are mostly oil-in-water emulsifying agents. Most of the creams produced are therefore of the oil-in-water type. In some cases, mixed systems are obtained.

Dragoco, Holzminden, Federal Republic of Germany

Dragovit F   Effect: Prevention of dermal dryness and abnormal keratinization. Constituents: Esters of 9, 12, 15-linolenic acid and 9, 12 linoleic acid. Vitamins A, E and D$_3$, cholesterol and a stabilizing tocopherol complex.

Bactericide MB imparts the necessary stability and keeping power to cosmetic products, and protects them against the formation of mould and germs causing fermentation or putridity.

Bactericide MB develops its preservative effect in the weakly acid, neutral, and weakly alkaline ranges. PCL-solid, self-emulsifying

'Self-emulsifying' PCL-solid is available in the form of a water-in-oil emulsifier and of an oil-in-water emulsifier. PCL-solid (self-emulsifying) contains approximately 50 per cent of the components of synthetic plumage oil of water-fowl, which is of predominantly branched chain structure.

Extrapone VC   Oil-soluble complex of vitamins and active substances. Dragoco Extrapone V.C. is soluble in oil and can thus be used in skin-function oils, massage oils and in all kinds of emulsions. Dragoco Extrapone V.C. is added to the liquefied oily phase of emulsions. Addition: about 10 g per 1 kg of finished product.

Dragocid Forte   Use: 1 per cent in creams, liquid emulsions, shampoos, etc. The classic phenolic preservatives, as is well-known, are mostly inactivated in the presence of non-ionogenous emulsifiers. Special care is indicated in preserving oil-in-water emulsion, particularly if these contain nitrogenous materials. Here, the use of 1 per cent of Dragocid Forte is recommended. Sterile raw materials, aseptic operations, with possible addition of 5 per cent propylene glycol, are advisable.

Emulsifier 14086   Complex of polyoxethylated sorbitan esters, non-ionogenous. Appearance: white substance of hard waxy consistency.

Prosolal S8   Photo-protective substance.

Prosolal screens off the short-wave ultra-violet radiation which produces erythma so that the skin is protected from photo-injury, but does not weaken biologically valuable radiation.
Use: As a 5 per cent addition to sun-screen oils, creams and lotions of the oil-in-water and water-in-oil types, sunscreen aerosols, etc.

Emulsifier 8475   Self-emulsifying glycerol stearate. Appearance: white, waxy substance.

PCL-liquid, water-soluble   PCL-liquid, water-soluble, a branched chain fatty acid containing 13 mols of ethylene oxide (14 mols of EO), is a faintly yellowish liquid with a faint characteristic odour. It is used as super-fatting agent in aqueous and low-grade alcoholic solutions as well as in active detergent substances for the purpose of improving their dermatophilous properties. Naturally PCL-liquid (water-soluble) can, in view of its hydrophilous character, be used also as an oil-in-water emulsifier.

Active substances Contain highly unsaturated fatty acid esters, wheatgerm oil, vitamin oil as well as the oil soluble vitamins, mainly vitamin D_3, A and E.

Hydroviton is based on special amino acids, a buffered sodium lactate complex, urea, allantoin, and special skin-wetting substances which control the moisture content of the skin.

Hydroviton is a water-soluble liquid (also available in cryst. form); the pH of which is within the range of that of the acid-coat of the skin, and which is added to the aqueous phase of emulsions; it does not give rise to difficulties during processing.

Emulsifier Dragil Self-emulsifying, specific glycol stearate. Appearance: white, waxy substance. Emulsifier Hydro-Myristenol 14082 Polyoxethylated fatty acid ester, non-ionogenous. Appearance: white to ivory paste to waxy.

Emulsifier apicerol 14081 An absorption base which is based on lanoline bees-wax and enables the simplified production of skin foods and cold creams. Appearance: almost white, heavily viscous.

Henkel International GmbH, Düsseldorf, Federal Republic of Germany

Amphocerin® Fatty alcohols and their derivatives. Emulsifying agent and ointment base, type W/O.

Cetiol® Fatty alcohol/fatty acid ester. Oil components and solubilizers

Comperlan® Fatty acid ethanolamides. Foam stabilizers, viscosity factors, re-fattening agents, solubilizers.

Cutina® Mono-di-glycerides. Consistency factors, cream and emulsion bases, type O/W, pearly lustre former.

Dehydazol® Carboxy methyl cellulose. Thickening agents, stabilizers.

Dehymuls® Ester combination of higher-molecular natural raw materials. Emulsifying agent and ointment base, type W/O.

Emulgade® Fatty alcohols, fatty alcohol sulphates and non-ionic emulsifying agents. Cream and emulsion bases, type O/W.

Eumulgin® Fatty alcohol polyglycol ether. Non-ionic emulsifying agents, type O/W.

Eutanol® Liquid fatty alcohols. Oil components and solubilizers.

Preservative C Preservative based on mono-chloroacetamide.

Dehydag® wax Fatty alcohols and fatty alcohol/fatty alcohol sulphate mixtures. Consistency factors, emulsifying agent and ointment bases, type O/W.

Nasuna® Mixtures of condensed chain polymers containing hydroxyl groups. Hair lacquer bases.

HD oleyl cetyl alcohol Liquid fatty alcohols. Oil components.

Texamid® Alginic acids, their salts and esters. Thickening agents and stabilizers.

Texapon® Fatty alcohol sulphates and fatty alcohol ether sulphates. Detergent raw materials for shampoos and bubble baths.

Viscontran® Methyl cellulose. Thickening agents and stabilizers.

Introduction to perfume

Contents

The designation 'perfume' combines two Latin words: *per* – through and *fumum* – smoke. It derives from the religious custom of burning herbs to let their fragrance rise toward heaven at worship to please God or the gods. This ritual was also carried out for special ceremonies such as marriages and funerals. Heat frees essential oils containing aromatic substances which ascend with the smoke. Incense was used, as far as we know, by Aztecs, Incas, Mayas, Egyptians, Greeks, Romans, Sumerians, Buddhists, Zoroastrians, Christians, Jews and Hindus. The burning of incense is still a ritual in some churches. In the Old Testament it says: 'Thou shalt make an altar to burn incense . . .' (Exodus 30) or 'for till that time the children of Israel burnt incenses . . .' (4 Kings 18).

In Ancient Greece perfumes were in common use. One even went so far as to soak the wings of pigeons in fragrances and let them fly in the hall at a banquet to fill the air with pleasant odour. The Ancient Romans were very fond of perfumes and added them to their oils, creams and bath essences. These fragrances all originated from plants, as other sources were not yet known.

We associate fragrances with memories; we recognize them but often we cannot describe the composition of odours. To choose the right perfume for a particular type of woman, we must not merely consider whether she is feminine, sporty, dark, brunette or blond. The fragrance should be tested on her skin, as it undergoes changes when in contact with temperature, acid, and skin oils. The same scent can smell completely different: on one person disagreeable, but delicious on another.

Terminology

The harmony of odours is called 'bouquet'. Blenders produce the harmonizing effect. The topnote or *tête* adds life to the perfume and when opening the bottle, it is the fragrance escaping first. Then follows the core (*coeur*) and body (*corps*), while another scent is the *fond* or base of the perfume which develops last. The modifier rounds the fragrance off and the fixative prevents a too-rapid evaporation. The Ancient Egyptians utilized a fixative that held the scent of a perfume from around 1300 BC until the present day. Fixatives come from animal and plant sources but are mainly produced synthetically. The fixative is an aromatic substance itself and strengthens the tenacity of a perfume.

Use in cosmetics

For various reasons perfumes are a necessary ingredient of most cosmetic preparations. Their main purpose is to cover the original odour of the raw material, but they additionally extend character to the product. Because of its aesthetic appeal, perfume is a pleasant and delightful attraction for the consumer. There are a great many perfume compositions enabling the manufacturer to meet every consumer's individual taste.

To obtain and produce certain fragrances often presents a difficult problem to the perfumer although there is such a wide range of raw materials. We distinguish between three sources: plants, animals and chemistry.

AROMATIC SUBSTANCES FROM PLANTS

Plants are a natural source for perfumes. Of the thousands of plants on earth, about 1700 contain aromatic substances in the form of resins, balsams and essential oils.

Essential oils

As opposed to fatty oils, which are also obtained from plants, essential oils are volatile and evaporate. They are extracted from different plant parts, usually by water or vapour distillation, and sometimes through absorption into certain fats (*enfleurage à froid*) and extraction through organic solvents, e.g. petro ether. The essential oil of the citrus fruit is pressed from the skin of the lemon, orange, bergamot, mandarin or grapefruit. Balsams and resins are used as both fragrances and fixatives in perfumes.

Essential oils in plants are not single chemical units, but alloys of complicated chemical compounds. They occur in great variety, and not all their components have an odour. Country of origin, place of growth, and methods of harvesting and extraction all influence the quality of these essential oils. The time of year and even the time of day make a difference in their quantity and quality. Some plants develop different oils in their various parts, e.g. the flower, the stem, the root and the leaves.

As previously mentioned, natural essential oils can be irritating to the skin and can cause its discolouration (berlock dermatitis). Only the essential non-fatty oils are of interest in perfumery, not the fatty plant oils like coconut oil and olive oil.

Essential oils are largely unstable. They are susceptible to light, heat, and oxidation. Light catalyses the process of chemical reaction. Therefore, perfume kept for a long period and opened numerous times undergoes a change in both scent and colour.

Essential oils used in perfumery come from flowers grown in Southern France near Grasse, in Spain and in the Balkans. Bulgaria is best known for its rose fields and is the main supplier of essential oils for this well-liked and popular fragrance (attar of roses). Spices come from the Orient and tropical countries.

Sachets

Pure plant compositions favoured for their delicate odour have been made into sachets for many centuries. These are small cloth bags containing the aromatic parts of plants crushed or pulverized. Leaves, petals or buds are dried on a screen in a warm, shaded place. They are turned over daily in order to dry thoroughly. Artificial heat can also be used to dry plant parts, but the heat should go no higher than 35–40 °C. Outside or room temperature is definitely to be preferred as it is more gentle and less damaging to the essential oils.

The ingredients for the sachet are then mixed in a jar where they are kept over several weeks and stirred now and then with a wooden spoon. Sachets are placed in linen and clothes closets. Examples for the preparation of a sachet are:

Sachet Maréchale
20 g sandalwood
20 g orris root
10 g cloves
10 g cassia
10 g rose petals
4–6 drops bitter almond oil

Rondelitia
16 g lavender blossoms
1 g allspice
8 g orris root
4 g cloves
16 g bergamot or bitter orange peel
16 g rose petals
30 g vanilla pods
1 g cinnamon (bark)

Rose sachet
20 g rose petals
5 g sandalwood
10 g vetiver (root)
15 g rose leaves
or
40 g rose petals
5 g sandalwood
5 g orange blossoms
3 g peel of bitter orange
2 g vanilla pods
2 g magnolia petals

Cologne sachet
50 g orange blossoms
4 g lemon leaves
3 g calamus (root)
3 g lime peel
5 g lemon peel
8 g rosemary blossoms
2 g sandalwood
2 g orange peel

Orange chypre sachet
40 g orange flowers
15 g coriander (fruit)
20 g mint leaves
5 g benzoin (resin)
10 g vetiver (root)
10 g calamus (root)
5 g oakmoss

Floral chypre sachet
5 g oakmoss
60 g rose petals
5 g patchouli
70 g orris root
10 g lavender blossoms
20 g sandalwood
10 g jasmine blossoms
5 g vetiver (root)

Some flowers cannot be used when dried even though they have a beautiful scent when blooming, for the scent is lost through the drying process.

In the fourteenth century aromatic substances, scent apples or pomanders were carried to guard against infection.

AROMATIC SUBSTANCES FROM ANIMALS

They serve mainly as fixatives, to invigorate the aroma and to perfect the fragrance by rounding it off. In concentration, scents from animals have an unpleasant odour, and can, therefore, be used only highly diluted. They are added to precious perfumes.

Fragrances of animal origin have played a part in the art of perfumery since ancient times. Hard-to-obtain substances are always thought of as the most valuable and desirable, and this applies as well to these animal secretions.

The best known animal fragrances are : ambergris, musk, zibet, castorium and the muskrat secretion.

Ambergris

This is a dark waxy substance with a very disagreeable odour which is found floating on tropical waters and after storms on the shores of Madagascar, Java and Japan. Ambergris is eliminated by the sperm whale and found in the intestines of dead whales. It is produced when the sperm whale is sick. It is lighter than water and as it does not sink, it may float for years before being fished out of the sea. The longer it drifts on the ocean the more valuable it becomes.

Ambergris may be soft and black, or firm and grey. The most precious is the grey ambergris, also called *ambra grisea*. It is rare and expensive. For a long time the origin of ambergris was unknown and it became a subject of many legends. However, the main constituent of ambergris is a fat similar to cholesterol and two of its major chemical parts can now be produced synthetically. Added to perfumes in a minor quantity, ambergris gives a fine note and helps in retaining the odour.

Musk

This is a brown secretion derived from a gland beneath the abdominal skin of the male musk deer. This animal lives in the Central Asiatic uplands, on the Tibetan slopes of the Himalayan mountains. The gland containing musk is developed when the deer is approximately 3 years old and its odour serves to attract the female deer. The animal has to be killed so that the hunter may obtain the gland, which is then dried and traded. As hunting of the musk deer has taken place for this purpose over centuries, it has become scarce, and musk one of the highest valued of all fragrances.

About 80 per cent of the world market is Tonkin musk but Hankiu musk, which is extremely rare, is more precious. In concentration musk has a penetrating, sickening odour; therefore, it can only be used in very small quantities, diluted in a solvent.

Musk is first mentioned in history when it was presented to the East Roman Emperor by Sultan Saladin in 1189. In the Orient it had long been applied as a perfume concentrate by sovereigns, rajahs and their concubines. Like ambergris it had the reputation of being an aphrodisiac. After its introduction to Europe, musk became a greatly valued addition to fragrances and is now a popular supplement to many of the most exciting perfumes in combination with flower essences. It is also contained in sachets and expensive soaps.

Chemically it has not been possible to imitate musk as it is found in nature, although one part of it became known, namely astrotone. The inventor of nylon, Dr Wallace Carothers, came across this compound during research.

Zibet or zibeth

This is secreted from a gland of the civet cat, zoological name: *Viverra civetha*. This cat is a small beast of prey found in Asia and Africa. In Ethiopia it is kept as a house animal also exported from there into captivity. The zibet is a yellow-brown fatty substance which is removed from the gland with a spatula or spoon every second week. The cat does not need to be killed in order to obtain zibet, which is found in both the male and the female animal.

Only a part of the zibet can be produced chemically, i.e. civeton, a ketone. Zibet is mainly added to perfumes for perfection of the fragrance.

Castorium

This is a gland secretion of the beaver. It comes nowadays from the Canadian beaver but the Siberian beaver was formerly the principal source of supply. Since the beaver is also valued for its fur it is becoming increasingly rare. The Canadian beaver produces less castorium than the Russian beaver. The odour of the Canadian castorium is reminiscent of fir trees, while the Siberian castorium has a leathery scent. This is probably the result of a difference in nourishment, the leather odour coming from the birch bark on which the Siberian beaver feeds. Most animals dispose of substances like castorium in the urine, but the metabolism of the beaver stores it. The contents of the beaver gland is a yellow-brown or brownish black liquid, which is found in both male and female animals. Castorium contains a mixture of about 100 chemicals, only half of them so far identified. It adds a spicy flavour to fragrances.

Secretion of the muskrat

A secretion from this North American mammal is a recent addition to perfumes. Only the male has the valuable scent gland, and in order to obtain the secretion the animal has to be killed.

The scent of the muskrat secretion is said to have a finer, less animal-like odour than that of the musk deer. It is lasting and powerful. The muskrat secretion is used in perfumery as a replacement for the real musk or as an addition to improve its fragrance. It will probably find its way into the most costly perfumes.

Muskrat secretion is chemically similar to that of the musk deer and the civet cat. Two chemists, P.G. Stevens of Yale University and J.L.E. Erickson of the University of Louisiana, succeeded in increasing the odour of the muskrat secretion approximately fifty times by oxidating its almost odourless 90 per cent portion to ketones.

SYNTHETIC AROMATIC SUBSTANCES

Certain essential oils can be reproduced synthetically, while others can be synthetic to a certain degree. Some aromatic substances are half synthetic, that is a chemical added to an isolated natural fragrance. Others are the chemical imitation of a natural scent, while the third type are purely synthetic creations unlike any aroma found in nature. Synthetic essential oils can be made in large quantities and are therefore less expensive than their natural counterparts.

The following is an excerpt from *The Practice of Composition* by Helmut Fuehrer, Dragoco, Holzminden, Germany:

'Perfumery is an art rather than a science, and hence the perfumer must be an artist rather than a chemical scientist. The perfumer should use essential oils, odorants, extracts, animal drugs, and bases the way the painter uses his colours. There is a long way to go from an odour accord to a high-quality, distinguished perfume. Careful dosage and unerring use of the tremendous range of raw materials are required to create a new odour by way of a well-balanced, intimate mixture, which must not be obtrusive but be able to please the wearer. For optimum results, close attention must be paid to possible reactions within the composition and to the stability of the perfume. The perfumer works with his nose. Daily practice is capable of developing anybody's olfactory sense. To have a good nose means to have a marked memory for odours, which still does not suffice, however, to make a good perfumer. Talent, imagination, long years of experience on the job, good taste, quick comprehension, good adaptability, absolute olfactory and gustatory senses, and a certain amount of intuition are what make the successful perfumer.

The commercial success of a new fragrance is dependent on the perfumer's specific, artistic, or even brilliant ideas. He should know that there is nothing 'incompatible' in the practice of composition, and that an apparent odour clash between two products can frequently be made to disappear by adding a third one as a connective link combining both odours. Fellow perfumers frequently ask about present fashions in the field of perfumery. There are no fashions in perfumery; it is the fragrance of the current bestseller which is fashionable.

The work required to learn the practice of composition is difficult and sometimes monotonous. No composer can write a symphony without having for years studied music, scales, and harmony. By the same token, intensive studies of odours are necessary to attain perfection and success in perfumery.

Female consumers do not choose their perfumes, but take them over, and this for various reasons. A lady may buy a certain perfume out of snobbishness because it has been lauched by a given fashion creator and, when asked its name by a friend, she will be able to assert that this is the new perfume by – , the well-known creator. If in the course of time, however, there is no favourable reaction from herself, her husband, or her friends, she will reject the perfume. If, on the other hand, a lady receives compliments on her good taste on the first day and is asked the name of her perfume thereafter, she will be flattered and wear the perfume by – – for years. Another reason for accepting a perfume may be the fact that it has held a leading position in the market for a long time.

There are other cases where a first-class perfume was rejected upon recommendation in a perfumery store, but recognized as good, and bought, later. What could have caused such a change in opinion?

1 In the store in question, the perfume was applied to the skin of the hand as is customary with lipsticks and creams. The specific odours of the glove and the skin were not taken into account. Hasty testing under unfavourable conditions has failed to permit proper evaluation of the characteristic fragrance.

2 The perfume was smelled merely at the opening of the flask. Improper evaluation was due to the fact that only the volatile topnotes were perceived, which fail to reveal the main character of a perfume. The true, clinging fragrance was thus completely ignored.

3 The fragrance was perceived on a friend and was found appealing afterwards. In consequence, the perfume is adopted. Such cases are very frequent.

As a general rule, the consumers are not in a position to evaluate perfumes properly. Perfumers should also employ test persons and await their reactions. If no comment has been received after a few days, the perfume may be considered a failure. If, on the other hand, several of the persons concerned make statements to the effect that the new perfume is wonderful and that they have been asked its name and where it can be bought, the perfume has been accepted and it may possibly turn out to be a success.

Essential oils, animal drugs, infusions, extracts, bases, and odorants are mixed under the control of highly sensitive precision scales. Utmost care in dosing and precise knowledge of the wide range of raw materials available will lead to the creation of new odour complexes, which must never be obtrusive and must be so as to be accepted by the final consumer.

Fragrances have magic power. There is nothing in the world equally capable of calling things to memory. An odour complex capable of calling to mind the splendour of roses must necessarily have some connection with rose, and one that makes us think of the ocean must have some rough or salty quality. The perfumer can conjure up countless delights which are then filled into tiny bottles – delights which are all the more valuable if the perfume is a novelty. We, in our hectic time, love what is new. Fragrance has been important to men and women since time immemorial, and has produced peculiar effects both physically and mentally. Mantegazza, the well-known Italian philosopher, was

not too far wrong in saying that fragrances are a weapon in the hands of love. Fragrances will forever be a delight to humans, as long as they will preserve their joy of life and beauty. Thousands of years have passed since the time when the first fragrant fumes, the earliest perfumes, arose from the hands of man, but ointments, makeup, precious stones and costly perfumes are as indispensable to the glamour of beautiful women craving admiration today as they were in those times long past.

When Loos, the well-known Viennese architect, saw his portrait made by Kokoschka, the Austrian painter, he said: 'This portrait is more like me than are my actual looks.' He meant to say that the artist had been able to visualize in his painting not only his model's features but also his inner life. Similarly, the perfumer should not be satisfied with reproducing a floral odour true to nature, but he should know how to 'vivify' it. Beside approximating as closely as possible the fragrance of a given flower, his composition should represent the entire complex of pictures arising before our inner eye while the flower is brought to mind. This complex may include, in addition to the actual fragrance of the flower, the odour of the leaves around it, or even that of its calyx or stalk. A cool fresh note can be reminiscent of dewdrops, while a delicately woody or mossy shade may suggest a forest. These accompanying odour shades can imply an environment or a background capable of more vividly setting off the flower visualized. It may be necessary at times to overemphasize some components of the floral complex at the expense of others for optimum concurrence with the odour image concerned. The violet, for example, usually smells sweeter, the rose fresher, and the narcissus used to smell much more of 'chemicals' and less appealingly than the corresponding floral perfumes must smell so as not to disappoint us.

Lilac exhales a predominantly green odour during the cool humid hours of the morning, while a note suggesting a mixture of heliotropin with a trace of phenylethyl alcohol is distinctly perceptible on dry sunny days. Lilac in full bloom and close to withering frequently betrays with unpleasant distinctness the presence of indole. Certainly none of these individual odour stages, if reproduced true to nature in a perfume, would be regarded as a good or even a natural lilac fragrance. The perfumer must make at least one compromise in order to obtain such a fragrance. As can be seen, the perfumer cannot fully agree with Plato who defines art as 'an imitation of reality'. It is imagination which plays a predominant part in composing floral perfumes where a standardized or idealized bouquet is to be composed with a natural flower motif. Here, the perfumer can either feel called upon to amplify or to accentuate a fragrance which, in its natural form, is faint or scarcely typical, as is done, for example, in hay or amber perfumes; or he can modify and convert into perfumes even obtrusive odours which, in their natural form, are not entirely pleasant, such as those of Russian leather, Pogostemon patchouli or Tonkin musk, by combination with refreshing, powdery, flowery, or basic complexes. In either case, it will be up to the perfumer to choose the correct way towards his end.

In former times, every perfume had to be flowery, and compositions without jasmine and rose were almost unthinkable. Present-day fashions prefer racy types with strong emphasis on character; they are far from limiting themselves to sweet, soft, and unobtrusive effects. Perfumes should, however, be of natural tonality, and synthesis should not predominate. While perfumers in former times were thrown almost exclusively upon natural raw material –mainly floral oils – in bouqueting in accordance with these demands, synthetic odorants with their clear, typical notes are the predominant shading materials in present-day perfumery. Care should be taken in each instance, however, not to obscure prevalence as a guiding motif of the natural odorant or complex selected, which as a rule is indicated also by the name of the perfume concerned. The perfumer has complete freedom, on the other hand, in purely fantasy perfumes as long as he conforms to the fundamental requirement that his composition should display a pronounced odour character which is perceptible throughout each phase of the odour sequence and will remain distinctly prevalent after the topnote has subtilized and the perfume begins to fade away. Imagination always needs some suggestion from the outside to become creative, the formation of clear, sharply defined images being a necessary prerequisite. Only factual experiences consciously or unconsciously perceived by our senses are capable of impressing the mind in such a way that it will be able to produce images independent of nature, purely individual and hence original, i.e., visions.

Surprisingly enough, the impression which triggers the image, and the image so produced or its expression, need not necessarily be within the domain of one and the same sense organ. An olfactory perception, for example, can produce an optical image, such as green odour, bright odour, etc., or it can be associated with an imaginary feeling of touch or temperature. This is exemplified by the description of odours as sultry, stinging, or heavy. Causes and effects can be interchanged here, and the relations between the senses can vary. The sensitivity, the type, and the intensity of the reactions are highly individual. A balsamic odour may produce a certain more or less clearly defined taste image in some, call to mind a melancholy tune or a minor chord in others, or bring forth an idea of sultriness and heaviness.

A musician presented with both a lily-of-the-valley and an amber perfume and asked to associate one with Mozart and the other with Chopin will scarcely hesitate. He will associate the sweetly delicate fragrance of lily-of-the-valley with Mozart, and the sensuous odour of amber with Chopin. Similarly, perfume designations affecting the senses so that their reaction produces a sensation which corresponds to the perfume's effect will doubtless enhance the latter. This effect will be all the more powerful where the name of the perfume is capable of evoking a mood whose imaginations affect several senses.

It should be recalled in this connection that the art of perfumery – like every art – has its origin in the erotic and magic or mystical fields, and that even we are largely influenced by these psychic forces that are frequently dormant in the subconscious mind of modern man. When they are roused by a word, and by the image corresponding thereto, the receptivity in respect of the fragrance will reach utmost intensity. It can be said in conclusion that the name of a fantasy perfume has a substantial share in its effect and in its success, if it produces sensual images, and hence moods, which harmonize with the perfume's odour effect. Classical examples of such designations are *Nuit de Noël, Soir de Paris, Printemps de Paris, Duke of Kent, Après Minuit, Fruit Vert, Crêpe de Chine* and *Forêt Vierge*.

It is a beautiful and pleasant belief widely shared by the general public that a great emotional experience or profound mood suggested by the name of a perfume has induced a perfumer to create his work of art. As a matter of fact, however, even the greatest masterpieces in the perfumistic field owe their existence to other, more concrete impulses. Many of these are based on very characteristic and interesting natural and – even more frequently – new synthetic odorants or odorant complexes. These are used as foundations and individualistically combined with other components in such a way that the particular effect that has inspired the perfumer is amplified or enhanced by contrast.

Let it be repeated: It is the perfumer's personal feeling which makes all the difference. While his expert knowledge and olfactory memory make him capable of composing a formula harmoniously, it is his sensitivity, his imagination, and sometimes his sense of humour, his desire to prompt spontaneous interest and pleasure in others, and his love for his work, which are more sure to allow him to please others than can any formula.

What harmonics is to the composer, the technique of composition is to the perfumer; he combines topnotes, core odours, fonds and fixatives into perfect symphonies of fragrance.'

A few examples are given below

Topnotes
acetophenone
benzaldehyde
menthanyl acetate
Brazilian rosewood oil
mandarin oil
benzyl cinnamate
coriander oil
dimethylbenzyl carbinol
petit grain oil, Paraguay
p-cresyl isobutyrate
eucalyptus oil
lavender oil
bergamot oil
dimethyl acetophenone
anise oil
peppermint oil
isobutyl ester
oil of thyme, red
hyacinth absol
lemon grass oil

Core odours
cinnamyl acetate
dill oil
heliotropin
violet oil absol
wild thyme oil
amyl benzoate
calamus oil
phenylethyl isobutyrate
verbena oil
cinnamon-leaf oil
myrrh extract
rosemary oil
geranium oil
citronellyl benzoate

ambrette seed oil
celery-seed oil
ginger-grass oil
rose absol
anise alcohol
neroli bigarade

Fonds and fixatives
angelica-root oil
birch-blossom oil
civet absol
iris extract
jasmine chassis
musk ambrette
musk ketone
tarragon oil
tonka extract
aceteugenol
benzoin
costus oil
ethyl vanillin
Ambrofix N
oakmoss extract
sandalwood oil Mysore
isobutyl quinoline
muscarine
Phenomuscol
vetiver oil Bourbon

Colognes and toilet waters

These are diluted perfumes. They refresh, relax, cool and disinfect. Anoldus Villanovis, 1235–1312, first made scented waters on an alcoholic base. Later on a number of fragrant waters became known, including *Eau de senteur, Eau d'ange* and *Eau d'or*. Particularly famous was the *Hungary Water* or *Eau de la Reine de Hongrie*, first introduced by Elizabeth, Queen of Hungary, in the fourteenth century. The recipe is supposed to have been developed by a hermit. An old version gives it as follows:

750 g fresh rosemary tops in full bloom soaked in 5 litres of wine spirits for four days and then distilled.

The queen, it is said, because she used it regularly as a cosmetic, was still so beautiful at the age of seventy-two that the King of Poland proposed to her.

The best known scented water is *Eau de Cologne*. It was invented by an Italian immigrant to Germany in the seventeenth century and became considered in the following century a miracle water: it was administered internally and externally, for health and as a perfume. Two names play an important part in the history of colognes, Johann Maria Farrina and Paul de Feminis. As was the case with similar waters in those days, their colognes were looked upon mainly as medicine.

The name cologne became a general conception for all scented waters. Besides *Eau de Cologne* which took its name from the city of Cologne on the river Rhine, lavender water and verbena water *Eau de Verveine,* became popular.

The purity of the alcohol and the length of storage time are of importance to the quality of colognes. Long storage develops a harmonious, full fragrance. Essential oils and chemical supplements are added to colognes depending on the bouquet desired.

Colognes are stored in glass or stone containers to mature and during this time they undergo certain changes due to room temperature. They are mixed and stirred until ready for use.

Generally the fragrance of a cologne or toilet water evaporates more quickly than that of a perfume, although certain ingredients are added to lengthen their effect. We find the least concentration of the fragrance, in colognes, then *Eau de toilette, Eau de parfum* and the highest in perfume. Cream sachets are of greater tenacity than alcohol-based fragrances and therefore are suitable for women with a dry and poorly-circulated skin.

PERFUMES

Perfumes are a solution of perfume oils with pure ethyl alcohol. This alcohol has to be of excellent quality with no specific odour. The fragrant oils are the expensive part of the perfume and give it longer tenacity. As the French perfumes contain the highest percentage of fragrant oils, their prices are justified.

The centre of perfumery is Grasse near Nice in Southern France. Here the most famous fragrances are composed and find their way all over the world.

Many of the traditional recipes have been changed and refined so that their original formula can hardly be recognized and only the name remains. New, exciting fragrances are always being created by the perfumers; to come across them for the first time is like a culinary experience.

Perfuming of cosmetic products

Present day sales psychology has proven that the success of a cosmetic product in the market depends greatly upon its packing and odour. The consumer is attracted by these two factors, appealing to the senses of sight and smell. Although a woman might be acquainted with the fact that the unperfumed product is generally non-irritating, she prefers her cosmetics to be scented. For this reason, the perfume industry has developed a number of perfume compositions that agree with different skin types (crematest perfume oils).

Helmut Fuehrer, Dragoco, Holzminden, Germany, in his brochures entitled *Up-to-date Dosing of Perfume Oils in Perfumery Goods and Cosmetics* and *Up-to-date Ways of Perfuming Aerosol Products*, advises as follows: The question is frequently raised as to whether or not a given cosmetic preparation has been sufficiently perfumed. Practical experience is a necessary prerequisite in determining adequate dosage.

Fragrances of appealingly-perfumed toilet waters and cosmetic products are of substantial importance to modern daily life. Not only do they prompt sales and consumption, but they are decisive also as regards consumer acceptance. Hence producers of perfumery goods and cosmetics have ample reason to make every effort with a view to ensuring pleasant fragrance and adequate dosage of perfumes in the finished products they put on the market. Discrete and effective camouflage of specific odours of raw materials is a major consideration.

PERFUMES

Toilet waters containing ethyl alcohol extracts, or perfumes, should, as a rule, contain 15 to 20 per cent of perfume oil (including such infusions as amber, ambropur, musk, civet, castoreum, etc.), which should be made up to 100 per cent with highly concentrated ethyl alcohol (spiritus vini, approx. 95 per cent) of neutral odour. Mixtures should be stirred well. Storage periods of two or three months will enhance the perfumistic quality of the final product.

Eaux de parfum (*eaux d'extrait*) display the same odours as the corresponding extraits (perfumes), but at a weaker concentration. 7 to 10 per cent of perfume oil (including infusions), and about 0.5 to 1.2 per cent of isopropyl myristate, for example, are made up to 100 per cent with highly concentrated ethyl alcohol of about 95 per cent. A finished product is thereby obtained which, while less odorous, is preferred by many consumers on account of its favourable price. Additions of 0.5 to 1.2 per cent of isopropyl myristate can be made, if desired. They will cause a film to be formed on the skin or on the inside of garments to which the perfume has been applied, so that the fragrance will persist longer. Isopropyl myristate can be added also to extraits (perfumes), but such additions must be preceded by solubility tests in that larger perfume components are used in this application.

Eau de toilette should contain about 2.5 to 7 per cent of perfume oil and, of course, additions must be determined in dependence on the odour intensity of the perfume concentrate used. The product is then made up to about 85 per cent by volume with distilled water and 95 per cent ethyl alcohol.

Eau de cologne should be adequately perfumed with 2 to 4 per cent of perfume oil; it should contain 75 to 80 per cent of ethyl alcohol – based on pure alcohol – and should be made up to 100 per cent with distilled water.

Cologne water (classic *eau de cologne*) usually contains 2 to 5 per cent of perfume oil (a mixture of citrus oils, such as bergamot, lemon, orange, lime, and citron oils as well as oils of neroli, lavender, rosemary, petitgrain and some rose and jasmine oils, etc.); it should contain 75 to 85 per cent of pure ethyl alcohol and the rest should be distilled water.

Preferably suited for the purpose on account of constant quality and favourable price are RCO Bergamot Oil, RCO Bergamot Oil tsqfr., RCO

Lemon Oil, RCO Lemon Oil tsqfr., and RCO Bulgarian rose oil (RCO – aliphatic acyl radical).

Lotions or cleansing *Eaux de cologne* should contain readily soluble perfume oils; essential oils free of terpene, such as RCO Bergamot Oil tsqr. or RCO Lemon Oil tsqfr., should be used in the perfume compositions. The dosage should be determined by the strength of the ethyl alcohol used, i.e., in dependence on the odour intensity of the perfume oil. 0.8 to 1.2 per cent of perfume oil are generally added to a finished product in dependence on its alcohol content of about 30 to 40 per cent by volume.

Lavender water (*eau de lavande*) should contain about 3 to 4 per cent of perfume oil and ethyl alcohol of at least 75 to 80 per cent by volume. Preparations containing ethyl alcohol, such as hair lotions, pre- and after-shave lotions, or skin tonic water, should be perfumed at a rate of 0.5 to 0.8 per cent, depending on the strength of the alcohol.

If these products are made with isopropanol (isopropyl alcohol), it will be well to conceal or to improve its specific odour (isopropyl alcohol has a very pungent odour) by adding 0/018651 Isodorant or 0/028540 Isodoryl.

Also, the perfume component can be increased up to 0.8 to 1.2 per cent. Creams and liquid emulsions should be perfumed for discrete but easily discernible immediate odour effect and aftersmell. In dependence on the formulation employed, the raw materials used, most of which have specific odours, cause some concern to the perfumer. Perfumes must be selected so as to conceal specific odours effectively. While the immediate odour effect should not be too faint, the perfume should not be too obtrusive after the preparation has been applied. Crematest perfume oils, which have been clinically tested for skin tolerance, should be used here with a view to avoiding irritation of the skin by the perfume oil. The use of these tested Crematest perfume oils offers a high degree of safety to the producer of cosmetics. Apart from many possible applications in the field of skin cosmetics, Crematest perfume oils can be recommended also for use in preparations for baby care. For full display of these Crematest perfumes – which are available in a wide range of clinically tested odour compositions – in skin cosmetics, additions of 0.5 to 1.0 per cent, depending on type of emulsion and anticipated end use, usually suffice to provide strong fragrance.

VANISHING CREAMS AND FACE CREAMS

Where the raw materials used have no distinct specific odour, 0.3 per cent of perfume oil represents the lowest limit for the desired odour effect. These creams are usually based on stearin or self-emulsifiers and require less perfume than do greasy creams (skin foods, etc.), in which the fragrance is somewhat diminished by the specific odour of the raw materials used. The perfume dosage can be increased to 0.5 per cent in vanishing creams and face creams.

Skin foods and cold creams containing large amounts of oil or fat need more perfume oil. Doses of 0.5 to 0.8 per cent are advisable. 0.3 to 0.4 per cent of perfume oil are generally added to cleansing cream.

All liquid emulsions, no matter whether they are of the oil-in-water or water-in-oil type, i.e., cleansing emulsions, face milk, hand and body lotions, and antiperspirant creams, which contain large amounts of water, require about 0.3 to 0.5 per cent of perfume, and additions of up to 1 per cent are permissible.

Lipsticks, the composition of which makes for a strong fatty odour, require perfume additions of about 1 per cent for effective camouflage.

Cream perfume is usually scented with 2 to 3 per cent of radiating perfume oils. It contains virtually neutral emulsifiers, about 60 per cent of distilled water, and approximately 32 per cent of 95 per cent ethyl alcohol. Solid cream perfume calls for 10 to 12 per cent of perfume oil.

Shampoos (based on soap) are perfumed at a rate of 0.5 to 1.2 per cent, and the successfully tested Shampootest perfume oils should be used in this application. Shampoo bases must not, of course, irritate the mucous membranes of the eyes. The amount of perfume oil to be used in bath foams and baby shampoos naturally depends on the type of fat employed. Fragrant bath foams should contain 3 to 5 per cent of perfume oil. Satisfactory odour effects can be obtained with additions of 0.5 per cent in shampoos based on detergents. 1.0 to 1.2 per cent of perfume will suffice in foaming shaving creams in view of the large amounts of soap contained therein. 0.5 per cent of perfume oil is usually required in nonfoaming shaving creams to be applied without a brush.

1.5 to 2.5 per cent are generally used in bath salts, depending on type of perfumes used. The following perfume dosage has been successfully tried out in the production of powder.

In baby powder the perfume component should not exceed 0.3 per cent (Crematest perfume oils); 0.5 to 0.75 per cent can be used in face powder and talcum powder; large doses of 0.8 to 1.2 per cent can be included in foot powder.

Sun oils and sunscreen creams are perfumed at a rate of 0.3 to 0.7 per cent (or even up to 1 per cent in individual instances), and Crematest perfume oils should be given preference with a view to skin tolerance.

Hair creams, hair conditioners, and hairsetting creams are generally perfumed with 0.5 to 1.2 per cent additions of perfume oil.

Doses of 0.5 to 0.75 will suffice in brillantine (solid or liquid) and hair oils, skin oils, skin tonicizing oils, and massage oils should contain 0.3 to 0.5 per cent, or even higher percentages of perfume oil, depending on specific odour; the use of Crematest perfume oils is advisable here.

In toothpastes the dosage generally amounts to about 1 per cent, depending on the flavour intensity of the aromatic oil.

Mouthwashes are flavoured at the rate of 2 per cent and higher.

Perfuming is, of course, of major importance in aerosol products. In aerosol perfumes, *eaux de toilette,* and *eaux de cologne*, the perfume oil is the sole active component, whereas spray deodorants and space deodorizers contain additional main active components.

The same applies to aerosol spray deodorants and hair lacquers. Ordinary toilet soaps usually contain perfume oil components in the amount of 0.5 per cent to 1 per cent. Other toilet soaps include 1 to 1.5 per cent of soap perfume oil.

Higher demands are, of course, made on luxury toilet soaps by the consumer nowadays, some of which concern additions of dermophilous fats and intense, persistent scents which must be perceptible throughout the time of use. While the desired results are obtainable with perfume oil additions of between 2 and 3 per cent, the incorporation of larger doses presents difficulties and requires adequate experience. The dosages given for the perfuming of individual products are the result of practical experience and are

intended as general directives for suitable experimentation by the processing industry. There will, of course, be variations due to the odour intensity of the perfume oils used, and larger or lesser amounts of perfume oil will be required as the case may be. In composing perfume oils for desired odour effects it should, of course, be kept in mind that mildly flowery odour notes will radiate less intensively in the finished products than, say, full spicy to powdery odour accents.

Tests made for the purpose of determining whether a given finished product has been sufficiently perfumed should be based on varied dosage in order to be able to determine the exact concentration required for optimum odour effect. Smelling tests of odour samples should be made in odourless rooms by several persons, including consumers. Consumer tests are of decisive importance. Conclusive odour tests – particularly in the case of alcoholic preparations – should be postponed until the products have been stored for adequate periods (three to four weeks), to allow sufficient time for the perfume to ripen. In addition, proof must be obtained that the perfume is compatible with the finished product.

There is a surprising number of trade-marked products which cannot do without perfumes. Many a branded article owes its popularity in no small measure to some specific odour. The extent to which the sales appeal of any given brand is affected by its odour is well known, and hence the requirements perfumes have to fulfill are becoming more and more exacting. Fragrant articles sell better, and this applies not only to soaps, cosmetics, and perfumeries, but also to many aerosol products, which are becoming increasingly popular.

Odours are capable of creating likes and dislikes, as can everything in our environment. Hence perfumes and their precise dosage are of major importance also to the sales success of aerosol products. Aerosol products, as viewed from the perfumisitic angle, can be divided into two main categories:

Group one includes products where perfumes, while ranking among auxiliary constituents, are of considerable importance in that they are designed to mask unpleasant odours of industrial ingredients in accordance with market requirements, i.e. they are to exert a camouflaging or compensating effect. It frequently happens that the chemico technical industry requests masking perfume oils for aerosols to be added to malodorous end products for complete odour neutralization. The final product is thus expected to be odourless. The odorant industry is, however, unable to comply with such requests.

It is a known fact that there are no positive or negative odour complexes which will finally cancel out, yielding zero as a final result.

Group two includes aerosol perfume (extrait), aerosol *eau de toilette*, aerosol *eau de cologne*, aerosol room sprays and body deodorant sprays, hair lacquer (aerosol base), shaving foam (aerosol base), sunscreen aerosols, etc. While perfumes are the sole components in the case of the first three preparations, they rank among the principal active ingredients of the solution of active substances in the case of the others.

Perfuming and odour camouflaging present numerous problems in connection with the various aerosols. Attention must be paid not only to possible chemical and physical reactions with other active ingredients, but also to the composition of the propellant used. The composition of active solutions and the type and amount of the propellant used have a major bearing on final results. As is generally known, a very volatile topnote is first perceived in testing perfume complexes on the skin or on test strips. The secondary and final, more or less continuous, odour accord largely depends on the varying volatility of the individual odour components. The situation is different in the case of aerosol sprays in that the less volatile ingredients are sprayed along with the highly volatile ones (topnote), and the entire odour complex is perceived all at once. The individual odour components do not succeed one another as usual, and hence the odour impression seems changed as a sweet, sultry fragrance is perceived immediately.

The odorant industry contributes a substantial share in the perfuming of aerosols by developing new perfume-oil compositions, which are subjected to prolonged storage tests for aerosol resistance. Major producers of perfumeries and aerosols are therefore taking advantage of the perfumistic and aerosol experience gathered by the manufacturers of odorants with a view to securing specific odour complexes from the wealth of aerosol-resistant perfume-oil compositions available.

The perfume oil and its fragrant radiation play a predominant part in aerosol body deodorant sprays. These products are designed to scent their users with a crisp smell of cleanliness. Bactericidal substances with their slightly phenolic odour sequence must be efficiently masked by the perfume oils, which are added in proportions of 1.0 to 2.0 per cent calculated on the active substance.

The perfuming of antiperspirant aerosols is a difficult proposition. These are either aqueous sprays containing dissolved aluminium salts, such as aluminium hydroxychloride, or anhydrous aerosols containing Rehydrol ASC, an aluminiumhydroxy-chloride-propylene glycol complex soluble in alcohol. Only very few perfume compositions are sufficiently stable in these media.

No difficulties are presented by the production of non-alcoholic dry deodorants and of personal sprays of similar composition, thanks to the availability of clinically tested Crematest perfume oils which are very well tolerated by the skin. The use of these successfully tested Crematest perfume oils gives the cosmetics producer a high measure of safety. Fatty acid esters and fatty alcohols are used as solvents.

PART II
PRACTICE

The cosmetic institute

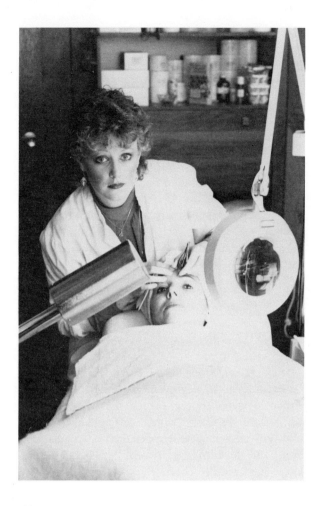

Contents
Planning and recording   Retailing cosmetics
Conditions

Before opening an institute, and starting to work on your own, it is an advantage to obtain practical and business experience to inspire self-confidence. A background in sales will help you to deal with clients, for successful selling is not a gift but an acquired ability. Never underestimate the responsibilities entailed in running your own business. A knowledge of bookkeeping, and management skills are prerequisites. Legal advice, information regarding insurances and government regulations, and assistance in advertising and accounting can prevent mistakes and many unpleasant occurrences.

PLANNING AND RECORDING

Set up a working plan so that no time is wasted, particularly if you have employees or an assistant. The operation will then run smoothly and appointments can be kept punctually, extending to the client an atmosphere of ease. She will not feel rushed, and will realize she is being dealt with individually and competently. Keep a card for each customer recording the following at her first visit:

Name _____
Address _____
Tel. No. _____
Profession _____
Skin Type _____ Tonus _____
Oil Content _____ Sensitivity _____
Turgor _____ Circulation _____
Skin Texture _____
Thick – Thin – Normal _____ Skin Marks ___
General and Special Remarks _____
Pores _____
Body Build _____

Also note each treatment as follows:

Treatments
(Quoting preparations used)

Date, Cleanse, Massage, Mask, Pack etc., Extra
specialized, Make-up

This chart gives you the opportunity of getting all the items necessary for her treatment ready in advance. By showing such personal interest, you will increase her confidence in your abilities. Attach to her card a list of any cosmetics she buys from you; enter the date of purchase so that you can remind her to renew her product before she runs out of it. She will appreciate your way of looking after her.

If you are employed and issue a bill for the cashier list all extra services rendered for your client, to check them out herself. Do not forget to discuss with her any addition to the treatment, informing her of the reason, benefit and cost, so that she may choose whether she wants it or not. The sale of cosmetics for use at home should take place as a result of skin analysis, treatment and recommendation.

RETAILING COSMETICS

Retailing cosmetics to any great extent, or setting up a boutique, requires capital. If you lack sufficient funds start out with a limited stock; a selection catering to the most common skin types and conforming to your treatments, will be adequate for some time. You will soon get to know your clientele, enabling you to have your supplies adjusted to their needs and requirements. For make-up choose the most popular shades. It is not advisable to over-stock, but on the other hand you must not run short, and be unable to fulfull your client's wishes. A minimal initial stock will grow gradually and automatically with the demand.

CONDITIONS

The treatment booth in the cosmetic institute must be light, friendly, airy, properly heated, have a hot and cold water supply and enough space for the aesthetician to work. It must certainly also comply with government health and sanitation regulations. Walls and floors must be washable and thus easy to keep hygienically clean. The booth should be soundproofed so that outside noises penetrate as little as possible, and do not interfere with the quiet, harmonious atmosphere needed to relax the customer so that she may fully benefit from her treatment. All this adds to the success of an aesthetician's endeavours.

Decor

Choose gentle, comforting colours for the decor of the room, preferably pastel shades, in only one tone or varying gradations. Your choice extends a personal touch, creating certain special surroundings. The ceiling should be kept white. Colours and in particular patterns must be avoided. The client will be looking up while resting in her chair and to be confronted by colour or ornaments over any length of time is irritating. Keep your booth tidy, neatly arranged and serviceable to show efficiency.

Illumination

This should create a warm environment in which the client feels reposed. Indirect lighting, pink or yellow bulbs, emit a candle-like softness without making the room dark. The aesthetician's work lamp must, of course, be bright. This light source is limited to one area and lit only when necessary during the treatment. It is switched off immediately if no longer required. Have bulbs attached to both sides or around a mirror, never above only, as headlights shade features unfavourably, spoiling your achievement.

Equipment

Have plenty of small towels available for compresses, and terry-cloth or washable blankets to cover your client for comfort. Washable head bands, scarves or caps to protect her hair from becoming greasy or wet, are an essential part of your equipment. Containers to dispose of used towels and waste should be close within reach to prevent the aesthetician from moving around and disturbing her client. A service trolley near the chair should also be part of the booth's furnishings. Cosmetics, bowls, cotton wool, sponges, tissue, disinfectant, comedone extractor, tweezers, small and large brushes (for application of masks, packs, lipstick, powder, etc.), spatualae, make-up tray and other items for a treatment should be accessible on the trolley.

An adjustable, sturdy stool should be provided for the aesthetician to prevent her from having to lean over and developing back aches or tired feet. Otherwise she is not able to carry out lengthy or successive treatments.

The reclining chair for the client is the centrepiece of the treatment booth. It must be anatomically appropriate and comfortable, simultaneously allowing the aesthetician to work without strain. It should be of a solidly constructed quality with convenient arm-rests. A relaxed, calm client is the first prerequisite for a good, successful facial treatment. As it requires an expensive initial investment the chair should be versatile enough for flexible use. It may be fitted for an addition of service to the neck, *décolleté*, back and body. For universal adaption the foot-piece must be moveable for pedicures and the chair must be able to flatten out for waxing or massage.

A magnifying light should be one of the standard fixtures, unless a lamp and magnifying glasses are preferred. They enable the aesthetician to obtain a precise impression of the complexion, assist in comedones or milia removal, shape eyebrows and perform many other treatments.

A woodlamp, a black light special hand magnifier, indicates oily and dry areas. Skin testers reflect an enlarged picture from a negative taken from the skin surface. They will determine the pH or pigmentation as well. There are a number of apparatuses that go hand-in-hand with the manual treatment, not only those specialized for the face but others for the entire body. A vapozone or steamer softens the tissues like a compress, prepares for the removal of impurities and for specialized procedures. It stimulates, opens pores and hydrates. Volatile ingredients may be added so that they are applied to the skin together with the steam. Through the presence of ozone, the vapozone also disinfects. It is often an asset in back treatments.

Other items The cosmetic institute should also contain a double boiler or wax melter for depilatory and paraffin wax. A fridge is useful to store fresh fruit juices, infusions or cosmetics that are susceptible to spoiling. Electrophoresis and an apparatus for muscle exercise are valuable additions to the institute's equipment. They can be employed in combination to combat cellulite. Sometimes battery-run apparatuses are preferred because of an aversion to electrical appliances or electricity on the part of either the client or the aesthetician.

Sprayers that apply liquids directly to the face are hygienic because they do not come in touch with the hands. In the long run they will prove more economical than pouring from a bottle, which gives reduced control.

Treatments

By providing vacuum massage in a cosmetic institute, a local reduction of fatty tissue can be obtained and the cells stimulated. With regard to ultra-violet or infra-red light, eletrophoresis, high frequency or vibrator equipment, refer to the physics chapter.

Sanitizers or sterilizers are discussed under 'Hygiene'.

For the entire body iozone baths, saunas, airstream/ underwater massage, body massage, shiatsu, acu-pressure massage, yoga and other treatments can be made available. These should preferably be carried out with the co-operation of a professional masseur, educated in the different fields. The aesthetician is not everywhere recognized to qualify for body care including these subjects.

If you wish to introduce epilation, it also requires a specialized knowledge and training in electrology. With all appliances it is advisable to undergo instruction as offered by the manufacturer as there are constant changes and modernizations.

To set up your manicure table you must have an assortment of the most popular nail polishes, cuticle remover, basecoat, topcoat, detergent for soaking nails, cuticle oil and hand lotion. Manicure implements include steel nail file, emery boards, cuticle pushers orange wood stick, cuticle nippers and scissors, nail brush, nail buffer, finger bowl, container for cotton wool and disinfectant. Have a manicure cushion for your work. Take fresh towels and tissue for each client. Fasten a small bag to your manicure table so that you can dispose of cotton and tissue immediately. Equipment for pedicure is dealt with in the respective training manual.

From time to time you should arrange a Consultation Day to which you ask your clients to invite their friends. It will give potential clients an opportunity to learn about your profession, to discuss their cosmetic problems and to choose the right cosmetic preparations from the plentiful variety available.

From all other means of reaching a broader range of future clients by media advertising, a repeated ad in the women's section of the local paper has still proven the most successful.

Treatment in the cosmetic institute

Contents

FACE TREATMENTS

The outstanding service extended in the cosmetic institute is the care of the face. Hands, feet and all other parts of the body are included in the conception of the Entire Body Cosmetic, which no doubt is just as important. The face, however, requires our greatest attention. It is the most remarkable part of our appearance, and at the same time the least protected and often most sensitive skin area.

The aesthetician follows these steps in a face treatment:
>   preparation,
>   cleansing,
>   diagnosis,
>   manual massage,
>   mask or pack,
>   make-up.

The work-place is set up according to the client's record of previous appointment. All products and necessary equipment must already be on hand at the time of the customer's arrival.

Preparation

If it is the client's first visit to a cosmetic institute, tell her when she makes her appointment how much time you will require for her treatment, so that she may arrange her day accordingly. Suggest a longer period than you usually require as you are not acquainted with her skin type. Devote extra time to her, explaining the steps and counselling her regarding home care.

The client who has been to an aesthetician before knows the massage includes shoulders and *décolleté*, so she will dress appropriately. Point this out to a new client ahead of time: she might prefer to wear a two-piece outfit in order to take off the top during treatment. If she goes to the hairdresser the same day, she should be advised to make her appointment after seeing you, as head coverings or steam may derange her hairstyle.

First stages   The aesthetician helps her customer to remove dress or top and asks her to slip out of her shoes. Her jewellery is placed in her handbag (purse). Assist her to lie down, making her comfortable in the chair. Cover her with a blanket, and place a small towel along the *décolleté*. It must be renewed when damp or greasy. A scarf will protect the client's hair, a head band along the hairline holds it firmly in place. When putting this on the aesthetician should support the client's neck for comfort. Scarf and band are fastened sidewards, not at the back of the head, to avoid pressure.

A piece of plastic material or cap can replace the scarf; however, cotton feels better and is more appropriate as it can be washed properly. The aesthetician should avoid allowing the scarf and band to get wet: do not apply compresses too high over the forehead. The scarf and band are not reused; each client receives clean material.

While you prepare your client, you inquire regarding her plans for the rest of the day. They direct the treatment itself and make-up. If she has no special engagements the regular routine is followed. Otherwise the aesthetician should choose a pickup mask rather than one for the particular skin type.

To avoid reddening an already well-stimulated complexion, comedones or other blemishes are not touched unless absolutely necessary, so that no marks appear on the skin. To prevent redness and puffiness, the eyebrow hair is only tweezed if necessary. Mild preparations are used, bearing in mind that bringing out the best in the complexion should make it glow delicately.

Ask your customer the colour of the dress she will be wearing for a special occasion, and the kind of accessories. The latter might determine the shade of the nail polish, e.g. gold, silver. Advise your client how to maintain her make-up for several hours so that she will look just as fresh and attractive at the end of the occasion as she did at the beginning.

Cleansing

To start the treatment, slide the shoulder straps down the upper arm of the client until they are covered by the small towel over the *décolleté*. If striplashes are worn, hold the upper eyelid firm at the temple and remove carefully towards inner corner of the eye grasping them at the base. A cleanser is distributed with even, gliding, upward movements over *décolleté*, neck and face. The numerous agents available from different manufacturers provide something for every skin type. Dip your fingertips into lukewarm water before continuing the treatment; have a bowl of water right next to you for this purpose. Repeat the same smooth massage motions as before with wet fingertips thinning the emulsion out (cleansers are hydrophile). Wash off the emulsion with cotton starting from the *décolleté* towards the forehead. If so required take clean cotton balls and repeat. Finish cleansing with cotton containing freshener or astringent. Astringent requires moist cotton, as undiluted it would be too concentrated and would aggravate the sebaceous glands. Straight astringents are reserved to close pores of certain skin types before moisturizing or for disinfecting when terminating a treatment.

Eye make-up removal with pads or liquid is done before applying astringent or freshener. Work with light hands and hold the orbicularis at the temple.

Diagnosis

The skin diagnosis is the most difficult part of the aesthetician's task. Even though the skin has been examined conscientiously, free of cream and make-up and using all available means, errors can still occur. It is best to wait at least half an hour after cleansing before examining the complexion, to allow swelling from moisture to go down. A magnifying lamp is of great assistance in determining the skin type. Look carefully at all facial areas: you will notice how the skin differs. Give a magnifying mirror to your client so that she may judge for herself, and explain to her why and what you recommend as well as how you intend to direct your treatment. The obvious image of her complexion in the mirror will convince her.

The next steps depend upon the diagnosis. The following is established and recorded on the customer's card: kind of pores, skin colour (pigmentation); impurities (pustules, comedones, milia, etc.); abnormal hairgrowth (where); special marks, i.e. warts, freckles, pigment spots, naevi, milia, telangiectasia, scars; thickness of adipose tissue; wrinkles; bone stucture and blood circulation. By touching the skin surface gently with the fingertips you discover cysts, keratosis and skin thickness. Gliding along the lower and upper eyelid you can determine the tonus if not obvious! The skin will be loose, lids perhaps a little puffy if the tonus is reduced. Should there be no other device, a simple method to establish turgor and oil content is to press a transparent, smooth spatula against the skin for a short while, then pull it away parallel to the surface. Repeat on different parts of the face: forehead, temples, cheeks etc. On the forehead we have many sweat glands and the sebaceous glands on the nosetip produce more sebum; thus the result will of course vary. Testing an oily skin you will discover a greasy film and tiny water drops on the spatula. The drops will evaporate rapidly, leaving only the sebum. If the sweat glands are underfunctioning, few drops or none will be seen. A dry skin leaves hardly any oily film on the spatula.

To check sensitivity either glide with the spatula's edge along the inside of the arm or over the *décolleté*. First a white line is noticed which on a touchy skin turns red or even rises slightly.

The results of these tests guide the diagnosis and the choice of preparations used for treatment. Two different skin types in the face, as found in combination skin, are handled accordingly. Specialized attention can be given by choosing equivalent masks for the two varying parts.

A well-circulated complexion does not need any further stimulation during treatment. This applies to preparation and massage as well as compresses and steam. Stimulation is reserved for the pale, dull-looking skin which needs to be revived.

Manual massage

In a basic treatment the aesthetician massages after cleansing. The cream for the massage must have a good gliding capacity and is selected for the skin type. Some preparations are hard to smooth out, so that it is necessary to dip your fingers in warm water now and then during massage.

After massaging the cream is removed with warm compresses. Ask your client to lift her head and shoulders. Place a compress over her shoulders, back and neck, taking off the cream. While you apply the compress, which can be quite warm, advise her to breathe in. Blot with a tissue and cover the back of the chair with a dry, clean towel. Let the client lie down again, supporting her with your arm.

Face compress For the face compress, gather a towel at both ends, forming a loop which you place around the chin and along the cheeks so that both ends meet on the forehead. Remove cream from the face, neck and *décolleté*, using several compresses. Make sure that the skin is not greasy when you finish. Blot face with a tissue, tearing a hole in the centre for the nose so your client can breathe. Grasp tissue at chin and pull away towards forehead. Use tissue over neck and *décolleté*. The skin is always blotted after a compress or steam to remove excess dampness.

A very sensitive person might feel uncomfortable having her face closed off completely by a tissue. Dab off moisture carefully instead, avoiding covering the face. This individual should also never receive a compress on the eyes, which might have a similar effect on her.

Mask or pack

Proceed with a mask or pack. Both usually stay on for 15 minutes and are washed off with compresses. End the treatment by distributing freshener or astringent. Now you may apply moisturizer as base, foundation and make-up.

Ice cold compresses are used exclusively for a poorly-circulated skin, and may alternate with hot compresses for skin stimulation. Warm compresses are employed for all other skin types. They are calming and relaxing. Herbal extracts or infusions can be a supplement to compresses.

Steam or vapozone follows the massage. The skin is prepared for removal of impurities. Do not steam a sensitive complexion longer than 3 minutes. An oily or thick skin can easily take up to 20 minutes. Warm compresses can replace steam if necessary, but are not as effective. Vapozone is easier on the tissue than a steamer and therefore serves a particular need in the care of more vulnerable skin types. Due to the vapozone's disinfectant properties it can be applied before and after extraction of comedones, milia etc. The advantage of the steamer is that plant infusions and essential oils can be added, profiting certain skin types.

Removing impurities After the skin has been softened, the face is blotted and comedones and other impurities may be easily removed. The comedone extractor is a metal stick with a small hole at one end, which is pressed against the plugged pore. The sebum is emptied into the opening. The fingers of the left hand stretch the skin during this procedure to convey firmness and resistance. Deep comedones can be loosened with a suction cup and then extracted. The areas around the nose are more sensitive than other parts, so exert little pressure when working in these areas. Examine hairline and ears to find comedones. To extract them manually the fingertips should be covered with clean tissue. A comedone extractor makes control easier and is more hygienic. Beware of hurting the skin with your fingernails, and check that the comedone extractor has no sharp edges. Have cotton wool and disinfectant handy while you work, and use it continuously to disinfect comedone extractor and skin.

The milia needle should be well sterilized before each use. Break skin carefully over milium or pimple with yellow head. The milium is taken out with the extractor. Dab cotton ball with alcohol against lesion. Do not press with fingers to remove pimples as this brings bacteria and pus into the surrounding tissues. Milia around the eyes should not be touched; the client must be referred to a doctor.

Go over face with disinfectant or medicated astringent, followed by vapozone and/or healing pack or mask (chlorophyll, camomile). Cream-steam gives a supple texture, widening pores simultaneously. If massaged with a special preparation it can be applied immediately after cleansing; otherwise it must be used later on.

Dyeing of brows and lashes as well as depilation of facial hair is carried out before the massage. Shaping of eyebrows is done after the massage. Should there be reddening due to depilation, do not massage here; cover instead with soothing cream.

Peeling prepares for specialized facial treatment and is done immediately after cleansing. Fading of freckles and chloasma by means of phoresis is preferably carried out prior to the massage, so that as little oil as possible is on the skin. Phoresis can replace the mask for a dry, mature or seborrheic complexion. There are ampoules for the care of all skin types. The manufacturer indicates the method of use for his product.

Muscle exercising by alternating current can be done after the manual massage, possibly only on certain muscles in want of it. Use of other apparatus as mentioned in the foregoing chapters can be included in a facial treatment. Full training is essential to employ these continuously-improved appliances for best profit to face and body.

An active woman pressed for time appreciates a partial massage. Back, shoulders, arms or legs are tense. Massaging these areas is pleasantly comforting, making it possible for her to relax and collect energy within a relatively short period. Infra-red light used for five minutes preliminary to massaging will enhance the result.

Ultra-violet light is best applied to a seborrheic and acne skin at the very end of the treatment immediately before make-up. Vapozone and ultra-violet lamp, U.V./H.F. respectively, are only allowed for a very short period, if applied in one treatment together, to avoid overexposure.

Use the time while your client has the mask or pack for giving a manicure.

General points

Be helpful to your client when she gets up and dresses. Accompany her to the door without rushing, take your time for further consultation if necessary, to guarantee the outcome of your work.

Facial treatments for men are carried out on the same principles as for women, with the exception that cotton is replaced with tissue. The fine threads stick to the hair of a man's beard.

Plan your work, be organized, not to have to look for items once you start. Dispose immediately of used towels, cotton, and tissue. Do not put your fingers into cosmetics; take a clean spatula each time. Close containers to prevent evaporation or oxidation of the ingredients. Collect tools during treatment in a bowl; clean and sanitize or disinfect them immediately upon terminating your task. Your last client must find the work area just as tidy as your first.

Avoid unnecessary movement and rushing around. Do not talk continuously; it is disturbing to your customer besides giving the impression of insecurity. Needless to say, hands must be kept clean. They are washed before and in between treatments. They should not convey odour, i.e. from cigarettes or sweat, or otherwise be unaesthetic. Dress clean and appropriately. Wear no jewellery, so that hands can be kept immaculate. Be well groomed, not over-done. You are yourself your best advertisement.

Select first-rate, appropriate material for your work, which you must always carry out conscientuously to the best of your knowledge and ability. Do not touch anything not pertaining to the scope of your profession. Realize its limits. Only the most proficient aesthetician has a chance for success in the competing market.

ALTERNATIVE AESTHETICS SERVICES

Essential oils in aesthetic treatments have gained popularity in the past. They and other plant extracts represent an alternative or complement to conventional face and body care. They are favourable for the varying skin types and trouble spots. The external employ of aromatic substances is of foremost interest to the aesthetician. Properties ascribed to essential oils in aromatherapy are psychological and physio-logical, counteracting stress and fatigue.

For the skin they are moisturizing, toning, stimulating, anti-bacterial, anti-toxic, clearing, regenerating, strengthening and balancing. They contain some of the best active ingredients for physical care, besides aromatic compounds, sulphur, vitamins, enzymes, iron, phyto-hormones and others.

Essential oils are distinguised as:

Top note oils: Very volatile, stimulating – sage, lemon grass, eucalyptus.

Middle note oils: Evaporating at body temperature, medium stimulation – geranium, lavender, rosemary.

Base note oils: Slow evaporation, so-called fixatives, comforting, retaining their odour – sandalwood, ylang ylang, cypress.

Face treatments For face treatments, a total of two to three drops of one or different oils can be incorporated into the device at the nozzle of a steamer or on cotton or gauze wrapped over it. The steam passes the aromatic substance carrying it to the client's skin.

Compresses

Compresses, either hot or cold, holding essential oils are for face and body care. Any material absorbing moisture like gauze, cotton or towelling is serviceable. It is soaked in a solution of a cup of water with about six drops of essential oil. To keep the compress moist a steamer may be applied over it. Cold compresses sooth and reduce swelling.

Hot compresses containing aromatic substances are to improve circulation, increase absorption and open pores. Cover with waterproof material or place steam over it to maintain temperature.

Compresses on body parts can accompany treatments dealing with cellulite and aromatic body massage. The body is worked over with light effleurage movement utilizing essential oils as a gliding medium. It may be combined with lymph drainage or reflexology of the feet. (Please note the laws of some countries do not permit aestheticians to carry out body massages.) The oils for massage purposes can be obtained in a ready-made form or can be mixed, using mineral oil as a carrier in a relation of about six to eight drops of aromatic concentrate in 250 cm³.

The effectiveness of essential oils can be furthered with the assistance of infra-red rays originating from a lamp or electrode of a high frequency apparatus.

In a steam bath an aromatic pine oil may be useful to enhance perspiration.

Body wrapping

Body wrapping is done in different ways aimed at the elimination of tissue fluid that has collected in body parts revealing cellulite. Wrapping is to reduce the unsightliness and firm the tissue simultaneously. One of the approaches in achieving this has been a wet loose wrap of warm bandages pre-soaked in a herbal solution. The client is kept warm with blankets. It is of great importance that the client is comfortable and does not feel cold during the procedure. Another method is to massage the afflicted area gently with a slimming gel. Again, the client has to rest at ease for about 60 minutes.

For effective spot slimming, wraps of figure-shaped foam rubber compresses cover the body part. The compress is soaked in a plant extract from, for example, algae. It contains chlorophyll, carotene, vitamins and minerals. Heat is applied over the area by infra-red rays or a thermal blanket. Preparation can be carried out by a local massage prior to the wrap to increase surface temperature.

Application of warm paraffin over herbal oils improves the circulation and circumscribed cellulite and can replace wraps, to some extent.

The entire body may be anointed with extracts from angelica, lavender, lemon, thyme, arnica or algae. The client is lightly wrapped in foil and the lounge covered by an electric blanket or an infra-red light applied over her. After 30 to 60 minutes she receives cold compresses or has a shower, depending upon the consistency of the ingredients of the plant matter used. A resting period of 20 minutes follows.

Improvement of skin and cellulite depends on the client's co-operation. A sensible diet, exercises, sauna, steam bath and jacuzzi, are supportive to the institute's treatment.

The skin types and their treatment

Contents

SKIN TYPES

The first and most important part of skin care is diagnosis before treatment. This directs the cleansing, care, protection and beautification of the complexion. The decisive points are:

1 cleansing according to:
  a) skin type,
  b) sensitivity,
  c) outside influences,
  d) make-up.

2 care according to:
  a) moisture content (turgor)
  b) oil excretion,
  c) sensitivity
  d) muscle firmness (tonus)
  e) texture.

3 protection against environment factors.

4 make-up to beautify the complexion according to personality and fashion.

Following is a description and distinction of the skin types with caring advice according to their condition.

The normal skin

Normal skin has neither the disadvantages of the dry skin nor of the oily skin. The pores are fine/or medium, the blood circulation is good, the skin looks and feels firm and smooth and is rosy, or brownish in colour. The functioning of the glands is regular, with balanced moisture and oil secretion. The skin texture is neither too thick nor too thin. The skin is free of unnatural hair growth and disturbing marks.

Treatment Cleanse: hydrophile lotion or cream. Freshen: mild freshener. Massage: gliding cream. Vapozone or steam: ten minutes. Masks or packs: moisture, protein, lubricating, chlorophyll, camomile. Moisturizer or moisture cream. Any make-up can be chosen. Daytime protection over twenty: moisture cream; night: semi-fatty cream. Do not experiment with this skin type and never use regenerating or highly 'nourishing' preparations until the age of about 25. Proper functioning depends upon environmental influences and skin structure. First signs of dryness show on upper cheeks.

The task of the aesthetician is to treat this skin professionally, to postpone the natural process of aging, and to emphasize its beauty by a carefully chosen, decorative make-up.

The dry, fine skin

Dry, fine skin has no visible pores, is thin and smooth. There are no comedones. This skin type suffers from lack of moisture and oil. The complexion is pretty but sensitive to cold, sun and overheated rooms, making it feel tight. It easily shows telangiectasia and has an early tendency for wrinkles. If this skin is not taken care of the negligence revenges itself in fine lines, early crows' feet and premature aging.

Treatment Cleanse: mild soothing lotion, cleansing cream or hydrophile oil with camomile. Freshen: freshener with no alcohol contents. Massage: (omit pressure), gliding cream, camomile cream. Vapozone: five to ten minutes. Masks and packs: protein, moisture, lubricating, oatmeal, vitamin F and A avocado oil, algae extract. Moisture cream. Make-up preferably on an oily base.

For daytime care, moisturizing preparations or semi-fatty creams; night 'nourishing' cream, eye and neck cream. (Strongly perfumed products should be avoided.) This skin type needs protection against the drying effects of sun, wind and heat. Soaps and detergents may be irritating. For washing with water add water softener, witch hazel or a few drops of lemon. Do not use glycerin preparations, as these may attract and withdraw moisture.

The sensitive skin

Sensitive skin has fine pores, a generally smooth surface, thin layers and few comedones. Sometimes we find telangiectasia and sensitivity to pressure. It may be pale or have a tendency to reddish, nervous marks and skin irritations (burning sensation).

Treatment Cleanse: hydrophile oil or mild lotions preferably with camomile extract. Freshen: freshener without alcohol. Massage: W/O emulsion, low perfume contents; camomile cream (gliding massage, avoid stimulation). Vapozone: 3 minutes. Masks and packs: moisturizing, hamamelis, lubricating, camomile, soothing, kaolin. Moisture: O/W emulsion. Make-up: light and moist.

There should be no frequent changes in caring products and if so, first make a patch test in the bend of the elbow.

The sensitive skin reacts to climate, pollution, food, cosmetics, or tension. A change in environment from city to rural areas, or dry climate to moist climate, may impove its condition. In many cases the sensitivity lessens with ageing. This skin needs protection, and in winter the day moisturizer should be replaced by a light, fatty cream.

The allergic skin

Note: Before using a cream, lotion, pack or mask containing fruit or herbal extracts, it is advisable always to ask about possible allergies. Hypo-allergenic products have been tested to exclude to a great extent skin reactions. However, there still remains a chance of some skin intolerance.

Treatment Cleanse: hypo-allergenic lotion. Freshen: freshener without alcohol. Massage: un-perfumed gliding cream. Vapozone: 5 minutes. Masks and packs: hypo-allergenic products. Moisturizer: hypo-allergenic. Make-up: hypo-allergenic.

Avoid stimulation and products with plant extracts. If in doubt, make a test for tolerance. For at-home care use hypo-allergenic products. Good skin care in polluted areas and dry climates protects this skin and reduces reactions. In case of obvious irritation, consult a doctor.

The thick, large-pored skin

This skin is not sensitive and generally looks dull and uneven. Cleansing is most important to avoid formation of comedones.

Treatment Cleanse: lotion, cleansing grains, washing gels, (use facial brush). Freshen and stimulate: astringent. Massage: regenerating, stimulating creams. Vapozone or steam: 20 minutes or soften with hot compresses. Enzyme peeling. Massage: regenerating, stimulating creams. Masks and packs: fruit, honey, cream steam, clay, stimulating, moisturizing, vitamin

A. Compresses: hot and cold, sea water. Moisten: carotene lotion, moisture creams. Any make-up may be chosen.

The purpose of treatment of this skin type is to stimulate the blood circulation so that the skin can function better. For daily care use moisture and stimulating preparations.

The poorly circulated skin

This skin is generally dull, pale and needs stimulation. The texture may be medium to thick and is not sensitive.

Treatment Cleanse: hydophile oil, cream or lotion. Freshen and stimulate: astringent, witch hazel, freshener with herbal extract. Massage: herbal creams, orange cream, vitamin creams. Vapozone or steam with herb infusion: 10 to 20 minutes. Masks and packs: fruit, honey, orange cream, cream steam, stimulating, moisturizing. Moisten: O/W emulsion. Make-up to give skin a better colour. Cold water treatments at home, fresh air, exercising and sauna.

The mature skin

Tired or atrophic skin is generally pale and slack, with poor blood circulation, spots and wrinkles. Moisture (turgor) and oil are lacking. A test for skin tonus is to gently lift skin at the cheeks between two fingers, and then let go. Contrary to other skin types which smooth out immediately, the mature skin takes a long time to regain its normal shape. (The branch of study dealing with all the physical and psychological effects of aging is gerontology.)

In case of expression lines, there is little that the cosmetologist/aesthetician can do. Only the client herself can control her face. If the wrinkles are a consequence of the slackening of the muscles (reduced tonus), then the client can assist the cosmetologist's work by facial exercises.

Treatment Cleanse: cream or lotion. Freshen: freshener (herbal extract), diluted astringent. Massage: rich and regenerating creams (phyto hormones). Vapozone: 10 to 20 minutes. Masks and packs: fruit, regenerating, nourishing, carotene, egg, stimulating. Moisten: moisturizer for dry and mature skin. Make-up: on an oily base.

Now and then a series of specialized treatments are needed, with vials for regeneration and moisturizing.

In at-home care, stress moisture by day and lubrication by night.

The combination skin

Combination skin is partly oily and partly dry. The oily parts are generally chin, nose and forehead, the so-called T-zone. The upper cheeks may show enlarged pores and the dry areas may be scaly. As dryness is the dominant characteristic, the dry skin's daily care should be followed (see above). Two or three times a week, special attention should be paid to the oily parts (see below). Professional care is carried out according to the two different areas, i.e. for dry skin and for oily skin.

The oily skin (seborrhea)

Oily skin looks sallow, has poor blood circulation, large pores and uneven surface. This skin always needs a great deal of care and perseverance. It takes about a year to improve this tissue, and regular care has to be continued. There are two kinds of seborrhea, the dry: seborrhea sicca and the oily: seborrhea oleosa. A combination of the two is not uncommon. In seborrhea sicca, the oil secretion and the dead cells of the epidermis form fine, clay-like flakes, giving a misleading dry look.

In seborrhea oleosa, the skin excretes more sebum than is needed, so the face looks oily and shiny as do the scalp and hair. In both cases the stratum corneum is thicker than normal. In the ducts of the sebaceous (oil) glands, the sebum hardens causing enlarged pores and hence comedones. The head of the comedone turns dark from dust and chemical reaction (oxidation under the influence of the oxygen of the air.) The locations of the seborrhea are the scalp, chest and back (especially in the area of the vertebral column (spine) and of the sternum), as well as the face. Different factors encourage oil secretion – indigestion, lack of vitamins, illnesses of the liver, anaemia and also negligence.

The abnormal functioning of the glands may be furthered by a nervous condition, or the climate, i.e. in an industrial district where, through chemicals in the air, the skin is continuously irritated. The constitution and hormones can also influence this condition. The doctor should be consulted.

The seborrheic skin shows not only the above described symptoms but has the tendency for diseases and disorders like acne, rosacea and the seborrheic eczema. Fresh air, sun, also sunlamp are recommended, and special attention to body care. For cleansing of this skin type, use products with low alcohol content and no alkaline soaps. Otherwise it could result in a higher oil secretion through irritation.

Treatment Cleanse: with hydrophile oil with camomile, special lotions for oily skin, gels, washing grains, (use facial brush). Freshen: special lotions (e.g. with sulphur) also witch hazel and other herb extracts, (rosemary, sage). Disinfect: with witch hazel lotion or astringent. Massage: lemon cream, medicated cream. Vapozone: (ten to twenty minutes) steam with camomile, cream steam to soften skin and open pores in order to remove comedones. Compresses: hot and cold in turn in order to soften skin or apply negative galvanic current (phoresis) 3 minutes. Enzyme peeling. Masks: camomile, chlorophyll, protein, vitamin A, carotene, clay mask. An alternative in dealing with oily skin is desincrustation (deep pore cleansing) with the assistance of corresponding vials and phoresis. No preparations containing paraffin oil.

Cover spots where the comedones have been removed with azulene cream (camomile) and apply mask to the other parts of skin. 1 to 2 minutes U.V. light, following this, blue light. Use phoresis positive 5 minutes with vial for oily skin. Vapozone to disinfect.

A dark skin has a greater sebum excretion and perspires more readily. It can tolerate heat and sun better than a light complexion but is less resistant to cold temperature. The thicker epidermis (stratum spinosum and granulosum) makes it more durable, requiring not a great deal of support. The large amount of melanin present makes it harder to detect redness, irritations, impurities and imperfections. All this is of importance when dealing with it cosmetically. Removal of comedones requires utmost care and a light touch, abrasive treatments are not indicated. After injury black skin has a tendency for keloid scarring and local change in pigmentation. A build-up of skin scales may give it an ashen, grey appearance. The products used in a treatment have to be mild, enzyme peels give an excellent result, mostly it can be looked after like other skin types if not oily. Black skin seems to have a natural resistance to current and apparatus may have to be set at a higher intensity.

Make-up for the oily seborrhea use water base or powder, for the dry seborrhea, liquid water base make-up in order not to make flakes show. (Special preparations containing, e.g. sulphur.)

145

For protection in the sun – for the oily seborrhea – sun lotions, O/W emulsions (no oils) this skin type can be exposed to the sun for a short time without protection.

For protection in the sun – for the dry seborrhea, O/W emulsion. Although this skin is not very sensitive, the skin around the eyes might be exactly the opposite and should, therefore, always be treated with special care. For home care, products for oily skin should be recommended.

Hair and scalp The client must also take care of her hair and scalp, their oils and skin scales (dandruff) may affect the forehead causing impurities. Blackheads or comedones, mainly those around the nose and ears, are generally soft and can easily be removed; those on the cheek bones and forehead are flatter and the sebum is harder, thus much more difficult to be taken out. For their removal, an instrument is employed, a comedone extractor. The instrument is ideal for professional use but at home, comedones may be removed by using the finger tips with tissue. If the skin has been hurt pigment spots remain for some time, therefore, great caution must be practised.

A well balanced diet seems to be of importance for an oily skin. It should include: vegetables, fruit, fowl, dark and whole wheat bread, lean meat, salads, cooked and broiled fish. The following should be avoided: highly seasoned and smoked food, pork, chocolates, fried potatoes, fried fish, sweets, cream, nuts and white bread.

The menstrual cycle

Additionally to the foregoing skin types we must remember that the female cycle does not only express itself physically but also influences the psychic state of a woman. It reflects on the complexion with a nervous sensitive reaction and not seldom by showing impurities. During these days, the skin should have a rest, mild and not irritating preparation should be used and, in general, touched as little as possible.

Effect of the seasons

The skin is an organ of the human body that is in direct contact with its surroundings. Therefore, it is constantly affected and influenced by its environment. This concerns, in particular, the climatic changes due to the four seasons.

In spring the complexion needs regeneration. Just like the whole body is tired after the winter months, the skin is likewise. Enzyme peelings, preparations with vitamins and herbal creams help to give it a new freshness and glow.

The summer, bringing a balance of vitamins, influences favorably the complexion which effects extend into autumn (fall). Moisture treatments, O/W emulsions and moisturizing, refreshing packs are recommended.

The autumn and winter months, with little sun, make the complexion dull and pale. The skin mainly lacks vitamins, i.e. A, E, and F. After fading of the summer tan, peelings and regenerating preparations assist in keeping a smooth, healthy looking skin. During the colder months creams (W/O for regeneration and with vitamins) and ultra-violet light are recommended.

	Youth	*Middle age*
	Acne	Rosacea
Comedones	Numerous	None
Lumps and pustules	Numerous	Lumps only
Scales	Seldom	Nearly always
Telangiectasia	None	Nearly always
Scars	Always	None

Typical skin problems at different ages

ACNE VULGARIS

Acne vulgaris is one of the most frequent skin disorders. It is found especially among young people during the years of development, approximately between 13 and 18. Though acne is common there seems to be very little that can be done to deal with it effectively. But, unfortunately, its consequence might be a psychological one on the young person suffering from it, whether a girl or boy, an inferiority complex may develop that only clearing the complexion can overcome.

The treatment of an acne belongs primarily in the hands of an experienced doctor as the reasons for it are not superficial but originate in a disturbance of the body system. The location of acne is not only the face but possibly also the neck, shoulders, back and chest.

The picture of an acne skin shows at the same time all three signs of this disorder, that is, comedones, lumps, infected pimples and on top, scars. The presence of all these symptoms is typical for the course of the disorder.

The process leading to it is as follows.

Due to overproduction, sebum congests in the hair follicle; the keratosis of the skin around the pore impedes excretion to the skin surface; excess of sebum interferes with the pH balance of the acid mantle; by decomposition of sebum and environment influences a lump is formed; the lump develops into a pustule that breaks open and after healing, leaves a scar.

The scars differ in size and shape according to the foregoing pimple. If there is infection in the pustule, it can develop into an abscess which leaves an ugly mark. Acne does not have a continuous, uniform look, that means, there is not always the same amount of blemishes. For example, before and during menstruation, in general, there is a heavier outbreak. Even healthy skin might have irritations and pimples during this time, which seems to prove the part that hormones play in this phenomenon. No doubt it appears acne is influenced by the hormone level of the body during puberty.

Also, digestion and the kind of diet a peson eats counts amongst the reasons for promoting acne. Too many carbohydrates, fats and spices stimulate the activity of the sebaceous glands and have a negative influence on acne skin. Acid fruit as well as sweets are not beneficial. But this is very individual and a client should experiment him or herself. Smoking should be omitted. It is recommended to drink camomile tea in the morning and evening as it supports regulating elimination. The task of the cosmetologist would be to remove the comedones to prevent development of pimples.

Treatment

Cleanse: medicated cleanser, facial brush if no open pustules. Vapozone or herbal steam: 20 minutes – removal of comedones. No massage. Mask or pack: with vitamin A (skin protection vitamin), soothing and healing e.g. camomile, camphor. Astringent acne lotion, moisturizer and covering make-up.

A lymph drainage furthers internal cleansing of the tissues. Though acne is not infectious, during treatment it is preferable to use tissue rather than towels, to avoid spreading of bacteria. All instruments used must be well disinfected.

For home care, if there is no doctor's prescription, special products are available from different firms.

After healing, acne skin can be treated as follows:
Cleansing with preparations for oily skin
Steam or vapozone

Peeling and massage with regenerating cream
Stimulating masks or packs
Infiltration of regenerating vial
Red light
Astringent
Moisturizer
Covering make-up

Skin disorders with a similar appearance to acne vulgaris can be caused by contact with chemicals, i.e. iodine, bromide, tar and certain mineral oils. The use of cosmetics containing impurified vaseline can lead to a skin resembling acne. For these reasons alone, the client needs to be referred to a doctor.

TELANGIECTASIA – ROSACEA

Rosacea can afflict men and women in the area of the nose and cheeks. The first stage, telangiectasia, is a consequence of an obstruction in the capillaries which follows an expansion of the vessels. Generally, this is an inherited weakness of the capillaries but can also be caused by too great an exposure to sun or cold, or wrong skin care. There is nothing the cosmetologist/aesthetician can do to improve such a condition. Stimulating products must not be applied to skin parts involved but only around them. This way the surrounding tissue is strengthened. Also, no massage in these areas. The treatment is carried out according to the condition of the remaining facial skin. For the marked areas a couperose cream proves beneficial.

The second stage of the disorder is rosacea where it comes to growths in the connective tissue and around the vessels. Rosacea is an appearance of a different age than acne. While acne is a disorder of puberty, rosacea starts around menopause in women. It has to be understood that there is no exact limitation in years.

Acne may persist until the age of 30 at which time rosacea can begin. In both cases seborrhea can be one of the initial states, but other factors e.g. constitution and hormones can play a part. The diet recommended for rosacea is similar to that for acne. Stimulants such as alcohol and coffee should be avoided.

Commercial cosmetics

Brand names of cosmetics can understandably not be mentioned or recommended by the author. The choice of product line is left to the preference of the aesthetician. Manufacturers offer a variety of formulations of cosmetics, techniques and approaches to skin care.

Fundamental ingredients

Fundamental ingredients of skin care products are:

Adeps lanae (lanolin), anhydrous – natural emulsifier, moisture retaining

Allantoin – soothing, healing

Beeswax – emulsifier, protecting, surfactant (surface active agent)

Boric acid – antiseptic, fungicidal

Ceresin – protecting

Cetiol (cetyl alcohol) – emollient, stabilizer

Collagen – moisture retaining protein

Elastin – moisture retaining protein

Ester – (plant or animal) lubricating (whether soothing or stimulating depends upon the kind of extract)

Eutanol – oily component

Glycerin – emollient, humectant

Hexachlorophene – antibacterial (limited use)

Hygroplex – humectant

Kaolin – absorbent, soothing

Lecithin – antioxidant, natural emulsifier, emollient

Menthol – cooling

Mineral oil (white) – protective agent, lubricant

Paraffin wax – protecting

Petrolatum (Vaseline) – smoothness of product, softening, smoothing

Propyleneglycol – moisturizing

PCL (Purcelline oil, synthetic) – lubricant, protecting

Rice starch – emollient, absorbent, protecting, soothing

Resorcinol – antiseptic

Royal Jelly (protein, carbohydrates) – caring

Salicylic acid – antiseptic, antikeratotic

Stearic acid – (fatty acid) consistency

Sorbitol – humectant, smoothing

Sulphur – antiseptic, healing

Titanium dioxide – opacifier, white pigment

Uric acid – humectant

Zinc oxide – protective, astringent, antiseptic

NMF – Natural Moisture Factor, a compound to improve storage of peripheral moisture in the skin, a natural or synthetic hygroscopic substance, a humectant.

Modern products are based on compositions of compounds formulated and tested by chemical and pharmaceutical companies. They receive their name from the producer and ingredients.

For plant extracts and further components reference is made to the chapters dealing with herbs and chemistry.

Face massage

Contents
Face massage   Alternative face massage
Lymph drainage massage

FACE MASSAGE

The facial massage represents a significant part of a face treatment. Although there are various apparatus available, they can never substitute the radiation of human hands. Only a manual massage can create a personal contact with the client, the calming, comforting sensation cannot be achieved otherwise. The valuable effects of an apparatus lie on a different base.

A manual massage counts amongst the indispensable steps in a face treatment together with cleansing, a mask or pack. Exceptions are, if the client has: a heart condition, high blood pressure, is running a temperature or an oedema of any kind. In case of telangiectasia, the afflicted area is spared, also no manipulations on pustular acne. Following cosmetic surgery it is for the doctor to decide when to start complete skin care again. (Reference: 'What to know about aesthetic surgery' as a general guide.)

The skin benefits from the massage by becoming soft and pliable, blood flow is activated allowing an improved supply to the cells, muscle fibres are strengthened and nerves soothed. Penetration of substance into the membrane's openings is furthered and skin cells are loosened.

The prerequisite to carrying out a knowledgeable, successful massage is the study of anatomy and physiology of the skin as well as of the facial muscles and their arrangement.

In practice the aesthetician arrives at how she wishes to arrange the variation of movements and which she considers of value in a specific case. It is a personal conception and matter of experience.

Conditions

During massage the client must rest comfortably to support complete relaxation. The lounge is adjusted and the client covered with a blanket to keep her from getting cool.

The aesthetician must have warm, clean hands and wear no jewellery.

A number of massage methods have been developed, distinguishing each other more or less by the sequence of the movements.

1 Friction – rubbing movement
2 Petrissage – kneading movement
3 Tapotement – tapping movement
4 Effleurage – stroking movement
5 Vibration – shaking movement

Massage movements must not be hasty but flow naturally one into another without abrupt interruptions or overexpanding the skin tissue. After the last step, hands should slide off slowly and smoothly.

A massage is carried out with a cream, using a cold cream for gliding effect or suited to the skin type. Before starting, cream is distributed over shoulders, neck and face, to allow gentle, even motions.

An example of a basic face massage follows:

Part one

1 Massage with both hands starting at the outer shoulder blades, describing three circles on the back. The third time, ring and middle finger go up the cervical vertebrae to the base of head. Glide back over shoulders with pressure. (This serves to relax the client.)

2 Hands at both sides of upper jaw, left hand stays in position, the right hand glides along the chin to meet the left. Stroke softly in turn from chin to *décolleté* (careful, no pressure on thyroid gland). Effleurage ultimately with both hands over *décolleté* and neck, until hands reach top of jaw, left and right.

3 Both hands circle with ring and middle finger from jaw top to centre of chin and back three times.

4 Left hand stays at left ear, right hand goes with small circles along chin to join left hand. Tapotement in turn with both hands (ring and middle finger), along chin from left to right and vice versa – several times.

5 Petrissage with thumb and forefinger, grasping the skin along mandible, alternately with both hands from left to right and reverse.

6 Vibrate with thumb and forefinger from centre of chin to upper jawbone. With right hand to right, left hand to left (three times). The power to perform the vibration originates from the pectoralis. Whilst the underarm remains stiff, the vibration is transferred to the face.

Comforting Movement

Part I Step 1

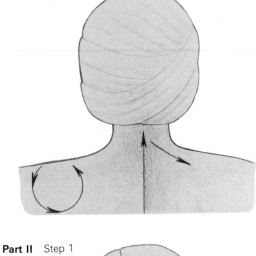

Step 2

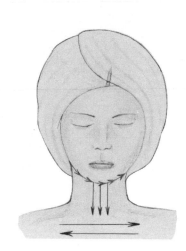

Part II Step 1

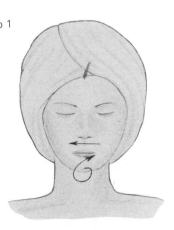

Steps 2 and 3

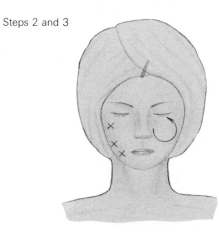

Part III Step 1

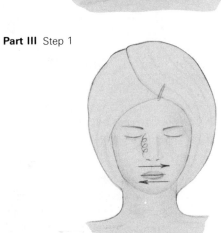

Steps 2 and 3

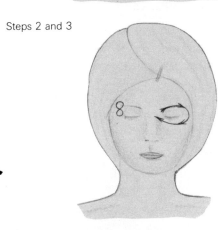

Step 4 – 'half-moons'

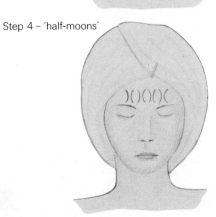

comforting movement

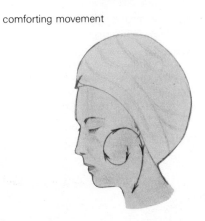

Part two

1 One and a half circles under chin, with left and right hand in turn (middle finger), procede with effleurage beneath and above lips.

2 Effleurage and massage in circles, nose-lip line right and left simultaneously, glide into massaging cheeks, first in small sections in circles, gradually increasing until complete cheek is covered.

3 Tap together, left and right, three times on two places of lower cheek and on zygomatic.

4 Tap on same places rhythmically twice with one hand third time with the other.

5 Press slightly curved hands against cheeks and pull away (three times). (A suction is caused, stimulating the skin).

Comforting Movement

Part three

1 Again, one and a half circles under chin with middle fingers in turn, effleurage beneath and above lips. Glide up to nose tip, massage nasalis in circles – don't press nostrils.

2 Proceed to bridge of nose, circle eyes simultaneously three times (starting from bridge of nose to temples, beneath eyes towards nose and back to bridge). Pull up eyebrows slightly, try to feel nerve points, handle skin under eyes gently.

3 Glide to temples and perform small figure eights over temples.

4 Circle eyes once more, go up to forehead and perform circles with right hand from one side to the other while left hand stays at temple. Small half-moons with both hands over forehead, one hand glides into the other. Friction over forehead, alternately with both hands (ring and middle finger).

5 Effleurage with palms of hands soothingly over forehead.

Comforting Movement

Note: Circles on nose and forehead upwards, on other parts downward. One hand must always remain on the client's face. The entire procedure is repeated a second time, omitting suction and tapotement. Massage takes 20 minutes.

Note: Comforting movement – cup hands over cheeks, curl up fingers, turn wrists inward, open hands gliding down shoulders.

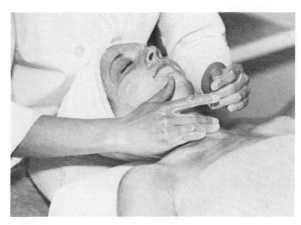
Effleurage over décolleté

ALTERNATIVE FACE MASSAGE

A massage with essential oils and creams containing active ingredients can be carried out when the client is under the steamer. This specialized service offered by the aesthetician benefits a mature, poorly circulated and large pored skin. Whilst the steam is enhancing stimulation and the tissues are rendered more receptive, the product can take greater effect.

A galvanic massage combines the benefits of soothing, relaxing manipulations and an ionization apparatus.

The contents of suitable vials for infiltration or an essential oil is distributed over the client's face, neck and *décolleté*. The electrodes are strapped to the aesthetician's lower arms. The massage movements are effleurage, moulding and light tapotement. Starting with soothingly pressing the flat palms against the *décolleté*, followed by effleurage and slowly gliding with both hands up the neck; gentle tapotement over the cheeks and nasalis; moulding hands over the temples and forehead; passing hands to cheeks and resting the fingers above and below eyes and lips; mould hands for a few seconds over the cheeks and jaws. As a final motion, return the hands to the forehead and hold in position.

The client perceives the contact of the aesthetician's hands on her skin instead of an apparatus attachment to be very comforting and reassuring.

Acupressure massage

Acupressure massage of the face is a finger technique based on shiatsu. The pressure is exerted on carefully selected points for the improvement of skin and muscle tone. Movements and pressure have to be of a distinct rhythm and intensity in order to be effective. This requires utmost concentration by the operator and adjustment to the client's sensitivity as well as her co-operation. In this massage procedure the aesthetician works with her bare hands only, without the use of creams or other gliding means. To master acupressure massage, thorough study and manual training are required.

LYMPH DRAINAGE MASSAGE

Lymph drainage is a clearing massage technique involving the lymphatic system. The method was greatly developed by Dr Emil Vodder of Copenhagen, Denmark. The manipulations are aimed at a more efficient back-flow of lymph from the superficial body tissues. Toxins and waste are removed from the skin and underlying structures to pass the lymph nodes and re-enter the circulatory system. Effleurage precedes and concludes facial lymph drainage. As we are not dealing here with larger planes, the movements are mainly restricted to small circles by middle and ring fingers, either stationary or in one direction of pressure determined by lymph flow and gland location. The fingers are placed flat on the skin and expanding, spiral, light pumping motions performed with increasing and decreasing pressure towards the lymph nodes. The movements over the glands are stationary. The lymph nodes in the locations touched during the massage starting in the shoulder girdle, are as follows:

1 axillary lymph nodes,
2 superficial cervical lymph nodes, along sterno-cleidomastoid,
3 mandibular lymph nodes,
4 pre- and post-auricular lymph nodes.

The steps in lymph drainage start at an area proximal to the body, working centrifugally, whilst movements are centripetal in order to prevent congestion of fluid in the tissues.

Lymph drainage steps can also be executed with the employment of ventuses of a vacuum massage apparatus with low intensity. The skin contact should be neither too smooth nor too dry. In order to equalize moisture on the surface, two to three drops of oil can be used in a manual lymph drainage, more would let the skin glide away from the pressure by the fingers.

Guide to lymph drainage massage of face and neck
Front view
Stationary circles – axillary nodes
Step: 1, 2

Stationary circles – along superficial cervical lymph nodes (2) pre- and post-auricular lymph nodes
Step: 1, 2, 3
Stationary circles – along mandibular nodes (along chin)
Step: 1, 2, 3, 4
Stationary circles – axillary nodes
Step: 1, 2, 3, 5
Step: 1, 2, 6
Final movements: 2, 1

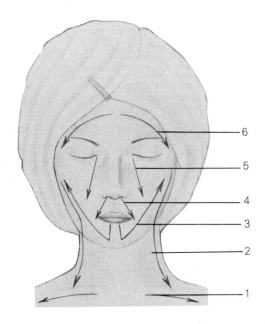

Back view
Stationary circles – axillary nodes
Step: 1, 2

Final movements: 1
The steps are repeated side by side on forehead, cheeks, neck, over décolleté and upper shoulder to cover the complete area. Effleurage in between steps and repeat stationary circles if considered necessary.

More time should be devoted to specific face sections if so required e.g. puffy eyes.

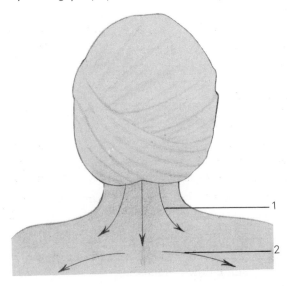

152

Masks and packs

Contents

Ready-made masks and packs   Paraffin masks   Peeling   Other packs and masks   Packs and masks to prepare at home

Masks and packs provide concentrated care when their ingredients are adjusted to the skin's needs. They are often grouped together, and their differences cannot be clearly outlined. As a general guide packs stay soft and can be easily removed with a compress; masks turn hard and are more difficult to remove. They may be softened first with a warm compress or water spray.

Both masks and packs may be applied with a flat brush, or with the fingertips if of a heavier consistency. The material is distributed evenly over face and neck, into the *décolleté*. Mouth and eyes are circled. Eyes receive a cotton compress soaked with water, eye lotion or a herbal infusion. Camomile makes a versatile extract and is preferred for sensitive skins.

Blue or red light over a mask or pack activates the process. Heat expands tissues and stimulates. Blue light is calming and relaxing. The two can be taken in succession; that is first the infra-red then the blue rays.

Masks and packs have a tradition of benefits. Many of their different ingredients have been known for centuries. At the time of Queen Elizabeth I, a pale complexion was in vogue. An old recipe for preserving a white skin reads: egg white, white poppy seed, powdered eggshell, alum and borax added to fresh well water, beaten until it shows foam on top. This concoction applied to the face three times a week was said to be very effective. There is no mention of how long it stayed on, how it was removed, or whether cream was used afterwards.

A wide range of masks and packs is available nowadays, suitable for any individual. A correct choice requires a profound knowledge of skin types and much professional experience. Herbal supplements for skin care have not changed fundamentally throughout history. They hydrate, temporarily firm, stimulate, lubricate and improve the texture in general. Only in a very few cases will a fresh herb ingredient be irritating, and then only if an allergy exists to one particular component. Cosmetic chemistry has developed a number of masks and packs in cream form on an oily or gelatinous base, as well as pasty, liquid, foam and powder varieties. The latter may be mixed with water, dairy products, herb infusions, diluted extracts, fruit or vegetable juices like tomato and cucumber, wheatgerm oil or other esters. Extracts are diluted approximately one to ten to give the proper solution. They extend moisture and enrich a mask or pack with phyto-hormones and vitamins.

Many ready-made preparations can be used at home to cleanse, freshen and stimulate in a quick application. They are convenient for a pick-up and stay on the face for 2 to 3 minutes. Masks and packs are taken off with warm, hot or cold water according to consistency and skin condition. Home application normally takes place twice a week, but should be restricted to once a week on a very sensitive skin.

READY-MADE MASKS AND PACKS

Oxygen masks

These favourably influence the oily and mature complexion, and can also be used on a poorly circulated skin but not on a fine and dry one. The substance stays on for about 15 minutes and is washed off with warm water. Following this a suitable cream is chosen for the oily or thick skin, or a regenerating preparation for the mature skin.

An oxygen mask can be combined with a firming mask for tightening of the tissue. This mask is peeled off after it has become firm. Oxygen masks can be enriched with lemon juice. (Masks ingredients: sodium perborate, kaolin, magnesium silicate.)

Stimulating packs

Stimulating packs (ingredients: essential oils, e.g. eucalyptus, arnica, cinnamon, thyme, cypress etc.) are for thick, poorly-circulated, oily and mature skin. They are on the market in the form of a cream or liquid. The pack is a preparation for a cream or treatment to follow. If massage is carried out with a regenerating cream, a stimulation pack is applied prior to the massage.

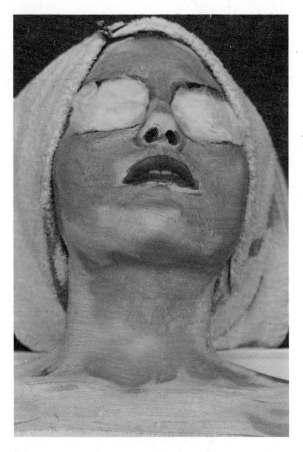

Facial mask based on kaolin after application

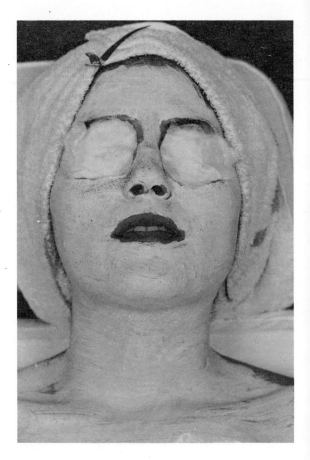

After twenty minutes the mask material has dried to a firm consistency

The complexion reacts to such stimulation by turning pink or slightly red depending on the skin type. The aesthetician has to stay with her client while this pack is reacting in order to be able to judge when it must be removed. Through stimulation exchange of substance through the cell membrane is activated and the skin is revitalized.

Regeneration packs

These containing plant or animal hormones, elastin or collagen are for the tired and mature skin. (Other components: cod liver oil, lanolin, whale oil, almond oil, wheatgerm oil, bentonite, colloid-kaolin.) They are also used as a special treatment in spring to freshen the complexion after the winter months, or in autumn to reduce damage from too much sun and dryness. The skin rejuvenates, wrinkles are softened and the tissue is strengthened in pliability. After 20 minutes the pack is washed off with warm compresses.

Regenerating packs come on an oily or colloid base or in liquid form contained in ampoules. Face, neck and *décolleté* are evenly covered with the material,

which is gently pressed into the expression lines with the fingertips. Remove with lotion after 20 minutes.

Firming masks

These tighten the skin temporarily. They are generally a thick liquid which firms when drying but are sometimes mixed from a powder by adding water, infusion or moisturizer. The latter makes the consistency smoother for application. The mask is washed off with warm compresses followed by a cold compress.

A contour lift is a preparation which firms but stays on the face under the make-up or cream. It is spread over face and neck in a thin layer, or patted on slack parts such as the neck, chin, nose and lip-line. It can be applied at any time and is not detectable.

'Nourishing' masks or packs

These are enriched with vitamins and contain plant oils like almond oil, cinnamon oil, etc. They make the skin soft and also restore the proper oil-and-moisture balance of the tissue.

Packs for acne-blemished skin

These contain sulphur, camphor or citrus fruit juices, rice starch, zinc oxide, kaolin, bentonite. They should be used about three times a week. They can be left on the skin for 15 to 20 minutes and are washed off thoroughly with lukewarm water.

Astringent masks

These contain herbs with tannin such as witch hazel or are made from citrus pectin and an addition of pharmaceutically effective astringents. They give resistance and firmness to the tissue and are used on oily, large-pored and tired skin.

Hydrating masks and packs are based on O/W emulsions or colloid substance. They are intended to retain and temporarily restore moisture on the skin surface. Their ingredients comprise: carotene, algin, uric acid, carob flower, glycerin, sorbitol, lanolin, elastin, essence of rosemary and different humactants. They cause a refreshing, cooling sensation. On a very sensitive skin apply an adequate cream under the mask first to avoid a tingly feeling.

Herbal masks generally on a cream base are lubricating and have herbal extracts aimed at different skin types i.e. chlorophyll, azulene, citrus and many more.

PARAFFIN MASKS

The skin is covered with cream according to a skin type, for example a sulphur preparation for the blemished skin, a herbal or vitamin cream for the mature skin, and so on. A bleaching cream can be applied under the paraffin mask to guard against freckles or pigmentation.

Paraffin is melted in a double boiler. Before application the temperature must be tested on the back of the hand to avoid burning and reddening the facial skin. A thin layer of paraffin is distributed with a brush over the cream. Thus the surface is closed off completely and the warmth of the paraffin enhances the process. After 15 to 20 minutes the mask is loosened at the sides and peeled off. The skin is soft and pliable so that comedones can be easily removed. Following this a skin freshener or astringent completes the treatment. Paraffin can also be applied over a gauze and be kept flexible with hot compresses or steamer which serve to maintain the temperature. This mask can be used without a layer of cream so that when it is removed small skin particles are sticking to the paraffin. It is not suitable for a seborrheic complexion.

There are further mask or pack-like treatments serving various purposes. Examples include:

PEELING

The process of superficial exfoliation of the cutaneous membrane is not to be confused with medical procedures and is frequently rather referred to as lysing.

Biological peeling

Ferments and enzymes are biocatalysts formed by living animal and plant organisms. They are protein compounds capable of producing or enhancing a catalytic reaction. In exfoliation of the keratinous skin surface, only those which split proteins are suitable. They include:

1 Pancreatin (pancreatic enzymes) – strongest peeling effect.
2 Papain (papaya enzyme) or bromelin (pineapple enzyme) – an efficient but weaker peeling effect.

Extracts from plants with a light peeling result are from the red algae (Irish moss), myrrh, aloe vera, comfrey, Peru balsam, quince seed. They combined with other plant matter have a planing as well as good cleansing action. The substance is kept moist and removed by compresses.

Although a peeling is a thorough surface cleansing, in some cases this does not suffice and should be combined with a deep pore cleansing by electrophoresis. This leads simultaneously to stabilizing the skin pH as the acid mantle has been removed by exfoliation.

A combination treatment referred to as ionto-lysing is mixing the peeling matter with the contents of a desincrustation vial. The solution is distributed over the facial skin and covered by an ionto mask for infiltration for 6 to 8 minutes. The moisture lets the skin become soft and swell so that comedones can be removed easily.

Peeling matter comes in a powder to be mixed with water or an ampoule of active compounds, in the form of creams, liquids or gels. The latter are based on latex, seaweed or agar-agar, combined with different other plant derivatives. After becoming firm with gummy layer can be peeled or rubbed off carrying away shedding skin cells.

For a better outcome of an exfoliation process on a thicker epidermis, warm, moist compresses or the steamer may be applied prior to the peeling, after cleansing, for about 10 minutes.

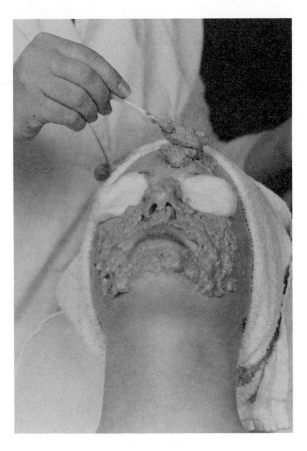

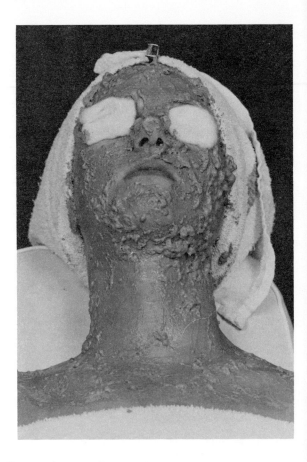

Application of a facial mask of heavy consistency

The mask covers face, neck and décolleté

In an enzyme peel the skin is cleansed thoroughly and a lotion containing 20 per cent alcohol is applied to the face, neck and possibly *décolleté*. The tissue has to be free of oil and completely dry before the peeling substance is distributed. This is left on for three to five minutes or according to manufacturer's instruction. The eyes are covered with a damp cotton ball to prevent particles of the substance reaching the eyes to cause irritation to the mucous membranes and eye ball. The peeling is rubbed off carefully with the fingertips of one hand in circular movements while the other hand holds the skin tight to produce an even surface and avoid pulling of the skin. The remainder is washed off with warm compresses. A massage with regenerating or nourishing cream or a pack follows. The skin has become more receptive to other matter and the surface, smooth and fine. Any unevenness disappears. Peeling is also carried out as a preparatory process before bleaching. A bleaching substance can be added to the peeling matter itself in the form of a 6 per cent solution of peroxide.

Peelings can be successfully done in a series of five to six treatments every third or fourth day. A peeling pack for sensitive skin will smooth the top layer of the epidermis. This is kept moist after application by means of a steamer containing plant infusion vapozone or warm compresses. The face is first covered with a gauze assisting in retaining the humidity. Compresses are administered carefully in order not to remove the peeling pack. This is either washed or rubbed off without pressure while still moist. Leave peeling on for 10 minutes.

Peeling is used to treat tired skin, seborrhea, blemishes, large pores, thick skin, keratosis, scars, freckles and pigment marks. Surface pustules are removed before peeling. The sequence would be: cleansing, softening (warm compresses or steam), removal of impurities, biological peeling, mask/pack or massage. If the client's face should be sensitive after treatment a soothing mask is recommended. She should be advised to use a good moisturizer and stay out of the sun for a day.

OTHER PACKS AND MASKS

Cream steam

This is for thick, mature, poorly-circulated or blemished skin. Apply nourishing cream in a thick layer, cut cotton wool in pieces and distribute on top after moistening with cold water. Ten hot compresses are applied in turn over the cotton or steam or vapozone for 15 minutes. Take off cotton, the cream with warm compresses; remove comedones if necessary.

Sea water packs

These may be employed for large pores, oily, blemished or poorly-circulated skin. They are also a stimulation for thick skin. The same procedure can be followed for other skin types by soaking the cotton in a herb extract suited to the skin type, rather than in sea water. Employ sea water or sea water salt diluted according to instructions. Cotton wool is cut into pieces and soaked in warm sea water, spread over the face and covered with wax paper, leaving eyes, nose and mouth free. The pack is removed after 20 to 30 minutes.

The minerals and iodine of the sea water revive and freshen the skin. To enhance the result apply red or infra-red light over the pack for 10 minutes.

Washing grains

Washing granules (contents: abrasive particles i.e. ground almonds, sea sand, oatmeal) cleanse, help remove comedones and stimulate. They are for large pored and oily skin and employed in back treatments. Moisten face and neck with warm water. Mix washing grains to a pulp with water. Apply with fingertips massaging over face and neck (on sensitive skin without pressure). *Do not use on open pustules*. Rinse off thoroughly with warm water or wash off with compresses. If skin is very oily, washing grains are advantageous for daily home care; otherwise they should be employed three times a week.

Petals

Petals made of silk or paper are used to combat wrinkles. They adjust themselves to the contours of the facial muscles when moistened and pressed against the skin surface. Each petal is impregnated with a thin layer of paste containing agar-agar, protein or algin, with a pH value between 5 and 6.5. Petals can be left on overnight. The skin is cleansed before application and creamed after removal.

PACKS AND MASKS TO PREPARE AT HOME

Proportions of ingredients in these masks or packs are more or less left to the user's judgement, always bearing in mind that the consistency should promote even distribution. Fresh fruit, juices or other ingredients should be prepared in small batches to prevent spoiling.

For dry skin

Cottage cheese–honey pack   Mix two tablespoons of cottage cheese with one tablespoon of honey and a little whipping cream. Remove after 20 minutes.

Egg pack   Stir one egg yolk with almond oil, apply with brush. Wash off after 20 minutes.

Linseed–milk mask Mix two tablespoons of ground linseed with warm milk and apply over face and neck. Remove after 20 minutes.

Milk–egg powder pack   Mix two tablespoons of milk powder with two tablespoons of egg substitute and whipping cream. Wash off after 20 minutes.

Banana pack   Squash one half of a banana. Mix with one teaspoon of honey and a little whipping cream. Wash off after 15 to 20 minutes.

Nourishing pack   Mix one and a half tablespoons of oatmeal or pulverized rolled oats with milk or yogurt, adding one teaspoon of honey, one egg yolk and three or four drops of lemon juice. The mixture should be thick but not dry. Cover face with gauze, leaving mouth, eyes and nose free. Apply pack over gauze. Remove after 15 to 20 minutes. Wash off remainder with damp, warm cotton wool.

For tired skin

Nourishing oil pack (only to be applied after the age of 30)

Warm almond oil, olive oil or wheatgerm oil in a double boiler. Cut cotton wool into pieces, dip into warm oil and distribute over face and neck, leaving nose, mouth and eyes free. Close off from air by spreading wax paper over the cotton wool. Keep on face for 10 to 15 minutes. If skin is sensitive, remove after 10 minutes. Remove remainder of oil with warm compresses. Apply lotion. (To avoid oxidation, do not keep oil in metal containers.)

Effect mask This mask for tired skin can also be used for large pored skin. Beat one half of an egg white so that oxygen can enter. Mix with a few lemon drops or orange juice. Oil the skin with wheatgerm oil, olive oil, etc. Apply mask over face and neck with a brush. Never leave on more than 10 minutes. Wash off thoroughly with warm water. Follow with cold compress.

Nourishing pack For mature and dry skin. Add one egg yolk to lemon juice. Stir with a few drops of olive oil until creamy. Wash off after 15 to 20 minutes.

Honey mask Beat one half egg white with two tablespoons of honey and one teaspoon of lemon juice. Wash off with warm water after 30 minutes.

For oily skin

Oatmeal pack Mix oatmeal with two tablespoons of liquid honey. Wash off after 15 minutes.

Cottage cheese pack Mix two tablespoons of cottage cheese with three tablespoons of fresh tomato juice. Take off after 15 to 20 minutes.

Clay mask Mix two tablespoons of clay with two tablespoons of honey, add camomile tea. Wash off after 20 minutes.

Egg white mask Beat one egg white. Mix with one tablespoon of clay and one teaspoon of honey. Wash off after 10 minutes.

For normal skin

Oatmeal mask Mix two tablespoons of oatmeal with a teaspoon of orange juice and a little whipping cream to make a slightly firm consistency. Apply thinly over face and neck with brush, wash off after 20 minutes.

Barley pack Stir two tablespoons of barley flour with camomile tea. Add a little borax and one tablespoon of freshly grated potato. Apply over gauze that has been shaped to the face, leaving mouth, nose and eyes free. Remove after 20 minutes.

Honey mask Mix two tablespoons of honey with three drops of lemon, apply with brush over face and neck. Wash off after 20 to 30 minutes.

Egg pack Mix one egg yolk with one tablespoon of honey, apply with brush on face and neck. Wash off after 15 to 20 minutes.

Cottage cheese–banana pack Mix two tablespoons of cottage cheese with squashed banana and some milk. Take off after 20 minutes.

For sensitive skin

Egg pack Mix one egg yolk with two tablespoons of oat flour and two tablespoons of whipping cream. Remove after 10 minutes.

Banana–cottage cheese pack Squash one half of a banana, mix with one tablespoon cottage cheese and a little camomile tea. Wash off with warm water after 10 minutes.

Cottage cheese–cream pack Stir whipping cream into two tablespoons of cottage cheese to form a soft consistency. Remove after 10 minutes.

For large pores

Yeast mask Mix two tablespoons of honey with two tablespoons of fresh yeast. Wash off with warm compresses after 20 to 30 minutes, then apply cold compress.

Clay mask Mix three tablespoons of clay with sage tea or fresh carrot juice. Wash off after 20 minutes.

For blemished skin

Yeast mask The yeast is mixed to a pulp with water and applied with the fingertips over the face and neck. When dry, it is rubbed off carefully. The remainder is taken off with a compress.

Against freckles and pigment spots

Bleaching Packs
1 Mix three tablespoons of lemon juice, three tablespoons of cucumber juice, one and a half tablespoons of honey, one and a half tablespoons of water, and one teaspoon of borax. This pack is left on the skin for 30 minutes – for single freckles, touch now and then with a cotton ball soaked in the mixture.

2 Combine two tablespoons of grated horseradish with two tablespoons of honey and a teaspoon of borax. Leave on for 30 minutes while horseradish clears and freshens the complexion. For a lighter effect stir grated horseradish to a pulp with milk and let soak for a few minutes before application. This mixture can be left on the skin for 30 minutes or more.

Cucumber juice whitens and also soothes the skin. Following are two suggestions for cucumber lotions:

1 Peel one or two large cucumbers and cut into pieces. Simmer in double boiler until soft, then squeeze through a linen cloth or run through a fruit press to extract all juice. Measure the juice, add one third the amount in elderflower water and a quarter of the amount in alcohol (ethanol). Shake the liquid well and store in a cool place.

2 Cut a cucumber into pieces, run through a fruit press. Mix juice with equal parts of glycerine and rose water. This liquid cannot be stored over a long period and should be kept in a cool place. It can be used as a hand lotion and for sunburn.

Eyes, brows and lashes

Contents
Treating puffiness and irritation   Dyeing lashes
and brows   Eye exercises

The eyes, the most expressive features of the face, display our emotions and thoughts. They and their surroundings often disclose our true state of health and fatigue more clearly than any other part of the body. Indications of aging are particularly hard to disguise in this area. Women throughout history have tried to draw attention to their eyes by framing them with eyeliner and dark lashes. They have even tried to accentuate them by enlarging the pupil with drugs like atropine (belladonna), a poisonous plant extract purported to give the impression of large, dark, mysterious, fiery eyes. This, of course, could damage the eyesight, particularly if employed over a long period. Recent years have brought a more refined development in the art of make-up, and ancient questionable procedures like this now seem ridiculous. Most of our decorative eye cosmetics are hypo-allergenic and can even be tolerated by a highly sensitive skin. But still there may be exceptions, and the aesthetician must always assist her client to find the most suitable product.

TREATING PUFFINESS AND IRRITATION

Many women suffer periodically from bags under the eyes and puffiness around them, which make their eyes appear small and tired, and take away their expression. Make-up is hard to apply and false lashes tend to irritate. The reason for this may be either an inherited characteristic or a temporary physiological imbalance before menstruation. Puffiness and slackness of the lids often appear during menopause. This is caused either by collection of inter-cellular liquid or dislocations of fat under the skin.

Warm and cold compresses followed by lubrication with eye cream or oil can be employed together with muscle exercise and vitamin preparations to reduce puffiness. In the case of the collection of fatty tissue, only the plastic surgeon can bring relief. After surgery the scars are hardly visible and can be disguised by make-up; about 3 months later they vanish. This operation takes years away from a person's age.

Irritated, red eyelids are treated with eye baths, using an eye cup or by applying cooling compresses. These may be made from diluted boric acid, witch hazel, wormwood or camomile infusions. Eye drops soothe and clear the eyes. If the cause of an eye disorder is not minor or obvious the client must be referred to a doctor.

Eye make-up: see chapter 'Make-up'.

DYEING LASHES AND BROWS

The eye lashes and brows are often lighter than the hair or do not match a changed hair colour. On a true blonde the fair lashes make the eyes look flat and dull. In most cases the tips of the lashes are lighter than the lash itself and therefore seem shorter. To obtain long, lasting colour without the use of mascara, lashes may be dyed. This procedure is efficacious for about 6 weeks until new hair grows in. Tinting provides shine, creating a natural-looking frame for the eyes.

Choice of colour

The colour selected for lashes and eyebrows must be the same as the hair or a shade darker. For a blonde, choose brown or charcoal; for a brunette, black or blue black. Care must be taken when selecting a suitable shade for a grey- or white-haired woman: charcoal or light brown may be used depending on the tendency in the colour of the hair. The aesthetician should also consult the client to see if she prefers to have her lashes darker than her brows. Changing from a brunette to a blonde sometimes leaves the eyebrows dark and harsh looking compared to the complexion and hair colour. They should then be lightened and dyed. This must always be done professionally with a product specified for the purpose. The eye area must be well protected with a cotton pad so that bleach does not come into contact with the eyes or mucous membranes. If the right colour is not available a variation in shade can be obtained by leaving the dye on for different lengths of time, or by repeating the procedure to make the hair darker.

160

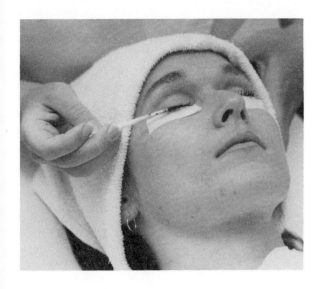

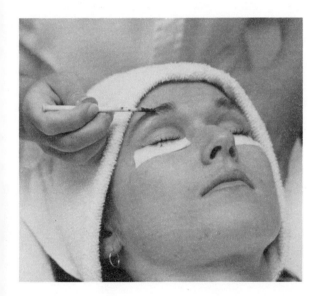

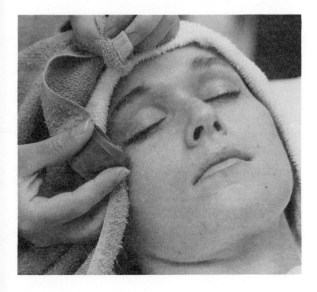

If the brows and lashes are to be dyed at the same time as the client takes a facial treatment, the dyeing takes place after cleansing and before the massage so that no cream covers the hair and prevents it from taking the colour. Brows and lashes must be free of cream, make-up and mascara. Eye make-up remover must be washed off with a cotton ball dipped in warm water.

Eyelash or eyebrows dye can be obtained either ready to be mixed or completely prepared. The dye in form of a cream is mixed with an equal amount of 3 per cent to 10 per cent hydrogen-peroxide (follow the directions of the manufacturer) in a small glass bowl shortly before application. Do not experiment with unprofessional material as it may harm the eyesight. The main ingredients in lash tints are the same as in hair colour, the difference is the concentration and way of application. There are three types of dye: natural vegetable dyes (e.g. henna), organic dyes (synthetic), and metallic dyes. The latter do not take as well as the two foregoing. (Please note: the laws regarding the use of these tints vary in different countries.)

Method

To prepare for treatment place a towel around the client's neck. Cover the skin around the eyes and brows with a thin, protective layer of Vaseline. A plastic shield or wet cotton wool shaped in a half moon should be affixed cautiously to the lower lid, pushing it with a small stick right under the bottom lashes. In this way both upper and lower lashes can be dyed at the same time. Tell your customer to close her eyes and not to open them until everything has been removed. Make sure that the shield does not slide away or becomes uncomfortable.

The colour is applied according to the manufacturer's or following instructions: a brush or applicator stick (with or without cotton wrapped around its tip) is used for the dye. Begin by colouring the lashes in a deeper shade, as the natural lash is generally darker than the brow. The eyebrows follow, starting from the bridge of the nose and working toward the temples. Work slowly and carefully so that the colour does not get on the skin or into the eyes. The dye is never left on longer than 10 minutes.

Wash off surplus colour from eyebrows with soap and water. Remove eyeshields by placing a piece of cotton on the lashes and blotting off surplus or wet colour. Grasp shield and cotton together at lower

161

rim, pull away in direction of the cheek. This prevents dye from getting into the eye. Clean lashes and under the eyes with damp cotton, then wash off with plenty of water. Some dyes only stick to hair and do not leave any mark on the skin. Stain removers are available if necessary, but most dyes may be removed by carefully washing with soap and water or a few drops of lemon. Soothe the skin with cream.

In the case of a sensitive skin the dye should be pre-tested in the bend of the elbow.

Shaping eyebrows

Dyed brows are usually tweezed after the massage, when the skin is pliable and pores relaxed by warm compresses so that tweezing is not uncomfortable. Otherwise cover brows with cream to soften before tweezing. Working with alcohol on a cotton ball, spread the skin between two fingers of the left hand and pull hair quickly. Approach the hair from the side to which it grows. Automatic tweezers do the best and fastest work for professional purposes. If the skin reddens easily or becomes puffy, it is advisable to remove the superfluous hair in two sessions. Follow with a cool compress and healing, soothing cream.

The eyebrows must not be thinned or tweezed excessively as they have the task of protecting the eye from dust and moisture. On the other hand a bushy brow makes a face look gloomy, while scattered brows give an untidy, unclean impression. For the flow of the eyebrows see the section on corrective make-up. It is determined by the proportions of the features and shape of the eye. Follow the natural brow, clean over the bridge of the nose and enlarge the area between lid and brow. It is definitely not advisable to remove eyebrow hair permanently to a fine line, as styles or personal taste may change. A natural brow always looks more attractive than one that has been pencilled in.

Wax for eyebrow removal does not allow as much control as removing hair by hair. Hot wax close to the eye is risky and cold wax does not work well on

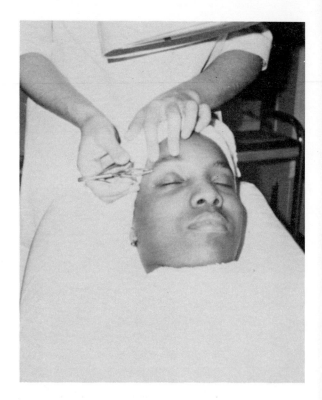

Eyebrow shaping

small areas. Using a razor near the eyes is also dangerous and causes the hair to grow back in stubbles.

Although there are several lash-growing preparations on the market, castor oil generally serves the purpose just as well. Brush it on carefully so that it does not burn the eyes.

If eyebrows are absent or very sparse, hair can be transplanted by surgery.

EYE EXERCISES

Eye exercises to strengthen eye muscles:
1 Roll eyes completely in a clockwise circular motion ten times, then repeat ten times counterclockwise.

2 Look from right to left ten times.

3 Look up and down ten times.

Hair removal (depilation, epilation)

Contents
Depilation   Epilation

Unwanted hair growth has always been a problem for women. Stronger hair growth which occurs on arms, legs or other parts as an inherited characteristic is called hypertrichosis. If hair appears on a woman where it is normally found only on men it is called hirsutism. The male hormones found in all women are held responsible. Changes at menopause or an irregular menstrual cycle may noticeably influence the pattern of a woman's hair growth. In these cases it is advisable to consult a doctor.

Fine fluff can be made less visible by bleaching with a cream made specially for this purpose. It is applied to hair on the face, arms, stomach, and thighs.

Methods of hair removal preferable for certain skin areas are:
  Shaving: legs, underarms
  Tweezing: face, breasts
  Depilatories: arms, axillae, stomach, thighs, legs
  Waxing: face, arms, stomach, thighs, legs
  Electrolysis: face, breasts, legs, stomach

DEPILATION

In the axillae, a razor may be used with great caution to avoid cutting. Shaving cream softens the skin and hair, and the arm is raised for an even, firm surface. Electric razors are less risky and are also convenient for removing leg hair. Improper hair removal under the arm may lead to a sweat gland abscess and swelling of lymph nodes. Shaving the face is not recommended. The razor cuts the hair blunt on the surface resulting in a thicker, darker appearance.

Pumicing

An old-fashioned method of hair removal on the extremities is twisting it off and out with a wet pumice stone by gentle circular motions reversed alternately to the left and right. Regularly done, the re-growth slows down. A special fine emery paper works similarly; the abrasive action wears the hair away at skin level. Working too fast and too much pressure, causes friction and soreness. Cream well afterwards. These procedures are not recommended for the tender facial tissue.

Tweezing

Automatic or ordinary tweezers may be used for manual hair removal. This method is generally chosen to remove eyebrow hair or scattered hairs on face and breasts, but it is impractical for dense hair. Re-growth becomes visible after 5 to 8 days. The hair is taken out with the root in the same way as waxing. The skin should be softened before tweezing so that the hair glides out easily without discomfort.

Depilatories

Chemical depilatories come in the form of cream, paste or foam. The chemical composition dissolves the keratin of the hair where it leaves the follicles. Re-growth occurs afer a couple of days. Before use of a chemical depilatory the skin has to be cleansed and rinsed thoroughly with warm water. The timing is indicated by the manufacturer. There is always a possibility that the skin may react with an irritation, but by applying a small amount of the chemical on a hairless spot on the arm, skin tolerance can be tested. After use of a chemical depilatory the skin surface is alkali and should not be washed with soap and water. Instead a vinegar rinse will neutralize and restore the proper acid balance. Follow with unperfumed talcum powder or a soothing cream. To avoid the discomfort of an inflammation from different chemicals brought together on the skin, deodorant or antiperspirant should be omitted for a day after underarm depilation.

Waxing

Mechanical-chemical depilation is accomplished by waxing. For depilation, the hair must have a length of at least half a centimeter for the wax to grasp and hold on to. Hair can only be removed where the shaft is visible on the skin surface.

Working fast and confidently is important. The client has to be comfortable, lighting must be good and the lounge, when depilating the lower extremities, is well covered with tissue.

Steps in depilation

1 From knee to ankle.

2 Angle legs, foot sole flat on lounge, depilate patella, watching direction of hair growth, depilate smaller sections one by one.

3 Client is placed in a prone position, the back of the leg is depilated, the knee bend again in smaller sections.

Ask the client to tighten muscles, facilitating wax application and removal. If thighs are done simultaneously, pay attention to direction of hair growth also in this section. The bikini and under-arm waxing is uncomfortable for the client.

Work efficiently and with skill, pay attention to the curvatures of the areas. In the small segments of the face, e.g. upper lip, cheeks and chin, hair growth direction is to be studied before depilation.

Depilation commodities may be firm or of medium viscosity. There are categories according to the state in which they are used, as hot, cold or warm wax. Hot wax is a mixture of resin, beeswax with additional cetiol, satol, azulene, vitamin E and others. After heating, the aesthetician checks the temperature and consistency of the wax so as not to cause her client any inconvenience.

Preparation

Before waxing, the skin is prepared by disinfecting it with alcohol and covering it with a fine protecting layer of talcum powder or mineral oil to prevent wax from adhering to the skin. The wax is melted in a double boiler or an appliance made specially for this purpose. The liquified wax is then applied to the skin with a spoon, spatula or brush in direction opposite to the hair growth, i.e. against the grain, so that the hair may stick in the wax. In order to be able to grasp the wax better, loosen the corner opposite the growth side from where it will be pulled off. When it is almost firm, it is removed with a quick jerk. Hold skin tight with your other hand at the side from which the wax is being taken off. To avoid breakage, a strip of material can be pressed against the still sticky wax, keeping it in one piece. Immediately after the wax is removed, place fingers or hand over the depilated area to sooth the skin. Apply a disinfectant or alcohol followed by a cooling cream or talcum powder. If a few hairs remain on the skin, they can be easily removed with tweezers. They will have been

already loosened in the follicle and should present no problem.

Even if great care is taken, a sensitive skin can show redness and can be raised after waxing. Generally this disappears within the next hour. Small blisters or hives may evolve the next day after first-time waxing. If this happens the area must not be touched with the fingers, but should be cleansed and disinfected.

Cold wax depilation is better suited for removing hair over a large area. The material is best serviceable at room temperature between 18 and 22 °C. Too hot, it turns into a liquid and no longer traps the hair but sticks to the skin. So-called warm depilatory waxes have to be heated to an adequate degree. Cold wax comes in a water-soluble emulsion of mainly waxes, fats and saccharides. It is, in general, well tolerated and can be washed off with soap and water. Because of the wax's water solubility it will combine with sudor. If there is an excess perspiration, cold compresses over the hirsute area will support the outcome of cold wax depilation. Stroke a very thin layer of wax over the skin in the same direction as the hair growth. The spatula employed should be perpendicular to the surface, pushing the wax ahead.

A strip of cloth or cellophane is pressed with the palm against the wax, which is then pulled off quickly against the hair growth. With cold wax the skin is disinfected with alcohol, before and after, ensuring that it is completely dry before depilation. The same goes for warm wax.

Waxing removes hair from the bottom of the follicle. Regrowth occurs after three or four weeks, depending on the general rate of hair regeneration. It will slow growth over the long run. *Wax must not be employed over imflammations, warts, moles, skin irritations, bruises, varicose veins and spider veins.*

EPILATION

Epilation is the technique of permanent hair removal. There are two methods, chemical reaction by Galvanic current, and diathermy coagulation by alternating current. The latter is the most popular though both may be combined in one apparatus. To become an electrolysist needs special training and practice and is only outlined here briefly. Prerequisites are manual skill, a steady hand, and patience. Client and operator must have perseverence to bring about success.

Conditions

The client must be in a comfortable position and the electrolysist must be able to reach her from all sides, working with a magnifying light. If the brightness bothers the client she should have a compress of cotton placed over her eyes.

Method

When epilating the face the electrolysist wears a surgical mask to avoid breathing into the client's face. The skin and the needle are disinfected before and after epilation with 70 per cent alcohol. A fine needle is inserted into the follicle along the hair root. The needle is insulated except for the outer tip which reaches the hair papilla. If there was no insulation scarring could occur on the skin surface where the follicle ends. By this method only the hair bulb is affected. The insertion of the needle is carried out at an angle in the direction of hair growth. On the left side of the upper lip, for example, the approach is from the left, while on the right side the electrolysist has to move to the right of her client. Needle removal is again parallel to the hair root. The hair is then taken out with tweezers. Many hours of practice are required to be able to insert the needle at the right spot, but if it is done properly there is a good chance of destroying the papilla. In order to discover the length of the follicle, a test hair should be removed and examined under a magnifying lamp.

The timer of the apparatus is generally set at half to two seconds. The intensity of the current plays a more important part than the timing in the destruction of the hair bulb. It can be set higher depending on the client's sensitivity and hair strength. First the dark and long hair which is most bothersome for the client is removed then the short, finer hair. There is generally a re-grown rate of 25 to 40 per cent depending upon whether or not the bulb had been reached in the papilla or the hair was in the process of shedding.

There are three stages of hair growth: anagen – active growth; catagen – shedding stage; telogen – resting stage. The hair has to be in the anagen phase to be successfully epilated.

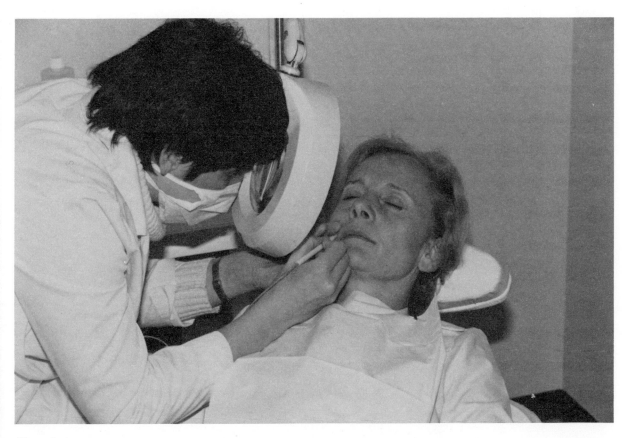

Electrolysis

165

The client is advised not to wash the area with soap and water and not to touch it with her hands to avoid infection. The skin should be disinfected and a soothing cream applied. A reaction may occur resulting in redness, hives or even small scabs. This will disappear within a few days.

The electrolysist must be well acquainted with the technical data of her apparatus and work with the utmost hygiene.

Counterindications

Counterindications for electrolysis are: if the client is indisposed, runs a temperature, is in the last months of pregnancy, has severe acne, skin disease, moles or infectious disease.

None of these depilation and epilation methods can be called optimal. It has to be decided in the individual case under careful consideration of the pros and cons which method should be given preference for success without repercussions.

Make-up

Contents
General Corrective make-up Evening make-up
Fantasy and masquerade make-up
Camouflage make-up

GENERAL

Make-up or *maquillage* is the art and technique of beautifying the face, discretely accentuating its natural attractions and correcting its imperfections. The skin requires good care to provide a successful background. A woman's personality must be taken into consideration, so that her make-up harmonizes with her whole appearance, and furthermore make-up must be appropriate to the place it is worn; on the street, at work, at home or at a social event.

For some modern women an individual make-up has become a necessary part of her apparel. Like her wardrobe it undergoes style changes from season to season. Just as she would not wear a dress that is outmoded, so she should not cling to a certain fashion in make-up that is outdated and no longer considered to be attractive. Extremes which render the face mask-like or too colourful should be avoided; the rule that understatement is always better than overstatement applies in make-up as well as dress. A young girl with a heavy make-up deprives herself of the charm of youth, while a mature woman adds years if her make-up is not delicate, natural and soft.

The light for make-up application has to be bright and not cast shadows, whether it comes from a lamp or originates from daylight close to a window. The face is cleansed, hands washed well and clean brushes, cotton and tissue set up together with the make-up items. Before starting with the first step, the features are studied carefully. For personal application a good-sized magnifying mirror is indispensible.

The movements when applying make-up are performed gently with a light hand. The steps are followed watching details and are double checked before proceeding. Do not rush. Judge each step of your work critically. Downward pointing lines make one look older and give the impression of sadness, if present around the eyes and mouth. They should be lifted, as make-up is not meant to project but to improve.

Preparation

In preparation for *maquilage* remove lipstick carefully with dry tissue without smearing it into the bordering skin. Cleansing lotion or cream is distributed in small quantities over the entire face with the fingertips in light circular motions, starting with the eye and mouth areas. The cleanser is removed with dry or moist cotton and repeated until cotton stays clean. For heavy or stage make-up a cold cream is followed by a freshener or astringent according to skin type. After cleansing face, neck and *décolleté* the following are applied in sequence:
1 moisturizer,
2 foundation and correction products,
3 rouge or blusher,
4 eye make-up,
5 powder,
6 lipstick.

Moisturizer

Moisturizer is used for protection and hydration. It is spread evenly with fingertips over face, neck and *décolleté* with a second layer over dryer areas. Let it soak in and blot excess with tissue. This is more gentle than wiping it off.

Foundation *(fond de teint)*

Dot foundation with fingertip on forehead, nose, chin, cheeks and neck. It is important to remember the neck, for it belongs to the facial unit in its skin colour. The foundation is softly and evenly blended into the skin with outward, upward motions.

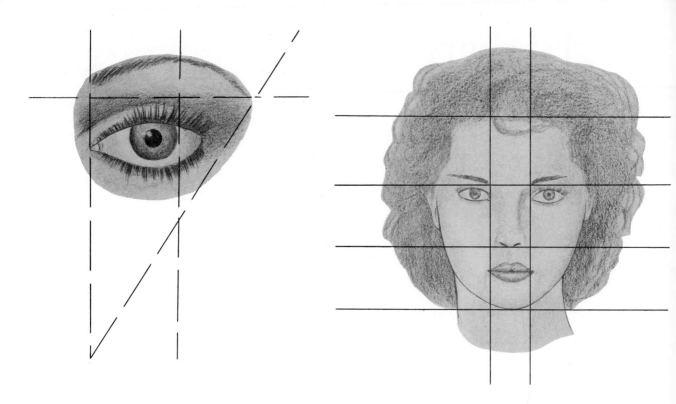

Chart for make-up application showing facial proportions

Note: the eyes should be one eye apart

Guide to perfect brow alignment

A heavy foundation is distributed with a damp sponge or with fingers dipped in water. Go over face and neck a second time, thinning out the emulsion letting it spread more easily. Extend it into the hairline, around the sides of the neck and into *décolleté*, if necessary, a deeply-cut back or bare shoulders also receive foundation. There are special preparations for this purpose that do not stain the dress. Eyelids and lips must be covered with the foundation. This serves as a base for eye make-up and lipstick, making eye shadow last better and preventing the lipstick from changing colour through the skin oils and acid. Blot off excess foundation.

Concealer or erace can be a liquid, stick or paste which serves to disguise imperfections. Using a lighter shade than the foundation, carefully press it in a semi-circle starting at the centre of the cheekbone and merging into the inner eye-corner to diminish undereye circles. The same highlighting can be done along the naso-labial fold to make it less obvious. Veins and spots can also vanish optically. The edges of the concealer must be well blended into the base. The technique and practice of camouflage to hide scars and colour abnormalities requires training and knowledge of specific products (see under 'Camouflage').

Foundation protects, adds colour and cares for the complexion. It may also act as a sunscreen if certain ingredients are incorporated. Foundation is the background of make-up and as such has to be immaculate and even. It can be of a lighter or darker shade than the skin depending upon the result desired. Foundations are in fluid, cream or cake form. The cake form is often medicated and has the greater covering power.

Foundation colours are governed by fashion, and must additionally be adjusted to skin tones, which can vary with the seasons. A basic rule is: to complement a pale, yellowish or olive complexion a rosy shade is best; for pink a beige; for a bronze, brown or black skin, a colour close to the natural nuance, as there are so many variations with sallow or reddish-brown undertones. Gentle green under-base diminishes a flushed, reddish complexion and mauve complements a very pale look. The foundation should always be transparent to allow the natural skin colour to shine through.

For large pores, first cover sparingly with a light base and then with a darker foundation.

168

Oriental make-up

Rouge and blushers

There are different kinds of rouge: cream, liquid, sticks and compressed powder. Cream rouge is the heaviest and can only be used with care. Liquid rouge is the most delicate and the easiest to control for a natural appearance. Place a small amount on three spots and blend it into the foundation. On a long face the dots are spread far apart on the cheeks, on a round face close together. Worn too high on the cheekbones, rouge gives an 'apple cheek'. As a general guide, it should be applied in a triangle reaching from the upper ear to the middle of the cheek and back to the earlobe. A darker tint makes a woman look older and a tender shade gives a younger appearance. Colour draws attention and distracts the eye from imperfections. Used on the temples close to the expression lines rouge can make them less noticeable.

Blusher and rouge give a soft, healthy look to the face. Their colours should fundamentally harmonize with the skin and lipstick but never be darker than the latter.

Blushers come in a stick, cream or powder. The cream or liquid goes over the foundation and the powder blush gives the finishing touch to the make-up after powdering off. A dab of blusher on the forehead, nosetip and chin besides on the cheeks, complements the all-over look. A young face has better blood circulation than that of a mature person, so a fine, rosy hue under the brows, a whiff of rouge on the earlobes and a little on the lower inside of the nostrils emphasizes a youthful appearance.

Rouge styles change and its application is a step in make-up requiring a lot of skill and practice. Some skins seem to absorb rouge and it has to be re-applied from time to time.

After completing the background make-up, continue with the accent make-up.

The eyes

Eye make-up has become the favourite of *maquillage* and its seasonal styles. Since its re-discovery the eye has become the most expressive part of the face, letting everything else recede. This has made it liable to constant changes: almond-shaped eyes, taking their pattern from the ancient Egyptians; round, *naive* eyes; deep mysterious eyes . . . there is no end to variations.

If you wear glasses to correct short sightedness, eye make-up should be applied more heavily than usual. It replaces the expression and beauty taken away by the glass. If you are farsighted, your glasses enlarge your eyes and your make-up should be lighter. Eye make-up must harmonize with the shape and tint of the glasses, and the brow has to be visible at least in part.

Glasses no longer serve exclusively to correct vision but represent a fashion accessory. The aesthetician can assist her client in the choice of the most favourable shape and create a complementary, personal eye make-up. The colour of the frame should be adjusted to the hair colour. A light frame gives a softer look than a darker. Bluish-grey and silver frames flatter a grey or white haired woman. Colourful frames should be left to the very young.

Smaller glasses are best suited for fine features, a large frame makes them seem even more delicate. Glasses worn further down the bridge of the nose shorten the nose optically and vice versa.

Artificial lashes are attached with the client's eyes semi-closed. The lids and hair must be dry and free of

To a round face, glasses with squares or geometrics give length.

A square face is balanced optically by round or curved frames.

Width is emphasized by round or rectangular glasses in an oblong face.

The triangular face is benefitting from an oval frame, slightly downward.

oils. Strip lashes are applied first, (recommended for the glue to adhere better) with the base conforming to the shape of the eye and lid. If too long trim at the outer corner. A dab of colourless nail polish will stop hairs from falling out later. Stroke surgical adhesive along base strip of lash with a toothpick; let it get tacky then fasten along hair roots at the border with the assistance of curved tweezers and an orange wood stick. The strip is first brought to the centre and then carefully adjusted to the sides.

Choose a natural lash for daytime and a fuller one for evening. There is a plentiful diversity, some being glittery, some with rhinestones at the base.

Permalashes give a perfect natural look. They may be single or in clusters and come in different lengths and colours as the foregoing.

Dip base in the glue provided. The lashes are individually attached with broad or curved tweezers, to the lower base of the hair, overlapping the natural lashes. All artificial lashes are shortened before being applied, and only added where natural ones are growing. Mascara, if used at all, is rolled on sparingly touching both lash rows together.

An eye liner creates the impression of longer lashes, imparts depth and enlarges the eye. Draw from the inner to the far corner or inward from each side, meeting at the centre. The fine line can be widened in the middle or towards the temple for a different effect. Extensions over the outer lid are done in accordance with the course of its brim and not allowed to become obvious. An almost invisible line along the lower lid or small dots in between the lashes can also be attractive. A heavy line looks harsh and makes the eyes seem smaller.

Eyeliner comes in liquid, cake, pencil and at times even in a shiny plastic fluid. Its choice depends on which one you prefer to work with. Shades of the liner vary from black, brown, dark green or blue to all pastel shades. Try two lines: a dark and then a coloured, blending into the eye shadow, or a smudged line of kohl or kajal.

Eye shadow makes eyes brighter and more expressive. It comes in crayon, cream, powder, liquid or stick form. Powder shadow is the easiest to work with and does not collect in the crease like cream, needing to be powdered off later. Creamy substances are only

170

Eye make-up application

suited for a very smooth lid. A dry applicator covered by cotton or foam rubber serves to work with the different consistencies; only for a liquid are fingertips or a dry brush used.

Eye shadow can be worn in many ways, covering the lid or reaching up to the outerpoint of the brow. In general the medium shade goes on the lid, the lightest under the brow and the darkest along the eye crease. There is a choice from a wide colour scale. The shade of the iris can be toned in with the colour of the dress, or a shadow selected corresponding to your eyes or dress alone. A dash of shadow along the bottom lid complements the colour of the iris.

Mascara   Stroke mascara on lower lashes and on both sides of upper lashes from roots to tips. An eyelash curler should be used before mascara to avoid breaking the hair. To prevent blinking, hold eye muscle firmly at the temple or open the mouth. Two or three coats of mascara lengthen and thicken the lashes, while powder dabbed on between layers furthers the outcome. By gliding the edge of a tissue along the lashes, excess mascara can be easily removed. Then the hairs are separated with a small brush or comb. Mascara which matches the shade of the iris or eye shadow dramatizes the eyes for an evening look when applied to the lash tips. Carefully painted lashes along the lower lid can optically replace missing natural ones.

Mascara is available in cake and wand form, with or without nylon fibres to build up lashes. For sensitive eyes cake mascara applied with water reduces the possibility of irritation. Brown and charcoal are neutral, complementary tones that go with many different hair colours.

The brow imparts more character to a person's face than any other area. Well-shaped eyebrows add to the harmony of the features and can be a means of carrying out corrections.

Brow shaping requires skill. Style alone does not decide the flow of the arch. The facial structure and height of the forehead must also be taken into consideration.

To determine the best course for the eyebrow, hold a pencil straight up from nostril to forehead. This is the place to begin the arch. Decline the pencil from this point past the outer corner of the eye, to determine the end of the brow. The peak lies over the outer edge of the iris. If this does not coincide with the given highest point, don't try to change it; keep it as a personal characteristic.

Bare patches and missing hairs are pencilled in with feather strokes. In order not to become too overpowering, colours a shade lighter than the hair or two shades combined, e.g. silver and charcoal, should be used. For example, for grey hair, charcoal, grey or even silver will give a natural and flattering look. Brush the brows, blending in the pencil lines and placing hair in the normal growth position. Cake powder with a brush provides easier application of brow colour, suited for a person with poor vision.

Powder

Powder is the oldest means of beautifying the complexion and hiding imperfections. Today, however, foundations and concealers offer better cover. Powder provides a matte finish to make-up and tones down excess colour, gloss or shine. It sets the foundation and extends a velvety appearance to the skin.

The powder should be translucent, lighter than the foundation or colourless to render it invisible and not to interfere with the make-up. Small amounts of powder are applied evenly over the face and neck with a brush or cottonball, creating a transparent, delicate layer.

For better control, fill a piece of cotton with powder, using the following method: Place powder in the centre, lift corners and gather in to enclose powder in a 'mushroom'. Dab on back of hand until powder penetrates ready for application.

For a translucent appearance, set make-up after powdering off by dabbing over it with a well moistened cotton ball or sponge, blot softly with tissue so as not to disturb the background. An ice cube for this purpose is reserved for individuals who perspire easily.

Powders of rice, wheat or other grains have good powers of absorption, but have to be specially treated to prevent them from becoming a breeding-place for micro-organisms. Natural silk micronized makes a highly valuable powder. It contains amino acids related to the ones in the skin. The silk fibre has a gentle shimmer as well as being absorbent and bacterio-static.

Powder serves as a restorative for make-up. Go over the expression lines with damp cotton and re-apply powder. For oily skin, add a drop of astringent on the cotton ball.

Lipstick

Lips must be dry and prepared with foundation and powder before lipstick is applied. A lipstick should be creamy, shiny, moist, not greasy, glide on easily and last a long time. To be up-to-date means to change the shades within the personal colour scheme according to seasonal fashion colours.

Powdering-off with the use of a brush

Lips must be dry before lipstick is applied. Outline them with lipliner or pencil, starting from the centre and working out towards the corners. Top and lower lip are drawn out to prevent colour from running into skin furrows. The lipline must be clean and clear, mistakes are removed with a cotton swab dipped into moisturizer. Proceed to fill in with lipstick, using a flat lipbrush and merging into the outline. Professionally lipstick is scraped off with a spatula and from there applied to the lips with a brush. The brush must never touch the lipstick itself for reasons of hygiene. For a fuller mouth, line only the middle curves of the lips. The lipliner can be darker or match the tint of the lipstick. An eyebrow pencil may replace a lipliner if it is not too obvious. Lipstick is blotted and applied again for greater longevity, powdering off between applications. Lipstick brightens the face and prevents the lips from drying out. Lipgloss gives an extra sheen.

CORRECTIVE MAKE-UP

Facial contour corrections are obtained by shading. Highlights bring features out and dark shades let them recede. An optical illusion like retouching a photograph can be achieved by make-up. With practice it can be developed into an art in perfecting facial features. Face shapes can be improved as well with the assistance of suitable hair styles.

172

The architecture of the face has to be studied to acquire knowledge about the location and function of muscles and bones. With few exceptions the face has two different halves; eyebrows, eyelids, sides of the nose, lips and muscle parts vary from each other. This can be minimized by skilful contouring, highlighting and shading, to bring everything into harmony.

To correct features, the desired changes are modelled into the foundation with a darker tone which can be another emulsion or a blusher with a brown tint. Blusher has the advantage to add life to the appearance and by adjusting itself becomes less obvious. The corrective shades have to be blended in carefully so that there is no visible nuance.

Basic face shapes

There are five basic face shapes: oval, round, square, oblong and triangle.

The oval face is easy to work with and its *maquillage* needs few or no corrections. The round face is shaded at the cheeks, and sometimes at temples and forehead as well to obtain the illusion of an oval shape. In order to avoid stressing the roundness, brows are kept straight. Rouge is brought closer to the centre to take away from the broadness of the face. Eyes are accentuated upwards to the outer brow tip. When making up a square face, the area from the jawline to the cheekbone is shaded darker. Eyebrows are kept shorter to diminish width, if upper face narrow, draw out wider. Rouge is applied close to the cheekbones. The oblong face requires shortening and the illusion of width. Eyebrows are extended further to the temples and rouge is brought up high to the cheekbones from the earlobes, forming a lengthy area at the sides. Darker shades close to the hairline and on the lower part of the chin draw attention away from these areas. The inverted triangular shaped face, with its wide forehead and narrow chin, provides various possibilities in make-up due to its asymmetry. It permits the most original and personal variations. Rouge is applied under the cheekbones. The brows can be arched according to the general ideal. The jawline is highlighted, while temples and sides of forehead are shaded. The triangular face with narrow forehead and wide jawline, also called pear-shaped, is highlighted on the forehead and shaded along the chin. The eye area is emphasized.

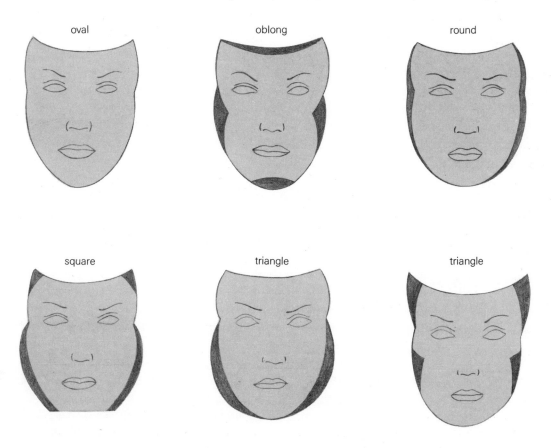

Basic face shapes and facial contour corrections

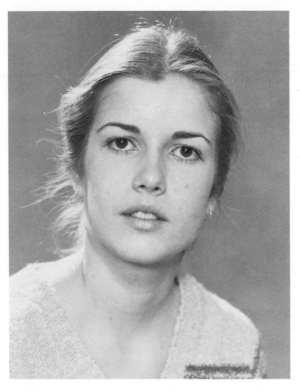 

Before and after corrective make-up

Correction of facial problems

Round forehead: receives a darker foundation.

Low forehead: lighter foundation, eyebrows not in a high arch.

Broad nose: dark shade on both sides, light stroke along bridge of nose.

Wide nose-wings: shade sides.

Long, pointed nose: lighten sides of bridge, darker stroke over centre, nose tip and edge of nostrils.

Short, flat nose: highlight along bridge of nose right to the tip.

Hook nose: shade over hook.

Crooked nose: straight highlight over centre, shade at sides.

Pronounced nose-lip line: highlight along crease.

Double chin: shade in a triangle starting at both sides of the chin ending in the centre of the neck.

Protruding chin: shade chin.

Receding chin: highlight in a triangle from lower lip along jawline.

Heavy jawline: create an optical effect by widening the upper part of the face with lighter make-up around eyes and on temples. Shade jaws darker.

Short and thick neck: darken at sides and highlight over middle.

Long, thin neck: a lighter foundation than on the face creates fullness.

The eyes

Eyes set too close together: shorten brows at bridge of nose and lengthen towards temples, apply eye shadow up and outward from outer eye corner.

Eyes set too far apart: eye shadow closer to the nose and not extended to the outer corner.

Round eyes: shadow placed on the centre of the upper lid and blended to the outer tip of the brow.

Heavy eyelids and bulging eyes: a dark eye shadow is blended in over the prominent parts.

Shallow eyes: shade with a darker tone over upper lid and below brow, a grey or brown line in the crease. If lid sinks in deeply, draw a line close to the crease to give the impression of an eyelid.

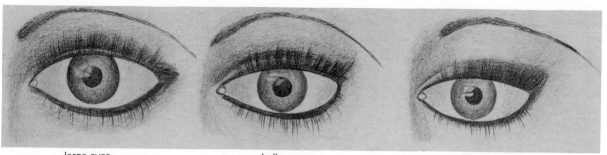

| large eyes | shallow eyes | close set eyes |

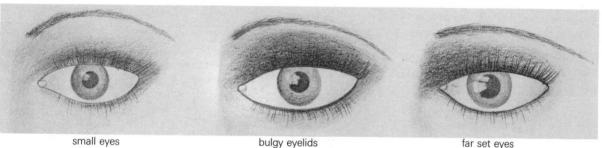

| small eyes | bulgy eyelids | far set eyes |

Corrective make-up

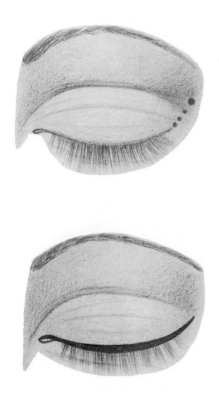

After determining length and location for extension of upper lid line when eyes open, the final point is marked and then drawn out. For a clear line the lid has first to be powdered off.

Length of artificial lashes is important in relation to the profile. The dotted line shows comparison with the tip of the nose.

Small eyes: highlight centre of upper lid and under brow, using heavier mascara or false eyelashes. Thicken eyeliner over centre. Eye shadow starting from the inner third or lower lid.

Almond shaped eyes: lighter eye shadow brought up from the crease close to the brow, heavier mascara over centre. Fine eyeliner and/or shadow along lower lid.

Tired eyes: eye shadow lifted closer to the brows, eyeliner very fine and in lighter shades, charcoal or greyish-brown. Powder eye shadow in delicate pastel tones.

Deep set eyes: strong colour above crease, blend out towards temples, highlight lid.

Droopy eyes: liner and mascara heavier towards outer upper lid, shadow drawn out to brow tip.

To create and emphasize:
a) depth in dark, lively eyes: light eye shadow on lower and upper lids, intensify in eye crease, dark eyeliner and mascara.
b) bright eyes: very light eyeshadow, eye crease softly outlined, light or metallic liner along lower lid border. The eyes are accentuated with dark mascara.

The lips

Although lip colours come and go, basically for blonde, red, white or grey hair a paler shade is more becoming. Brunettes including those with dark hair and a fair complexion should choose a clear red; brown to black skin, a tan or mauve.

Deeper shades subdue lips, lighter ones and lip gloss make them more prominent. Two lipsticks for each season, in more or less intensive colours of the same range allow for different effects and corrections in combination. The mouth is such a noticeable feature of the face that changes to it must be carried out in a subtle, immaculate manner, employing great skill. This can only be achieved by using a lipliner and lipbrush.

For correction of a small mouth (thin lips), trace a line outside close to the lip. Fill in with bright colour covering all areas. A darker shade in the corner of the mouth may improve the effect. Use lip gloss.

For a large, wide mouth, cover corners with concealer, apply lipliner away from outer edges, emphasize centre part of lips.

Full lips, camouflage lipline with foundation or coverstick. Outline right inside the natural border. If only one lip is heavier, shade darker than the other.

Uneven lips, choose medium shades, cover natural lipline, pencil in corrective line for an even contour, fill out with lipstick.

Correct a droopy mouth by lifting line invisibly at outer upper lip corners, or draw a tiny triangle over corners for a defined, curved lip.

EVENING MAKE-UP

Everything we have learned about day make-up also applies to evening make-up, the difference being in the amount of coverage. All exposed skin areas receive foundation: arms, décolleté and back, iridescent, pearlized powders create a magic glow on the skin's surface.

In order to reduce colour absorption caused by artificial light, a compensation in shades is required.

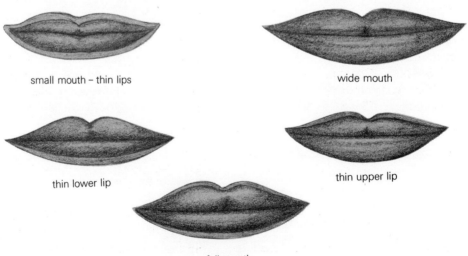

small mouth – thin lips

wide mouth

thin lower lip

thin upper lip

full mouth

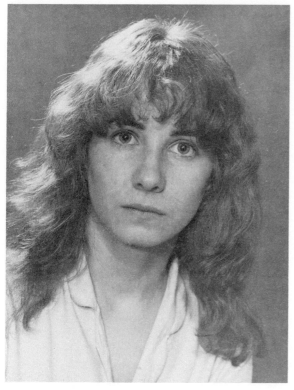

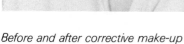
Before and after corrective make-up

The reaction of two different colours on each other in the illumination used at certain events must be considered. Orange and yellow fade in yellow lighting, and must be compensated with blue-red. Red light makes red seem paler, and should be counteracted with brighter red. Blue light is cold and unfavourable for any make-up: choose vigorous shades and soft, warm contouring. Lashes can be shiny and longer, but not too dark, lest they cast unflattering shadows.

Base the make-up for deep set eyes on clear, shiny tones, combined with gold, silver or bronze. Mica dust on lids reflects evening lights. A red dot in the inner eye corner and blusher along the lower brow make the face vivacious. Contour corrections are carried out with more contrast on a dark foundation. Shades and highlights are adjusted in harmony with the basic tone.

Features are contoured with a flat powder along cheekbones, sides of the nose, indention at lower lip and philtrum. Naso-labial fold, cheekbones, bridge of nose, under-eyes and any area to be emphasized or desired to protrude receives highlight.

In poor lighting shadows appear darker and shading needs to be done less conspicuously than in bright spotlights, where dramatizing is indicated.

Evening make-up is almost exclusively governed by the dress, and little attention is paid to the type of woman. Even if designed to be worn in a dim light, make-up application must take place in front of a well-lit mirror in order to be flawless.

If there is a blemish, never let it worry you: wear a *mouche* (beauty spot), dotted on or cut out from silk or velvet and kept in place by means of lash glue.

Mannequin (modelling) make-up

This is determined by bright lights. It should be well done without being overdone: foundation generally light; features corrected and highlighted, shaded under the cheekbones; eye make-up neutral (ivory/tawny/brown shades) suitable for all dress colours; artificial lashes.

For a dark skin: foundation adjusted to skin tone; eye – kajal liner; to stress upperlid emerald-green or lavender may be applied, the colour strongest along eyeliner fading out into the lid crease; artificial lashes; emphasis on cheek-bones and darken brows; shading the nose wings; make lips appear less full; lipstick brownish-orange tints.

Creating a fantasy make-up

FANTASY AND MASQUERADE MAKE-UP

Creating a fantasy make-up is the expression of joy of life at a masquerade or carnival. Artistic make-up is chosen which imparts an interpretation of the costume or dress. The eye is the main attraction; it is stressed by surrounding it with designs painted in gay, vivid colours. Follow its natural flow with your lines and work with upward motions. First outline the design with a pencil, later filling in the colours. There is no limitation to your imagination. If the costume allows, knee, leg and arm can receive abstract drawings. Paint a flower or butterfly on the part of the leg to which you want to draw attention.

Character make-up for a masquerade, such as a change to a different ethnic background, is available in complete sets from manufacturers. Various skin tones are also available as liquid make-up. They give a natural appearance and are easily removed with soap and water. For application follow the guidelines and charts supplied by the manufacturer.

Points to remember: take client's personality into consideration; adjust make-up to dress or costume worn; have the kind and motto of the event in mind; include hairstyle. Do not make client unrecognizable and keep make-up attractive.

CAMOUFLAGE MAKE-UP

Camouflaging skin disorders, inoperable abnormalities and disturbing marks, as are often the consequence of accidents, belongs to the daily tasks of a make-up artist. The aesthetician should acquire the know-how of these rewarding procedures to be of advice and assistance to her client. Artistic and manual skills enable her to obtain the utmost result in camouflage techniques. A prerequisite in mastering this art is product knowledge and the ability to select the proper nuances in relation to the skin's colour.

Only proven and dermatologically safe preparations should be used. The make-up material has to be waterproof, withstand perspiration, be neutral, hypoallergenic, of strong covering power and must

Fantasy make-up creating an effect by the use of black and white only

3 Have a fine brush available to disguise eye shadows, small scars and single blemishes.

4 Ring and middle finger are best suited to stroke and pat on a camouflage base (do not use index finger). For blending the edge into the surrounding skin the thumb has proven helpful.

5 The camouflage cream is spread evenly in a thin layer over the area extending 1 or 2 cm over the border.

6 Blend in with some rouge for a live, natural appearance according to individual skin colour; take the changes in the season and sun exposure into consideration.

7 The foundation is generously dusted with colourless finishing powder and allowed to set for up to 10 minutes until the material has dried completely. Now excess powder can be carefully fluffed off with a powder brush.

8 In order to extend a natural shine, the skin is sponged off lightly with a damp cotton ball.

The final, natural looking outcome of the make-up depends upon the aesthetician's aptitude. A well applied camouflage must, so to say, not be detectable and the skin not seem lifeless, and/or the face masky.

Application

The approach to concealing varies according to the mark present. A scar due to trauma or burn may be uneven, showing indentations whilst a nevus flammeus leukoderma, vitiligo and similar disfigurements are level with the healthy tissue.

If the area to be covered is lighter than the surrounding, one commences with a darker foundation, over which a second layer adjusted to skin tone follows.

In case of a dark patch, a light or white base is first applied with tapping movements. A second layer is mixed with a darker shade and blended over it. If the discolouration is not pronounced one can achieve a good result by the use of one shade only.

A sunken-in area receives a lighter all-over foundation than the healthy skin to counteract casting of shadows.

In a woman, the concealed area can easily be disguised and balanced by using an all-over make-up afterwards.

not interfere with or counteract the skin's natural functions. To be on the safe side, an allergy test should be carried out on a sensitive skin. To acquaint the client visually with the outcome of camouflage techniques show her photos of before and after performing corrections of skin faults.

The procedures are explained to the client step by step during make-up application, enabling her to look after herself day by day.

When choosing the proper hue for a skin, several make-up shades can be blended together to find the matching natural tone.

The aesthetician's nails must be short so that the material does not collect under the free edge and the client's skin is not injured.

General points

Observe the following:
1 Choose a working area with daylight and have a mirror available for your client to observe the application.

2 The skin is covered with a light moisturizer; a fatty cream would interfere with the make-up's consistency.

For cleansing, camouflage make-up may be carefully rinsed with water, if necessary, and dried by dabbing it off with tissue.

The make-up material can be removed with soap and water followed by a cleanser or special cleansing cream.

For pimples and spots, a moisturizer is distributed over the face. Camouflage cream in the skin's colour is locally applied with a large, flat brush and carefully blended into the surrounding tissue with the finger tip or sponge.

The areas are set with finishing powder. Foundation is now distributed over the complexion with light movements not to disturb the concealed marks, powdered off and make-up completed.

Back and décolleté

Contents
Back massage *Décolleté* massage

For a back massage the client sits erect. She holds a towel over her chest. A towel is also placed around her hips at the back. Cleanse back with cleansing lotion, apply skin freshener with cotton ball, massage with oil or body lotion.

BACK MASSAGE

1 Describe three circles from neck to shoulders, both sides at the same time, with pressure, with the palms of both hands. Glide back to neck with pressure (twice);

2 Small quick circles from neck to shoulders, keeping palms pressed firmly to skin (twice);

3 Lift left shoulder muscle with right hand, stroke muscle with left hand from neck to shoulder (three times), repeat same procedure on right shoulder;

4 Massage in circles down the spine – both sides – with both thumbs. Stroke upwards along both sides of the spine with the thumbs (twice); comforting movement: stroke soothingly with both hands at the same time, starting under shoulder blades, gliding in circles up to nape of neck, then down along spine to waistline;

5 From the spine along the ribs three small circles to the side – stroke back and glide into the next rib – stroke upwards along both sides of the spine with the thumbs;

6 Keep left hand on client's left shoulder and vibrate with right hand (thumb and index finger) down the spine; comforting movement: effleurage with both hands over scapulae down to waist;

7 Tap alternately with fingers spread over shoulder and shoulder blade, both sides;

8 Tap with back of hands in turn over shoulders and shoulder blades describing a figure eight (three times); comforting movement: lift lower shoulder blade at the base, left and right (hold shoulder with other hand);

9 Stroke over shoulders and down the back in large circles with palms of hands; comforting movement: apply hot compresses followed by arnica lotion or rubbing alcohol; distribute talcum powder over the back.

To combine a treatment with the massage, have your client rest on the chair in a prone position. Cover her with a towel to the waistline and place a small towel along her waist. Fold a towel to cushion her head.

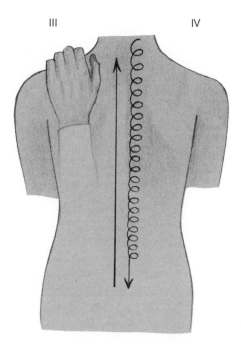

I II III IV

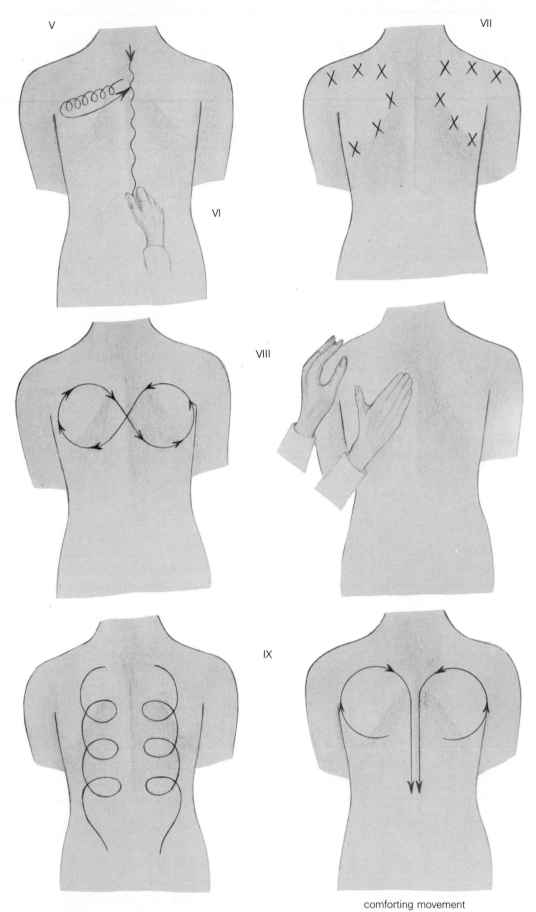

V

VII

VI

VIII

IX

comforting movement

Steps to back massage

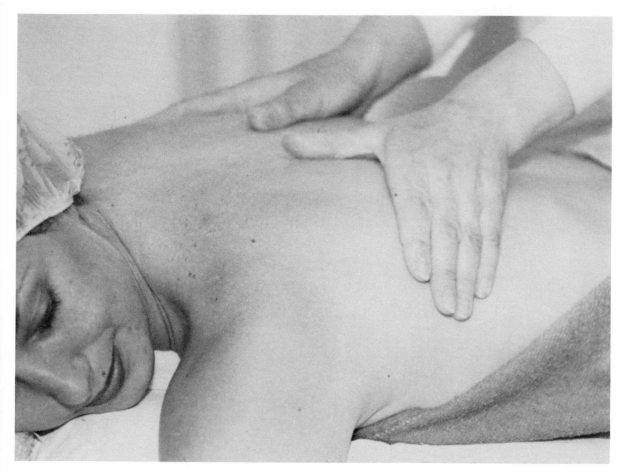

Application on the back in prone position

Variations of treatment

Variations according to skin type apply to the back as they do to the face. Vapozone, masks, packs, peeling and stimulating preparations may all be utilized to beautify and clarify the skin. Alternating current exercises the muscles on shoulders and back, releasing painful tension. Vibrators exert a deep, muscle-loosening pressure on shoulders. Cellulite on the nape of neck and shoulders is favourably influenced by phoresis applications with suitable preparations. Infra-red light before massaging (5 minutes) radiates comforting relaxing heat; the back can also be exposed to U.V. light at the end of the treatment if the skin is oily. Protect client's eyes, keep lamp at a distance of 75 cm to 1 m for 2 to 3 minutes.

Seborrhea oleosa may appear on the back and in the triangle of the *décolleté* as it does on the face, even though the remaining skin of the body is normal or dry. Comedones develop along the spine and sternum. After softening the skin, they are removed with a comedone extractor.

The aesthetician can only influence the area surrounding the bust. For firmness the client herself must strengthen the muscles through exercise and sport. The skin around the bust is cleansed with a lotion and freshener and massaged with a nourishing cream. After the massage a stimulation mask can follow and the bust muscle be exercised by alternating current. Never touch the bust tissue itself.

DÉCOLLETÉ MASSAGE

1 Three circles with flat hands from the outer shoulders towards bust;

2 Circle busts with light pressure from middle of sternum upward, to the sides, under busts and back;

3 Vibrate with thumb and middle finger along sternum upward towards neck;

4 Massage sternum with small circles (ring and middle finger); massage bust muscle upward with kneading movements;

5 Stroke alternately with both hands over *décolleté*;

6 Make small circles with thumbs over shoulders up to back of neck.

Bust muscle strengthening exercises

1 Fold hands in front of chest. Part palms and push together with a jerk without separating fingers.

2 Hold hands flat against each other in front of chest; keep together while moving arms over head to back of head. Return hands to chest, keeping them firmly together.

3 Stand a foot away from a wall; hold hands flat against wall, bend arms and push back.

Hand and nail care

Contents
Manicure   Hand massage   Hand exercises

MANICURE

General care

Hand care begins with prevention. Dirt and dust must not be allowed to grind deeply into the skin, particulary the cuticles, which like the nail grooves are often difficult to clean afterwards. Gardening is one instance where one should wear gloves for protection. Rubber gloves prevent contact with water or harsh detergents. If they are not lined, talcum powder should be inserted before slipping them on to absorb perspiration.

For stains from chemicals and dye, solvents and removers work well but are very hard on the skin. Subsequent washing and thorough creaming are necessary to restore smoothness. Very little can be done about tobacco stains on fingers. Rub with pumice stone, a lemon slice or try bleaching. The brown penetrates deeply into the skin layers and can only be lightened.

Soap, hand brush and pumice stone still prove the best way to keep hands clean. The pumice has to be moistened before use so as not to harm the skin. Soap particles are rinsed off with water containing a few drops of lemon or vinegar. The alkali is neutralized, leaving soft supple hands. Washing grains take away roughness, cream well afterwards.

When applying night cream before retiring, the hands should not be forgotten. Now and then a thick layer should be applied and a glove worn during sleep to thoroughly lubricate dry fingertips and cuticles. In addition brittle nails require a cuticle cream or soaking in warm vegetable oil.

Never go outside with wet hands; in low temperatures gloves must be worn at all times.

Chapped hands require special ointments, preferably containing vitamin F. These can be obtained from drugstores. In serious cases, the doctor must be consulted. The healing process is furthered with packs of unperfumed fatty cream. Cocoa butter, an extract of the cocoa bean, is an excellent protection and lubricant.

So-called blue hands, sometimes showing white fingertips, are a sign of poor blood circulation. Stimulation can be obtained by a hand bath alternating hot and cold water, finger-to-wrist massage, hand exercises, brush massages, compresses and infra-red rays. Red hands also indicate a need for the same treatments. The reason for the redness varies: it can be inherited, but is often due to internal or external factors. Red and blue hands have to be kept warm in wintry weather to prevent cold damage.

Damp palms signal a disorder of the sweat glands, arising from a nervous condition or an illness. To help regulate gland function, hands may be bathed in a plant extract (birch, hamamelis, arnica) or pharmaceutical astringents. Seek the advice of a doctor if perspiration is excessive.

Rough elbows and uneven upper arms are smoothed with an abrasive followed by a cream.

Professional care – manicuring

The name manicure originates from two Latin words: *manus*, the hand; and *cura*, the care. Professionally, hands are treated with compresses, massages, nourishing and regenerating creams, cream steam and phoresis, just like the face.

A paraffin mask makes the skin of the hands supple and resilient. A rich cream is distributed over the back of the hand, over which hot paraffin is applied with a brush. *Only* the back of the hand is treated. By covering the palm, the sweat gland secretion would be stimulated which, of course, is undesirable.

Ultra-violet light on hands and arms should be used only for women under 35. Women past that age must avoid exposing arms and hands to the sun. Ultra-violet rays intensify and encourage the development of brown pigment marks, the so-called age-spots. There is no remedy for them; they can only be made paler temporarily by a bleaching process (peeling and bleaching with the assistance of electrophoresis and suitable vials) which requires several treatments.

Unfortunately, hands are not cared for as often as they deserve, although it is true to say that the neck and hands of a woman give her age away. Hands should be gracious, the skin soft and the nails well-groomed. A pretty hand is an attraction, complementing the overall appearance. On occasion we are judged by our hands: they reveal our character, manifest our feelings and show our temperament.

The nails and their shape dictate the appearance of the entire hand. The nail has to be clean and healthy. Never use a sharp instrument to scrape under the free edge, as it may injure the skin and allow bacteria to penetrate. After washing, push the cuticle back with a damp towel so that it does not grow too far over the nail.

Once a week, a professional manicure is advisable.

Method
Following are the steps:
1 remove nail polish;
2 shape nails by filing;
3 apply cuticle remover (soften cuticles in soapy water);
4 dry fingertips, apply cuticle oil;
5 push cuticles back, trim with nippers where necessary;
6 clean under nail, file again (remove remaining roughness);
7 massage hand and arm;
8 free nails from oil and cream using damp cotton or brush (working downwards from lunula to tip);
9 apply base, polish coats and sealer (quick dry).

The manicurist always uses a small towel, serviette or tissue, when touching her customer's hand. She starts all steps in manicuring with the little finger of the customer's left hand. This gives the right hand, which generally is the working hand, a longer time to soak and soften in the bowl.

Nail polish is removed with polish remover (liquid or in a tube). Press cotton against nail, hold and wipe off. The grooves are cleaned with a Q-tip. Polish remover contains oils and is not harsh, like pure acetone. Brittle nails receive a warm lubricating bath of vegetable oil or lotion. Any oil surplus is removed with a compress. An O/W emulsion can be used for the subsequent massage.

Nails are filed from the sides to centre in one direction only, a precaution preventing cracks and roughness. Do not file deep into corners, so as not to hurt the cuticles and weaken the nail. Cutting causes splitting.

The shape and length of the nail is generally chosen by the customer, according to her taste and lifestyle. The manicurist can advise her as to styles and what shape would compliment her hand; square, round,

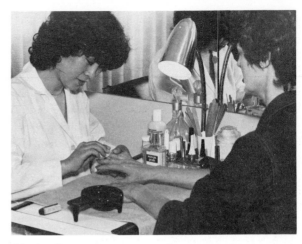
Manicurist carrying out a manicure

oval or pointed. The nails should always be a little longer than the fingertip in order to give protection, and kept at an even length to be well groomed. The middle finger grows faster and the little finger nail slower.

After filing, cuticle remover is brushed on and the fingers dipped into warm, soapy water to soften the cuticles. Then the hands are dried, cuticle oil is applied and the skin is pushed back gently with an orange wood stick wrapped in cotton. Exert no pressure: the lunula is easily hurt. Never use a metal instrument in this step and avoid harsh cuticle removers which corrode the horny nail substance. Skin particles like hangnails are nipped off. Hard edges at finger tips are taken away with a pumice stone. Bleeding of the cuticles can lead to severe infections. Cutting hardens them, encourages hangnails, and allows dirt and bacteria to collect in the cracks. A manicure for a diabetic must be given with much care: her cuticles must not be touched because of poor healing. *After use, all instruments must be disinfected.*

Polish After the massage, the polish is applied on a clean, dry nail. If possible, each layer of polish should be allowed to set before the next is applied. First, stroke over centre from cuticle to nail tip; then do the sides. Dip brush into polish for each nail. The base-coat evens out ridges, and the sealer protects the polish to make it last longer.

A nail polish is expected to be easy to apply, not to leave stripes, or discolour, correct unevenness, dry fast, and not to chip or peel. The base of nail enamel is nitro-cellulose, responsible for a hard, lasting film with resins for gloss and oils extending pliability. The organic solvents are ethyl and butyl acetate. Additions: proteins, acrylic and compositions of different lustre and colour matters.

The colour and method of wearing polish change with fashion. As a guide, the colour chosen should harmonize with the lipstick and suit the skin tone; a pink enamel is unfavourable for a rosy, and a yellow undertone, for an ivory skin. A brown hand is complemented by brown and orange tints in nail polish. Sometimes lunula or lunula and tip are left free of colour; sometimes the whole nail is covered. The latter method is preferred, as it gives an impression of length. This effect is also stressed if polish is applied over the middle of the nail, leaving a thin stripe at the sides free. The polish must not be too close to the cuticle at the lunula to allow air to reach it. A lengthening effect is obtained if the point of the nail is filed only from the fingertip. Polish should be applied evenly. Rather than patching chipped parts, renew the polish completely. The nail has to look immaculate, as the colour draws attention to it. Diluted nail polish never stays on long; therefore, the bottle must be closed promptly after use to prevent thickening by evaporation. Wipe off bottle neck to allow easy opening when next used.

Nail polish supports and protects the nail. To strengthen and harden it further, various products may be applied under the polish. Fundamentally, however, the consistency of the nail is inherited and determined by the physical condition of the entire body.

Some women are allergic to certain nail polishes. A test can be made by dabbing polish on a small spot of skin on the hand. The allergy can be to various ingredients in the polish.

Patching and mending With skill and practice cracked nails can be patched or broken nails mended. Artificial nails, if properly shaped in proportion to the hand and fingers, can bring about a great improvement. By making a person self-conscious about the looks of her hands, it can assist in overcoming nail biting. So-called perma-nails are built up to stay. The technique requires practice and skill. To provide good looking nails quickly and easily ready sized prostheses are available in different lengths and widths. Adhesive is distributed over a clean nail plate. The artificial nail is slid on from the tip and pushed against the cuticle. It is pressed onto the nail for about 30 seconds then cut and filed to required length and shape, followed by polish application.

Replacements of single broken nail tips is achieved the same way using pre-styled synthetic nail tips. They stand up well and can hardly be detected.

Acrylic nails can be sculptured on the shortest natural nail. The nail plate is roughened with an emery board to make the build-up stick better, a liquid is applied to dry the nail surface, which is followed by a formulated fluid to help the acrylic to adhere. A horse-shoe shaped foil is fitted under the free edge and by working quickly dipping a brush in turn into a liquid and a powder, a smooth layer is created resembling the client's own nail. After setting, the foil is removed and the new nail filed and buffered. The result is a strong, flexible structure.

A contoured nail can also be achieved by way of using a gel instead of the acrylic powder. This method seems to be faster and the liquids used do not have the specific odour as is the case in the foregoing. The forming of the nail is done with the fingertip gliding over the build-up to even out the surface. To further the hardening process, the prosthesis is exposed to a curing light. Visible light nail bonding results in a natural non-chipping structure.

Nail wrapping is an alternative to mending and re-attaching broken off nails. A silk fabric is cut into the nail's shape. The nail plate is slightly roughened and glue applied. The silk is adjusted smoothly to the nail surface. More adhesive fluid is distributed and after setting, the nail's edges are smoothened. The last layer of adhesive is applied and let dry, then the nail is buffered and finally shaped.

Splitting and cracked nails can be mended by a small piece of silk or special fine tissue dipped into nail hardener and placed onto the damaged area overlapping the edge. Whilst the hardener is still wet, the extension is carefully bent with the use of an orange stick, tucked and pressed under the nail to adhere, followed by a second layer of acrylic hardener. The area is then smoothened and let dry. It has to be observed that there is no ridge created between the attached material and the nail plate.

Nail painting or finger painting

This is a technique requiring steady hands and a magnifying light to be immaculate. There is a variation of all colours of specially formulated nail polish available as well as a supply of brushes for the creation of patterns and images on the nail plate.

Short nails can optically appear longer by drawing on vertical lines. For a different look, diamond studs and golden covers can be fastened to the nail surface.

Hand and nail shapes

1 Oval hand with oval nails is the ideal shape. Nails may be long and lunula left free of polish.

2 Dainty hand with small nails. Polish to cover entire nail. Choose light delicate colours.

3 Broad hand with wide nails. Nails must not be filed to a point and only extended 2 mm over the fingertip. For elongated appearance leave 1 to 2 mm free of polish at both sides.

4 Sturdy hand with square nails. Do not file pointed or longer than 2 mm overlapping the free edge. Leave sides free of polish about 2 mm or use darker polish over the nail's centre if nail plate is arched.

A flat nail plate appears more slender if a light stripe is drawn over the centre from eponychium to free edge.

Buffing

Buffing the nails was once in style, but is now mainly requested by men. A stick or powder is applied on the

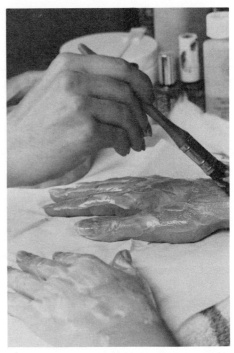

Paraffin is applied over the cream on the back of the hand

leather part of the buffer; the nails are then polished until they shine. Buffing with a buffer alone can take place before polish application to give the nail a smooth surface.

A manicure carried out by hand is, in general, preferable to one done by a machine, which can be hard on nails and cuticles unless the operator has had a great deal of experience.

Paraffin mask on the hand

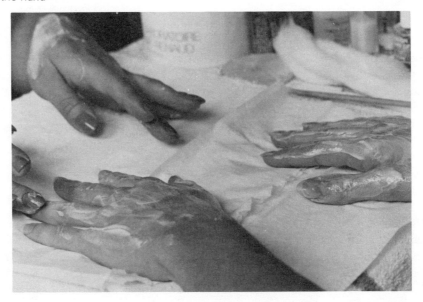

188

1

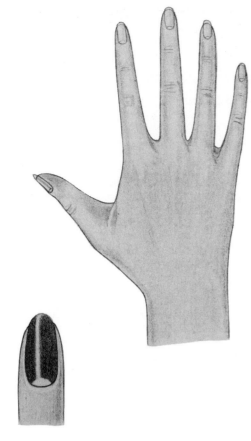

2

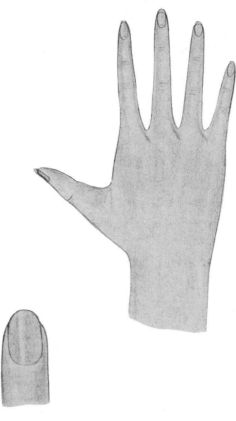

3

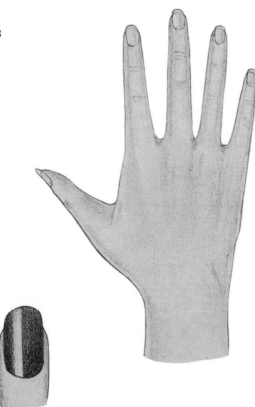

4

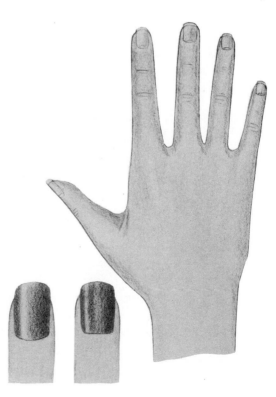

HAND MASSAGE

Distribute cream over the hand and arm, then:

1 massage cuticles with thumb of right hand;

2 massage fingers from fingertips towards hand;

3 massage hand in small circles along metacarpals towards wrist;

4 massage lower arm at ulnar side with three kneading movements towards elbow (two or three times);

5 cream elbow and stroke upwards with pressure from wrist to elbow;

6 press fist against palm and roll out (twice); criss-cross with thumbs firmly over clients palm from wrist to fingers:

7 using both hands, press sides of hand of customer, stroking down over wrist.

During the massage, always hold client's hand or wrist. Start with little finger of her left hand.

(For setting up a manicure table see 'The Cosmetic Institute'.)

HAND EXERCISES

When regularly undertaken in every spare moment, exercise strengthens and relaxes the hands and leads to controlled and gracious movements. Observe your hand exercises before a mirror. Even the least beautiful hand is attractive when its gestures are light, expressive and graceful.

1 move the hands in a circular manner from wrist, clockwise and counterclockwise;

2 bend hands from wrist backward and forward;

3 close and open hands;

4 spread fingers;

5 press fingertips of both hands together, repeat several times (the resistance strengthens the fingers).

Men's manicures are carried out the same way as for a woman except the massage extends only to the wrist. The nails are buffed or colourless nail polish is used. The free edge may be whitened with nail whitener.

Diet

Advise your client as to a diet for healthy nails:

calcium – fish, dairy products
iodine – fish, spinach
sulphur – cabbage, cucumber, onions
iron – vegetables, liver
copper – liver, fish
silicic acid – vegetables
manganese – fruit, vegetables

Kelp tablets contain minerals, iodine, proteins, some vitamins and unsaturated fats. They are a great help for weak nails and will also improve hair and skin.

Remind your client to use a pencil to dial a telephone number, and to pick up objects with the fingertips so that she may enjoy her manicure for a longer time.

At-home care

Contents
The face   The body   Facial (neck) exercises
and massage

THE FACE

Cosmetic care at home supports the work of the aesthetician, furthering the benefits of her treatments in the cosmetic institute. The client must follow her caring outlines to guarantee success. It is the task of the aesthetician to consult, demonstrate and make the customer understand why different cosmetic preparations should be used. The steps as well as the principles observed at home are the same as in professional care:

1 cleanse,
2 freshen (stimulate),
3 care (lubricate, moisturize, regenerate),
4 protect.

These are performed as given under 'Treatment in the Cosmetic Institute' according to different skin types.

The daily routine

This starts at bedtime for home care of skin and beauty. Thorough cleansing is the first prerequisite for a healthy, good-looking complexion. The skin is given a chance to recover without make-up, dust or other matter. A complexion that is left without make-up during the daytime needs cleansing as well, to remove pollution particles and glandular excretions accumulated on the tissue. Cleansing itself is carried out the same way it is done professionally: apply cleansing cream or lotion with fingertips; distribute by massage without pressure over face and neck; let set; dampen fingers and repeat the entire procedure; rinse off. Lipstick and eye make-up are removed separately. If the skin type requires, splash warm or cold water over your face; dab dry lightly with tissue; avoid rubbing, particularly around the eyes. Always stroke inward from temples to nose under eyes. Wipe skin with freshener or astringent on cotton ball, repeat with fresh cotton if necessary. Apply night cream or vial or combination of both. For complete renewal of make-up during daytime, take the same steps, using moisturizer instead of night cream. A 'nourishing' or other night cream is massaged over face, neck and décolleté. Do not pull the skin, as this can do more harm than good (massage instructions are given at the end of the chapter). Facial exercises should be carried out regularly, together with the foregoing steps for a good result.

Night cream can be patted gently in a double layer over the delicate skin around the eyes, as well as over the naso-labial fold. Specialized eye creams with valuable oils are available. Apply sparingly, dabbing off any cream still visible after a few minutes, as it no longer has any value. During sleep, the skin has time for regeneration.

Protection should be the primary aspect for day care. We are surrounded by many harmful agents in the air, by dust, chemicals, dryness and temperature changes. In the morning the face needs to be awakened just like the rest of the body. Cleanse, freshen, stimulate with astringent and/or water. Do not forget that softener, borax or a few drops of lemon juice should be added to water for a sensitive skin. Lemon juice is also useful for an oily skin. Apply moisturizer as indicated. It will simultaneously povide protection and a foundation base. The moisturizer is evened out with light, outward-upward motions. Make-up as described in the relevant chapter is next. The aesthetician advises professionally regarding colour and product and guides her client to make-up in harmony with her personality and lifestyle.

Masks

Now and then, a mask at home for a quick pick-up or between professional treatments gives the complexion a lift. The aesthetician recommends a product or recipe the customer can prepare herself. Steam your face if required, apply mixture, close your eyes, lie down, take a rest. The mask material is best distributed with a brush or, if no brush is available, you can use a damp cotton ball.

Preparations for home care should be changed from time to time and, of course, adjusted to the different seasons. This gives the skin new stimulus and shows a rewarding result. A series of regenerative vials applied at night in spring or autumn is most effective.

Eyebrows and lashes are brushed in the evening with castor oil or a preparation formulated to make the hair grow and shine.

Eyes

Eyes often look tired, and since they are emphasized by make-up they need very special attention. Bathe them with an eye cup using camomile tea, boric acid (diluted according to instructions) or plain, warm water. Place a cotton ball soaked in any one of these liquids on your eyes for a few minutes while you are resting. Sea water salt also makes a useful compress for the eyes. It must be diluted: one cup of warm water to a quarter teaspoon sea water salt. Compresses and eye bathing can do wonders, making your eyes look fresh and clear after only 10 minutes. To cool puffy eyes, cover for 10 minutes with a cotton ball dipped in cold water. Cream carefully around them afterwards.

Lips

Lips need protection against dry and cold, provided in part by a lipstick. When skiing or sun-bathing, use a good suntan lotion or cream. The mucous membranes of the lips are sensitive, and cracks in this area hurt more than on parts of the skin and heal more slowly. Cream and lip balm restore smoothness. To prevent small wrinkles close to the mouth, stretch the lips over the teeth and massage firmly with one finger around the mouth and over the lips, using your night cream.

Good teeth

Good teeth go with pretty lips and a well-cared-for complexion. Teeth too therefore need regular cleaning and attention. Floss daily and brush after each meal. For better circulation of the lips go over them gently with a soft tooth brush using cold water. The dentist has different options to improve the optical appearance of teeth.

Hair

For shiny, healthy hair, blood circulation should be furthered by massaging the scalp and daily brushing against the growth from neck to forehead. This cleans and lubricates the hair with natural oils.

Body and facial skin require proper oxygenation, a well-balanced, healthy diet and sufficient rest. Tiredness and strain reflect just as any irregularity on our complexion and on our whole appearance.

THE BODY

Cosmetic care concerns the entire body. It should include the good health and fitness that we need to keep up with our demanding daily life. Proper breathing, physical exercise, baths, saunas and a balanced diet combined with wholesome thoughts create a healthy, well-groomed body, inside and out.

Water and fresh air are two of the main sources of body fitness. They keep the skin elastic, fresh and young. Physical exercise and correct breathing as taught in yoga both have an inestimable influence on our general condition from the health and cosmetic point of view. The aesthetician should be sufficiently acquainted with yoga to recommend suitable exercises and be able to judge its benefits from her experience. Regular exercising while reducing helps maintain muscle tone. Sports of any kind suitable to health and age should be encouraged. Walking and swimming maintain fitness by exercising all the body muscles. Home exercise should be undertaken in the morning immediately after rising, before breakfast and if possible in front of an open window.

Bath or shower

Only a clean skin with a normal circulation can function well. A brush massage before the morning bath or shower gives a smooth, clear skin and should be employed at least two or three times a week. This massage can be carried out with either a dry or wet brush or loofah. Brush legs and arms upwards and the rest of the body towards the heart, in circles with light pressure. Follow with a warm bath or shower, then a quick, cold shower. The latter carries away soap particles remaining on the skin and awakens the system. Skin scales, dust, sweat and bacteria are removed from the skin by soap and water. Over-fatty soap – like baby soap – should be used for a dry skin; medicated soap for oily skin. A bath should never be excessively hot but should maintain a mild temperature, not more than 38 °C. Warm water tires and dries the skin so one should not remain longer than ten or fifteen minutes in the tub. Tap water is hard and needs additives to make it better tolerated by the skin. These additives soften the water, while their fragrances give a feeling of luxury. They contain relaxing, revitalizing or lubricating ingredients.

Additives Oil baths are intended for dry skin and coat it with a fine film. If not in the form of an O/W emulsion, they float on the water causing greasiness. Foaming cream baths combine lubrication and foam and are also suitable for dry skin. Foam reacts mechanically on the skin and has an invigorating effect. A foam bath without oil also provides cleansing, but a body lotion is needed afterwards. Gels are gentle cleansers, good for dry or sunburned skin.

A milk bath is an O/W emulsion serving mainly to perfume the water. Bath salts are water softeners which stimulate and cause a tingling sensation on the skin. Bubble baths refresh. All require creaming afterwards, as they cause an alkaline reaction and otherwise would dry the skin.

Algae-based additives appease nerves, relax muscles and clear the skin. Herbal essences have a natural, delicate fragrance. Soothing bath additives contain extracts of lavender, camomile, melissa and fennel. Plant extracts from rosemary, pine, horse chestnut and sea salt refresh and stimulate the circulation. They favourably influence an oily skin.

Medical bath additives must only be used on doctor's prescription. They are frequently derived from evaporation of natural well water, and serve distinct medical purposes – Pumice stone or peeling substances are used to make body skin more supple. Rough elbows, upper arms, knees and feet become soft and smooth. Apply body lotion afterwards. Wherever there is a sign of cellulite, regularly massaging with a cellulite lotion improves the skin's appearance.

Sauna   Many people do not take advantage of the benefits of a sauna, steam or hot air bath. Large cosmetic institutes often include a sauna. It can also be established in a private home. A steam bath in a small cabinet which leaves the head free will serve this purpose. If there is any doubt about health, a doctor should be consulted before a sauna or steam bath.

Prior to entering the sauna the body is cleansed thoroughly. Heat relaxes nervous tension and can replace, to some degree, physical exercise. Water and salts are given off in perspiration during heat exposure. Unless one is accustomed to a sauna, it is better to stay no longer than 10 minutes and not repeat. A cold shower or a dip in ice-cold water follows. Rest is required after the last cooling off, with no physical exercise which could overstrain the organism. In the sauna the metabolism is revived, and resistance builds up against colds and influenza. Saunas should be taken at intervals of approximately 1 week. In Finland, where a sauna has been general practice for centuries, its advantages have been praised in the country's literature.

Other means

Body massage is an important part of general physical care. A masseur often works in a cosmetic institute. This person needs specialized training, in addition to a general knowledge of nourishment and diet. These are dealt with in a separate chapter, as are hair removal, hand care, leg and foot care and hygiene.

An ultra-violet lamp may be employed to replace the natural sun during the winter months. Exposure has to be carefully monitored. Sun bathing unprotected in bright sunlight not only harms the skin but also irritates the nerves. The exposure over a long period can lead to lasting damage to skin tissue. A tan obtained in semi-shadow will last longer and result in more even colour. Skin exposed regularly to bright sunlight dries out and becomes wrinkled. For example, a person working in the open will often have a leathery, rugged looking skin, which guards itself against harmful rays by becoming keratotic.

Air bath   The advantages of an air bath are not widely known. This procedure must obviously be undertaken in temperatures that are warm enough to prevent catching a cold. The best place is a protected area and of course away from the sun. An air bath, once it becomes routine, can be carried out over any length of time. It intensifies physical resistance to colds.

Regular and sufficient sleep, at least eight hours a night, is one of the great beauty resources. It assists in maintaining a good mental balance.

The bust

The bust requires special attention. Unfortunately, styles are continuously changing from a small bust to a full bust and vice versa. Certain adjustments can be made through the shape of the brassiere, although this is limited. It is by no means advisable to experiment with hormones or homone preparations. To strengthen breast muscles and keep the bust naturally firm, arm exercises, swimming and not forgetting a good posture are the best precaution. Cold showers tighten muscle fibres. Breast and *décolleté* are included when applying moisture body lotion. To prevent neck and *décolleté* lines sleep without a pillow or only slightly elevated.

The bust is a fatty tissue and has a tendency to lose its form when body weight is reduced. When on a diet, bust muscles need regular strengthening exercise.

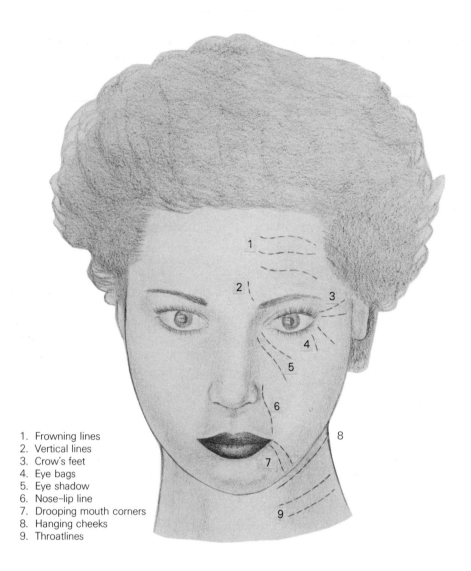

1. Frowning lines
2. Vertical lines
3. Crow's feet
4. Eye bags
5. Eye shadow
6. Nose-lip line
7. Drooping mouth corners
8. Hanging cheeks
9. Throatlines

This type of exercise should be started during adolescence as a prophylaxis. A proper, well-fitted brassiere helps keep the bust in shape. In certain cases the doctor must be consulted. Bust plastic surgery has been improved in recent years with procedures that generally show good results.

In conclusion, the aesthetician acts in an advisory capacity to prevent her client from becoming discouraged or confused by the many aspects of her individual caring programme. Going through the complete programme outlined may take too much time and energy, but at least give your client a choice and let her decide for herself what she wants to do. Morning and bedtime face and body care should not take longer than half an hour if developed into a routine. A thorough overhaul should be carried out in the cosmetic institute at regular intervals.

FACIAL (NECK) EXERCISES AND MASSAGE

1 Raise and lower the head back and forth with enough stretching so that you feel the muscles tightening and relaxing, breathing in with one movement and out with the next.

2 Turn the head with a jerk alternately to both sides.

3 Lean the head over to both sides of the shoulders.

4 Make a complete circle with the head, once clockwise and once counter-clockwise.

5 Pull chin forward and let go, then pull forward, leave in position and lean head back.

6 Move lips from left to right and right to left, stretching the muscle around the mouth.

7 Contract jaws firmly, making sounds 'o – – o' and 'icks' in turn.

8 Blow up cheeks very firm and let go.

9 Blow up cheeks and move air in the mouth from one side to the other.

10 Place ring and middle finger tightly on both sides of the temple, feeling eye muscles; close and open eyes firmly.

Note: Repeat every exercise five to ten times.

Facial massage, using night cream

1 Massage neck, sides, back and front, careful over front centre, avoiding pressure (thyroid gland) using both hands in a light, downward, circular movement.

2 Stroke alternately with both hands over *décolleté*.

3 Stroke with ring and middle finger, with pressure, from chin to upper jawbone alternately, left and right.

4 Pat energetically under chin and jaws with back of fingers, using both hands alternately and working from right to left and back again.

5 Push chin slowly and firmly with back of hand resisting pressure.

6 Massage in small circles with upward movement the nose–lip line, nose wings and sides of nose. (Press tongue tightly against inside of nose–lip line when massaging.)

7 Massage both cheeks in circles with upward movement and repeat same with cheeks blown up.

8 Stroke with middle finger above upper and below lower lip.

9 Massage around the eyes in circles, starting from bridge of nose. Go along eyebrows to temples, gliding underneath eyes back to bridge of nose. Pull eyebrows up slightly, stroke tenderly under eye.

10 Spread skin on temples, where crows feet appear, using forefinger and middle finger of left hand. Describe circles with middle finger of right hand over spread part; do not pull when massaging.

11 Massage forehead in circles with both hands (ring and middle finger).

12 Finish massage by stroking soothingly with whole hand over forehead.

Note: Repeat all movements several times.

PART III

BASICS OF STAGE, PHOTO, SCREEN AND T.V. MAKE-UP

Make-up for stage and screen

Contents

This chapter is an introduction and guide to different forms of make-up. It will be of use in camera and theatrical fields.

STAGE MAKE-UP

Just the basics of the many-sided art of stage make-up can be laid down here. Only practice can prove and teach perfection. If you wish to go into this field, art lessons will assist in providing the artistic skill you will require for your work. They will train your perception of details and inspire your imagination. A course in hairstyling and wig-making will be useful on occasions where there is no hairstylist available, especially if you are working at a smaller theatre.

The science of stage make-up is closely allied to costume and stage design. The human body can be completely changed or disguised by a costume, a person placed into an imaginary surrounding, the voice can be altered, but without make-up the facial expressions fail to fit into the part. The success of an actor or actress depends, of course, primarily on the performance; however, performance may be greatly enhanced by make-up. Make-up extends the ultimate illusion, and renders the artist authentic. Exaggerations must be avoided, as must insufficient make-up. With too little make-up, perhaps only a simple foundation, which neglects shading the features, the face of the actor on stage lacks expression or seems to be blurred. On the other hand too much make-up can result in caricature. Imperfections or mistakes made in the dressing room look much worse on stage. You can spoil the complete project by failing to realize what you are doing. You may hinder the actor with your make-up, instead of helping him perform his part. The audience particularly, appreciates the visual aspects of a show or play; therefore, poor make-up irritates and disappoints the spectator.

Lighting

The correct depth and intensity of theatrical make-up depends on the size of the theatre and stage, and the strength and colour of the lighting. If the theatre is large or the light is bright, colours must be intensified and stressed so that they are not faded by illumination or blurred by distance. Poor lighting gives abundant shadows, so that dark make-up tones must be moderated. Try out make-up before a mirror under both a powerful and weak light to judge the different effects. See that the colour of the light in the dressing room harmonizes with that on stage.

Red light absorbs pink, and takes away from red shades. It changes blue to violet and makes greens appear yellowish. It also intensifies brown almost to black. Thus under red light you must use soft brown shades, a darker rouge and deeper tones of pink for the foundation.

In a blue light, blue is not reflected and red becomes violet or, if it is very dark, almost black. Yellow turns greenish or even almost brown. Counteract this by applying a light foundation and lighter red.

Orange and yellow light require a control of blue, green and grey due to absorption. Apply more red and more intensive foundation. Browns must be deeper. Be careful with blues, which may turn greenish; light green fades.

Green light has an unfavourable, deadly effect on make-up. Under this colour avoid reds and browns. Red turns brown, browns nearly black. Choose a light, soft shade.

Pink, violet and day-light blue flatter the complexion. Violet light is the most favourable for make-up. Pink light requires more red, gentle blue less colour. In all, lighting colours and make-up shades react like mixing two paints on an artist's palette.

Clown make-up with use of a bald cap

Quick changes

If there is a minimum time available between two scenes, not allowing for a make-up change, colours can be subdued by a quick application of more powder. Other touch-ups or adjustments to the facial expression are sometimes also required between two scenes of a play when the actor undergoes mental or physical changes in his part.

Characterization

Get yourself acquainted with the contents of the play to learn the age, profession, personality and other peculiarities of the part the actor is playing. In an historical play, check pictures of the era for typical characteristics and beauty concepts of the time. For contemporary plays, less make-up is necessary. Features of the performer are perfected by corrective make-up, which must be applied artistically within the boundaries of harmony and taste.

We distinguish between straight make-up, when the actor or actress appears similar to his or her own personality and age in a contemporary play, and character make-up, when a transformation of some kind takes place.

Studying the face Examine first the face of the actor or actress to find the facial characteristics you wish to emphasize. Select those you believe are suited to the part. Do not try to change the face to a lifeless mask, but to an interpretation of the role. Adjust the actor to fit into the part by using his own features, or you may achieve a ridiculous result, failing in your endeavours.

Extras who represent crowds do not generally receive an individual make-up. To save time the same foundation and shades are used for them all.

A study of the structure of the skull is not only an asset but indispensible for character make-up. This is particularly true if the part requires the actor to appear older or younger than his true age. To change his features, you must know where the bones protrude and where the hollows are found in the skull. You must be acquainted with location and course of the facial muscles. A chart dividing the face into different segments facilitates shading the face, and shows where lines should appear when a young actor is made up to play the part of an aged person. There are three even sections: from the hairline to the bridge of the nose, from there to the root of the nose, and then to the chin. In addition two perpendicular lines may be imagined from the hairline along either side of the nose to the chin, touching only the nostrils.

In old age, the muscles sag and lines become deeper. The boney structure is more apparent and the face loses its soft, smooth, round contours. Hollows sink into the skull.

Muscle movements express emotions. Knowledge of the facial muscles is necessary to express emotion and character by means of make-up. A relaxed person or someone with a well-balanced disposition, for example, has no obvious emotions showing in his face; the muscles stay in their natural positions. Determination, greed, tiredness or physical and mental strain all reflect in the face. These can be successfully accentuated by following certain criteria. Bitterness shows itself in lines around the mouth, tiredness around the eyes, to name two characteristic marks. Sickness, drunkenness and insanity typically influence certain facial areas. Any condition of the mind affects the features, even if the person is not aware of it. In this modern age, we all generally enact a well-controlled mimicry. Our living conditions prevent us from showing our emotions. We try to overcome our feelings and shortcomings to mislead the world around us. For this reason, a character in a contemporary play cannot be stereotyped like a character in a play that takes place in a former century.

Certain parts require the actor or actress to appear ugly, sometimes asking for a drastic change of the features. Here disproportions and characteristics of the face can be stressed to make the part look realistic without making the actor himself unrecognizable.

Writers and poets have invented fabulous creatures in their plays. They resemble human beings in body, speech and gesture, but they depend on make-up to arouse the interest of the audience.

Light and shade are the principles of stage make-up used to create a natural appearance. In order to give a realistic, authentic interpretation of a character, the make-up must show the breaking of light on the muscles of the face, and the unevenness of the skin and bone structure. In profile, each shadow must have a corresponding highlight. This creates an optical illusion, whereas a flat line drawn on the face remains no more than a flat line even when seen from a distance. Shadows need highlights to make them plastic. Make-up should take only a short time once you have mastered the basic rules of handling the material.

MAKE-UP MATERIAL

Grease paint and body make-up

Several firms manufacture grease paints which are not damaging to the complexion even if used over a long period. They cause no irritation to most skin types. Grease paint comes in the form of sticks or paste. There is a great choice of shades, numbered differently by each manufacturer. Foundations come in a wide range suitable for all complexion colours, matching characters, races and age groups. The thicker grease paint sticks are for the foundation, thinner sticks for contours and wrinkles. The stick is applied directly to the skin and evened out with a damp sponge. The paste which comes in a tube or jar and is stippled on with a sponge, permits faster application because of its smooth consistency. If a stick is too firm, hold it in the closed hand; it will soon become soft and pliable from the heat of your body. Colours can be easily mixed in the palm or back of the hand. For a very oily complexion cake make-up makes a better foundation than grease paint; it requires no powder.

For a very dry skin, it may be necessary to use a fine film of moisturizer as a base, but this must be done sparingly to prevent grease paint colours from becoming soft and running into each other, particularly under the heat of stage lighting.

For the body, there is a liquid foundation and a cake make-up. To apply the latter a wet sponge is used. All parts of the body not covered by clothing must be made up. This make-up is later washed off with soap and water. Grease paint is removed with cold cream and tissue.

Other equipment

As well as grease paint and body make-up, the make-up box should contain tissue, cotton, brushes, spatulas, sponges, sticks, cold cream, a head band, scarf (for protection of hair and face when changing costume), comb, mirror, astringent, moisturizer, lip liner, brown and black pencil, mascara, false eyelashes, nose putty and other materials like derma-wax or latex and powder. Tooth enamel (white or black), spirit gum, crepe hair and scissors may also be necessary.

For a performance taking place in the open air, everyday make-up is adequate. It needs only a slight accentuation.

In order to prevent skin problems, stage make-up items must be kept immaculately clean. Cotton and tissue must never be re-used.

Application of make-up foundation

It is advisable to dress before applying make-up, so that it may not be damaged by putting on clothes. A towel or tissue protects the neckline of the dress. A head band holds the hair back. The skin is first cleansed, freshened and blotted dry with a tissue. Modelling of facial parts or application of prosthesis is carried out under the foundation.

If the complexion shows dark marks like liver spots, discolouration or unevenness of any kind, they are blocked out by a sealer. If the line of the natural brow requires change, eyebrows can be successfully 'soaped out' by a thick lather which is left to dry. Brow hair can be controlled with wax, spirit gum or a fine fabric, camouflaged by coverstick.

Foundation is then placed over the forehead, nose, cheeks, chin and neck, and smoothed out with a sponge to a fine layer. For a natural look, go carefully into the hairline, over the ears, under the chin and far back towards the neck. If a line revealing the edge of the grease paint base remains visible, it gives the impression of a mask.

Colour effects   Foundations containing warm shades of pink or red create a youthful impression. Cold tones of blue and grey give the complexion a sickly or aged look. The colour of the foundation also depends on the setting of the stage production. A man or woman living in the country is depicted with a fresh

201

skin, whereas somebody in the city may have a paler hue. A man working outside has a different complexion from one working in an office. Age also determines certain colour changes. Manufacturers issue pictures and descriptions to guide the right choice of grease-paint colours. Mixing them requires great care to obtain the correct effects and proportions. Mix small quantities and experiment.

General guide to foundation shades according to age groups:

> young to about 25 years of age – rosy,
> 25 to 45 years of age – apricot,
> 45 to 65 years of age – ochre (yellow-beige undertone),
> great old age – grey undertone.

Shading the contours

Remember, the heavier the foundation, the lighter it appears when seen from a distance. The darker the shadows, the more contrast they bring to the complexion and the deeper they seem. Shadows should be translucent, not dark blotches.

Shadows and lines are blended into the foundation so that you cannot tell where one ends and the other starts. To blend them, stroke or pat gently between them with the fingertip, using a brush for thinner lines. Practice on the back of your hand by drawing a line or triangle and blending it into the base. Blend a very light triangle into a dark foundation and a dark triangle into a light foundation. This will teach you the relation of light to dark and how dark make-up reduces size, and light make-up increases it. Highlights are also blended in this way. The hues of shadows and highlights depend on the foundation and should be chosen accordingly. A brown complexion naturally needs a darker highlight than a fair or pale complexion.

As mentioned before, modelling of features requires a knowledge of the facial skeleton to avoid application of light or shade in the wrong place. If bones were shaded or hollows highlighted, the face and its expression appear grotesque.

In both, straight and character make-up, features need shading for emphasis on stage, making them visible from the distance. For a perfect appearance, facial defects are corrected with corrective make-up. But without shading of the sides of the nose, temples, chin, cheeks, etc., the artist's mimicry would get lost.

Effects   When making up a character with a fat face, the fleshy parts dominate the bone structure. Fewer hollows and wrinkles are visible, even in old age. Few dark shades are used, and a light foundation is applied all over to stress fullness. Horizontal portions of the facial planes are also stressed, while eyebrows are made shorter.

An effect of leanness is achieved by highlighting the bones to make them even more prominent. Apply deep shadows and accentuate vertical lines for elongation.

The appearance of old age, when the adipose tissue decreases or increases, is produced by the preceding two make-up devices. Nose and ears also usually enlarge with advancing years. The middle-aged face shows the strongest, most expressive features. Through shading a double chin can be created optically, the nose can be changed in width and form, and the whole face can be made to assume a different shape.

In order to make wrinkles look genuine, they have to be located where they would naturally appear. To determine this and to avoid duplication, the performer should frown, laugh, squint, and make other mimical expressions while being made up. Wrinkles are never just straight, but come in waves. Work generously. Going into fine details would not make them show up, but just create a dirty surface. When drawing wrinkles, use a fine brush or stick to highlight and blend. We distinguish between a hard and soft edge, e.g. the lower edge of under-eye bags is a hard edge and is not blended, unlike to the upper edge, which merges softly and gradually. Neck muscles need modelling to complete an aged appearance. Freckles, pock marks and moles and so on are dotted on. Warts are usually moulded on. A scar is drawn with a light line in the middle and a reddish brown one on each side, blended into the foundation. A wound is made with a dark red line in the middle and pink at the sides.

Two different kinds of make-up will create an illusion: three-dimensional or plastic make-up and make-up applied in lines only, like that used for a clown.

Rouge

Cream rouge is applied on top of the foundation. Dot it on to the cheeks and blend in. Do not apply too high on the cheek bones. A dash of rouge goes over the forehead, nose tip, chin and earlobes. A dot is placed in the inner corner of the eye and some in the upper nostrils. Dark rouge on the lower part of the face makes a person look older. Powder rouge can be applied over the powder if still deemed necessary. Each make-up, including a dark complexion, needs rouge to become realistic and alive.

The eyes

In stage 'make-up', the eyes are more intense in colour than in everyday make-up. Too heavy an eye make-up must be avoided, however, or eyes appear like two dark hollows. To enlarge the eyes in a younger person, let liner on upper lid run out towards temples and extend artificial lashes. A thin line is drawn along lower lash base also extending over the outer eye corner. The space between the lines is whitened. For character make-up a change of the course of the eyebrow can assist to obtain a desired facial expression. Block out the natural brow and paint on a new brow after powdering off the face, or glue it on with crepe hair. Crepe hair is available in different shades to match the natural hair colour. To apply it, cautiously remove the foundation where the brow is to appear and brush on spirit gum to cover the area. Leave it to get tacky, then pull crepe hair from the braid and carefully press it against the gum with a cloth damp enough to prevent the gum from sticking to the fingers, the eyebrow is then shaped with scissors. To remove crepe hair, pull it off and erase the spirit gum with astringent or rubbing alcohol, rubbing off any residue with a damp towel.

Eyebrows create different expressions; for example, a short brow denotes stupidity; a straight, bushy brow denotes energy; and a brow close to the bridge of the nose or even extending thinly over it denotes firmness and sternness. A diabolic character is shown by a brow curving down over the inner corner of the eye. Racial characteristics are also marked by the eyebrow: for interpretation of an Oriental, the lines of the eyebrows and eye-liner go straight up towards the temples. Bulges over the eyes are moulded on. Tired eyes and eyes that have been crying show a pink rim. Witch's eyes have a red line around them.

False eyelashes are applied after powdering off the face so that particles of powder do not cling to them. Natural lashes are freed of powder before mascara is put on, or before they are whitened to depict old age. To cover the eye for a closed look, a piece of gauze is fastened with spirit gum over the eye socket, covered with foundation and powdered off.

MODELLING

Modelling may be done with nose putty; absorbent cotton and with spirit gum; derma-wax; latex; and other materials.

Method

This process of prosthesis is done before make-up on a dry oil-free skin. The procedure is as follows: break off a small piece of the nose putty stick, knead it in your hand to make it pliable, roll it and press it against the back of the nose, smoothing it out to the sides into the shape of the natural nose. For the tip of the nose, cheeks, chin, etc., roll putty into suitable shape and apply it in the same manner. Cold cream on the fingertips will prevent putty from sticking. By this method any shape of facial features can be obtained. Putty or wax can be applied over spirit gum and sealed with the same material. It is then covered with the foundation, leaving no demarcation line visible. Do not apply putty over the bridge of the nose between the eyes as it will loosen through muscle movements. Transformations must in no way interfere with the freedom of the artist's facial muscles and impair his mimical expressions. To change facial contours, you must be well-acquainted with the location of the muscles and their elementary motions. A putty nose or other prosthesis can be re-used for another performance if it has been carefully removed by running a thread along the natural nose underneath it.

Latex is the most versatile material for prosthesis over a larger area or pieces for scar build-ups and other changes of the skin surface e.g. extensive wrinkling.

HAIR

The beard or moustache worn by a performer can be made up of crepe hair or purchased ready-made. It must accord with the colour of the natural hair or wig, and with the thickness of hair growth. It is attached the same way as brows.

When applying a beard, do not forget that the hair also grows under the chin, and sometimes a little down the neck and into the sideburns. A beard is generally made of four parts: one under the chin, two at the sides along the jaws, and one under the bottom lip. (If you make it of crepe hair, remember the hair is thinner at the edges and thicker in the centre of the beard.) By putting the beard on in these sections, and using spirit gum in several layers, the performer's lip muscles are left free and his mimicry is not hindered.

The moustache is applied in two spots, left and right. If it has not been made on a flexible base, a ready-made moustache should be cut in the middle to prevent discomfort. Leave a space between the beard and the actor's lips. An unshaven face can be painted on with dots of a pencil. For a short beard, cut crepe hair into small pieces, pick up with a damp cloth, and affix by pressing it against the spirit gum. To make white temples and beard, use a spray. If a wig reveals natural hair at the sides, it should be sprayed to match the wig's colour.

Wigs

A good wig is often the most important part of a performer's make-up, for hairstyles clearly characterize certain periods of history. Grey hair and complexion colours sometimes indicate old age better than wrinkles. If a wig has a join, grease paint is used to cover the line on the forehead, blending it in with the foundation. To indicate baldness, make-up becomes lighter towards the top of the head. If the forehead is to show wrinkles, place one along the line of the join. Spirit gum is used to hold the wig firmly in place. To lower the forehead, the hairline is moved further down with a wig or lightly pencilled in. Pencilling can also create fullness if a man has a naturally thin hairline.

POWDERING OFF

Before powdering off, check your make-up critically. It is difficult to make corrections on grease paint once it is powdered off, as it will not blend in easily. Choose a light, translucent powder to set the make-up, one that does not interfere with shading and lines. Press it into the paint with a powder puff or sponge, wait a minute, then remove surplus gently with a clean cotton ball or powder brush. Over-powdering gives a dull, lifeless look. Excess powder can be carefully removed with a damp cotton ball.

LIPS

The lips are one of the last steps in stage make-up. To correct their shape, follow the same rules as in corrective make-up, using a lip liner and brush.

To create an old mouth cover it with foundation, do not use any rouge. You can draw creases over the upper and lower lip to give the idea of a wrinkled mouth. These lines have hard edges.

A tooth can be covered with white enamel for correction, or shortened and made invisible with black enamel for a toothless look.

The tooth is dried well, the colour brushed on, and the mouth kept open for a while in order not to wipe the colour off with the lips. Tooth colour is removed with cleansing tissue, followed by brushing of the teeth.

THE HANDS

Make-up should be applied to the hands after dressing. It must not be neglected, as it completes the overall appearance of the actor. Much is expressed by hand movements, they can dramatize and support the performer's mimicry. As they attract attention, they must harmonize with the age, skin colour, etc. of the part. In a straight make-up, the hands just need a foundation like the other uncovered parts of the body. The foundation can be made natural by stroking over it with the palm of the hand after evening out.

Shadowing of muscles in arms and hands is done lengthwise, downward and around the joints. Veins are emphasized by means of dark red, blue or grey colouring highlighted at one side and shaded at the other. The hands can be made to look short and fat with an even, light base, or skinny, by shading the sides of the hands and fingers. To depict a sick person or someone of great old age, the nails can be painted yellowish. Hands must be powdered off if grease paint has been used, otherwise it will come off on the objects touched. Do not forget to make-up bare feet and legs. Light red on heel and toes makes feet look young and natural.

CLASSICAL BALLET

In classical ballet the make-up for the dancer has to be created with strong contrasts to draw the attention of the audience. The face is seen from the distance and make-up worn by a person in constant motion. It has to withstand heat and perspiration, therefore has to be of a dry consistency.

Classical ballet make-up

To stress the romantic look of the danseuse, the foundation is very light and well covering. Sides of the nose are shaded and the zygomatic strongly

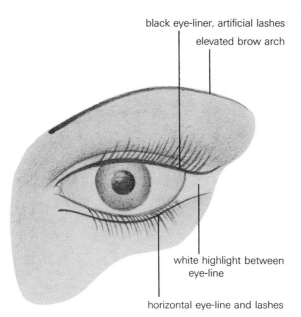

black eye-liner, artificial lashes

elevated brow arch

white highlight between eye-line

horizontal eye-line and lashes

Classical ballet make-up

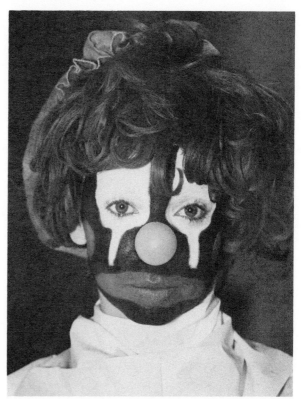

Make-up for a clown

emphasized with a dark contour underneath and a pearly bright highlight on the bone. The natural brow is blocked out in its outer part and replaced by a longer, higher arch. Eyes are enlarged by black liner along upper lid running towards temple and a horizontal straight line at lower lid; between the extension a white highlight; artificial lashes. Lips are contoured with a dark red or brown pencil, preferred lipstick colour: dark red.

Variations to this include dancers in modern ballets when bright colours are used in addition for cheek rouge and eye shadow.

CLOWN MAKE-UP

The make-up changes features completely to the traditional conception of clown, harlequin or buffoon, with a false nose and large mouth. It is to depict humour and amiability.

The brows are blocked out, followed by a well covering white foundation powdered off by colourless powder. The nose may be round or other shape (ready made prosthesis is available), eyes are stressed in size by designs around them, brows are pencilled in in a high arch. The mouth is outlined with a dark shade and filled in. Variations can be made by bald caps and varying wigs. For a happy clown make-up, enlarged mouth and eyes have an upward direction. In a sad clown, lines have downward trends.

Another example of clown make-up

Dietrich Fischer-Dieskau as Germont in 'La Traviata', Bavarian State Opera, and as Falstaff (Photos Sabine Toepffer, Munich)

PHOTO, SCREEN AND T.V. MAKE-UP

The lens of the camera registers irregularities of the complexion which are hardly noticeable to the human eye. Re-touching the negative can correct these faults to a certain degree if they are not too drastic.

For black-and-white

For this reason alone, grease paint cannot be used for black-and-white photos or films, including T.V. It would turn out as light and dark patches. The method of shading which so successfully betrays the eyes from a distance on the stage becomes absurd before the camera where it fails just like all the other tricks used to produce an illusion. A wig with a forehead piece becomes impossible, as it would be too obvious. Crepe hair and wigs must be applied to appear natural. For a man, no photo make-up is necessary in most cases. Everyday make-up is sufficient for a woman, except if meant to look eccentric or sophisicated. The natural shade of the skin must not undergo a drastic change. Pinks are to be avoided, and rouge, if applied to indicate fresh colouring, should be very light.

The best foundation colours for a black-and-white reproduction are found among the tan tones. A pink complexion looks dark and heavy rouge may even appear almost black. There is a special make-up in neutral shades for black-and-white which are lavender, darkish yellow, green, etc. On black-and-white photos, (T.V. or screen) colours turn out in a scale from white through various greys, to black. They show as follows: light blue turns white; red nearly always appears black; bluish grey and light yellow turn almost white; pink or purple, dark green and dark blue appear black.

For colour

In colour photography, T.V. and film, colours undergo changes. It is therefore helpful to know what make of film is being used and what specific reactions can be expected. T.V. make-up is governed primarily by reference to colour, secondarily by reference to black-and-white. As it is reproduced on two different screens (colour, black/white), make-up must be correspondingly effective. New products for screen make-up are constantly being brought into the market. Manufacturers indicate which colours are to be used for different makes of films.

Neutral shades are used for both foundation and contouring. The make-up material is not sensitive to heat. Professional make-up can be combined with products made for everyday make-up. Because of great changes in the fields of T.V. and film, a continuous development in make-up methods became necessary. The enlargement on the screen requires a natural look. Make-up must be carried out extremely carefully as it emphasizes every aspect of the skin, whilst on the small T.V. screen, make-up can be more generous and distinctive. The decorative part becomes most important, and maximum care must be devoted to details. The lighting in a film or T.V. studio can create an optical illusion. With this lighting, unlike the stationary lights on a stage, facial features can be changed, made older or younger, lines can be softened or deepened. This is not always successful as the camera's lens is not easily misled.

On T.V., lighting may cause a distortion of features: headlights bring out certain structures, shadows intensify. Experiment by casting light on a face from different angles. You will thus establish where highlights are being created, and where, how and why shadows are falling.

Character make-up

The film and T.V. industry have a great choice of actors available; they are not limited to an ensemble as in the theatre. The actor can be chosen to fit the part from the point of view of age and feature characteristics. This is fortunate, since character make-up cannot create so drastic a change as it can on the stage. It cannot stand up before the criticism of the camera. If a character make-up does need to be done, it has to be worked out to perfection with consideration of the three dimensions. Otherwise, it will seem untrue (see the general guide to stage make-up).

General points Much more time is needed for a transformation on screen compared to one on the stage, infinitely greater care and patience are required, for the end product must be perfect. It is advisable to make a chart of the make-up, as some films are shot over a period of time. Simplicity in make-up application, avoiding too many details, makes it less difficult. Prostheses must be used with maximum skill, and skin imperfections must be well disguised. The foundation is worked out artistically, employing delicate shading. Foundation is lighter for a dark skin and vice versa so that the skin tone appears neutral. Blending must be carried out accurately, preferably using a brush. Rouge is used in the same way as in everyday make-up. The red dot that is applied to the inner corner of the eye on stage, cannnot be used on screen as it would be too artificial. Eye make-up must be gentle and should only underline, except in parts where it is supposed to be obvious. For black-and-white, a black eye liner is too harsh; blue or grey looks softer. Women's eyebrows must be shaped and superfluous hair tweezed. A man's beard line is covered with a lighter tone than the foundation before all-over application.

Men's ears are made up in a shade darker than the face, because they often draw attention, especially under bright light. Men's features are modelled if lighting requires it or if protruding parts make it necessary. Lashes and eyebrows are darkened only if they are very light. It is better to grow hair than to use false beards, side whiskers, etc.

Special effects A middle-aged look on T.V. and screen can be achieved by using less make-up, a foundation of a sallow tone, by not covering the naso-labial folds and by leaving shadows under the eyes. Make-up for old age is done on the same principle as in stage make-up, but to obtain the three-dimensional illusion, it is done less with shading than with prosthesis. Neck and hands also belong here among the essential aids used to express age.

If you should want to make an old actor look temporarily younger, give a facial lift with elastic tape to raise sagging muscles. Wigs have to be good and natural-looking. The make-up material does not need much powdering off, unlike grease paint for the stage. Powder must be fluffed into a transparent layer. White talcum can be used to set the make-up instead of powder. Corrections can be made in screen and T.V. make-up after powdering off. The lips are made up as in everyday make-up (see corrective make-up). A man's lips are hardly ever coloured; if so, they receive a coat of the foundation over the rouge in order not to stand out. The make-up of the uncovered body parts must be kept in mind.

For a brown or darker complexion, choose a foundation with an equivalent undertone, shading and highlighting accordingly. The lipstick should have no bluish tint, but rather an orangy, brownish shade.

Children need no make-up, or very little as they have to appear as natural as possible. The reflections of different colours in clothing have to be taken into consideration when making up for colour T.V. or film, and the shade of the complexion adjusted. In black-and-white, when white or black dress is worn, the hue of the foundation for the skin has to be in relation to these tones, so as not to produce an extreme discrepancy; for example, one should not look very pale in black or tanned in white, unless this is intended.

Index

211